# Praise for
## *It's Not About Food, Drugs, or Alcohol:*
## *It's About Healing Complex PTSD*

---

"*It's Not About Food, Drugs, or Alcohol* should be very helpful for anyone who has or is struggling with any type of addiction to understand that their addictions are not their fault, and by healing their trauma, they'll heal the root cause of their suffering." —Pete Walker, MA, LMFT, Leading trauma therapist & author of *Complex PTSD: From Surviving To Thriving*

"Mary Giuliani offers her readers compassion, guidance, and hope as she peels back the layers of her journey through overcoming trauma. With each chapter, she disrupts the status quo's understanding of how we think, behave, and heal by offering approachable science-based fundamentals we should have all learned about in school. Mary's book explains how addiction, disordered eating, relationship issues, and more are linked to a common root cause of injury and walks the reader through a manageable process through which true healing can occur. As a psychologist and fellow human, I recommend this book to anyone who is curious about or is currently on the path to recovery." —Andi Fetzner, PsyD, Trauma Therapist & Educator

"Mary's touching memoir of her own struggle with substance abuse, obesity, and complex trauma exposes the historical lack of awareness the mental health community has regarding C-PTSD, which has caused people like her to be misdiagnosed with multiple labels from the DSM and delay the ability to seek proper trauma treatment. Mary's book is relatable and personable as it follows the courageous story of a woman that found deeper addiction recovery when her childhood trauma was named and acknowledged." —Melissa McManis, LCSW, Sexual Trauma Therapist, Southern California

"This book is a one-stop shop for people who think they may have or who know they have trauma. Mary has done the homework to read and share some of the most important information from the best books on the topic. Her story? She's lived with CPTSD, and she is here to help you survive the pitfalls and thrive with newly-identified superpowers that we actually can gain as the result of our experiences. Best of all, she shares her story with humor and humility, grace, and ultimately what we all need and can learn from her: a lifesaving and affirming dose of self-compassion." —Carey Smith Sipp, Director of Strategic Partnerships, PACEsconnection.com and author of *The TurnAround Mom*

"This book exemplifies how childhood trauma is relational trauma. Brimming with science-based research through a plethora of resources, Mary's book is a lighthouse nurturing those suffering in darkness with her guideposts supporting their healing journey. Ms. Giuliani's book needs to be available for the masses of humanity and has insight, wisdom, and lived experiences permeating through every page. C-PTSD is not your fault. Your brain is neuroplastic and wants to heal. A must-read for clinicians, therapists, cross-sector folx, and most importantly, YOU." —Dana R. Brown, PACEs Science Statewide Facilitator, Organizational Liaison, PACEsconnection.com

"Mary guides us through her personal recovery journey, offering hope and healing wisdom as we travel from not knowing it was trauma into triumph! Thank you, Mary, for this inspirational collection of personal victories infused with an impressive compilation of trauma resources and tools." —Teri Wellbrock, Host of The Healing Place podcast, Trauma-Warrior, Author, Speaker & Blogger

"This is such an important book for anyone struggling to have the life or love they want -- but especially necessary and empowering for LGBTQ women since our stories are so rarely told. Thank you, Mary, for sharing your healing journey so openly and including the discussion of homophobia as a source of trauma that we can and must heal from. You are a role model, and this book is full of information, guidance, wisdom, heart, and courage." —Ruth L. Schwartz, Ph.D., Director, ConsciousGirlfriend.com

Wise Tribe Media, Aliso Viejo, CA

ISBN: 979-8-9874660-2-5


Copyright 2022 by Mary Giuliani.  All Rights Reserved

Manufactured in the United States of America.

Library of Congress Cataloging-In-Publication Data

Giuliani, Mary M.


It's Not About Food, Drugs or Alcohol: It's About Healing Complex PTSD

By Mary Giuliani

—— It's Not About ——
Food, Drugs, or Alcohol

IT'S ABOUT
# HEALING
COMPLEX PTSD

——————

MARY GIULIANI

WISE
TRIBE
MEDIA

*For the survivors.*

*Because sharing our story is the single most powerful thing*
*we can do to heal ourselves and heal the world.*

# CONTENTS

---

## PART III – The Trauma Healing & Recovery Journey

## PART IV – The Gifts of The Trauma Healing & Recovery Journey

# INTRODUCTION

---

I decided to write this book because I wish someone had written it for me thirty years ago. Discovering that the root cause of my struggle with food, weight, drugs, and alcohol was a condition known as Complex PTSD—a more severe form of PTSD that developed due to my being raised in a chaotic alcoholic home was a pivotal moment that changed everything.

It changed how I viewed myself, how I viewed my past, how I viewed my future, and it even changed how I viewed humanity as a whole. Most importantly, it changed how I approached my recovery, to where I was finally able to find the healing and wholeness I'd been searching for.

Before learning in mid-life that childhood trauma was the root cause of so many of my lifelong struggles, I'd been on a thirty-year healing and recovery journey that started when I got sober when I was twenty-seven.

Even though I was in long-term recovery with alcohol, drugs, and food, had maintained a healthy weight for two decades, and had what most people would consider a successful life, behind closed doors, I still struggled and wondered…

- Why I had so few close friends and struggled to find a fulfilling, romantic relationship.
- Why I still had difficulty with food, sleep, and caffeine.
- Why I couldn't find the flow and passion I longed for in my career.
- Why, even though I'd overcome my struggle with addiction and severe obesity, I still had deep shame about them and felt the need to hide these and other parts of my past.

Looking back, I realize now that my addictions weren't my problem. They were my best attempt at a solution. The solution I needed was to stop the pain of living day in and day out with the anxiety, fear, loneliness, and shame that came from trying to cope with a brain, body, and mind profoundly dysregulated by trauma.

Discovering C-PTSD was behind so many of my struggles was what sent me on a five-year journey doing intense research studying leading experts in the field and experimenting with dozens of trauma-oriented therapies and practices to find the most effective methods for optimal healing.

This book is the story of what I discovered on my healing and recovery journey, what I did to heal, and how healing my trauma profoundly changed every area of my life.

It's also a how-to guide to support you to embark on your own trauma healing and recovery journey so you too can heal the root cause of your struggles, let go of the shame over what happened and how you coped, and as a result, experience the healing, connection, fulfillment, and peace of mind you deserve.

## What You'll Find In This Book

- I've blended memoir, science-based research, and a how-to guide for healing from C-PTSD and recovering from alcohol, drug, and food addiction, obesity, and how to forge and maintain healthy relationships.
- For my research, I relied on well-established experts in the fields of complex PTSD, adverse childhood experiences (ACEs), neuroscience, developmental psychology, attachment theory, polyvagal theory, and addiction medicine.
- For my how-to guide, I've relied on what I've learned over my thirty-year background in healing and recovering from my struggle with substances, food, weight, and codependency and my twenty-five-year background as a Master Certified Life Coach.

## Part I – What Happened to Me

- Join me while I look back through a trauma-informed lens on what happened to me growing up in a chaotic alcoholic home, where I began using food to cope at just five years old and, as a teen, turned to alcohol, drugs, and cigarettes.
- Witness the steps I took to experience the first major turning points in my life, getting sober and overcoming my thirty-five-year battle with food and severe obesity.
- Notice as I move through my adulthood, while sober and looking healthy and successful on the outside, how I continue to struggle since I have no idea that unhealed C-PTSD is operating under the surface, sabotaging my relationships, career, self-esteem, health, and recovery.

## Part II – My Discovery

- Witness the many aha moments, profound insights, and paradigm shifts I experience as I learn in midlife that my most difficult struggles in life have been caused by how C-PTSD has impacted my brain, body, mind, and relationships.
- Learn why talk therapy, spirituality, self-help, or 12-step programs can't completely heal trauma
- Learn about the invisible traumas—such as a child witnessing chronic tension or fighting between parents, or being raised by an addicted, depressed, anxious, or emotionally invalidating parent, and how they can experience just as much trauma as a child who was sexually or physically abused.
- Discover why C-PTSD is at heart relational trauma, why it makes personal, professional, and family relationships so difficult, and what you can do to heal.
- Learn how living in a homophobic culture and being raised in shame and fear based religions traumatize LGBTQ+ kids and accounts for why they grow up to struggle with twice as many addiction and mental health issues as their straight counterparts.

## Part III – The Trauma-Healing and Recovery Journey

- Learn from top C-PTSD experts what the most effective goals and approaches are to healing, what to expect, what you need to do to get started, and how to know if you are on track.
- Witness my journey of experimenting with various brain, body and mind oriented trauma-based healing and resilience-building therapies and practices and which ones I discovered to be the most effective in helping me to heal from C-PTSD.
- Learn how healing relational trauma can help you feel safe enough to enjoy the soothing connection that a romantic partner, close friendships, and a sense of community can provide.
- Learn how to replace shame, guilt, and regret with self-compassion, self-forgiveness, and self-acceptance
- Learn all the steps I've taken to achieve long-term recovery from my struggle with alcohol, drugs, and food, and the steps I've taken to maintain a 160lb weight loss for over two decades.
- Get clear about your healing & recovery goals and stay focused and on track through the included worksheets, quizzes, and questionnaires.

- Gain access to a 36-item menu of evidence-based trauma therapies, practices, and addiction recovery resources that I've found to be the most effective in healing from C-PTSD and achieving long-term recovery.

## Part IV –The Gifts of The Trauma Healing and Recovery Journey

- Learn how healing from C-PTSD was the key to unlocking my purpose and setting me on a path to doing the work I love and how it can be for you too.
- Learn the top seven gifts I've received from healing my trauma and recovering from addiction and what gifts you can look forward to by embarking on your own trauma healing and recovery journey.

## Appendix

Here you'll find over one hundred resources that have played a crucial role in helping me heal from C-PTSD and recover from food, alcohol, drug addiction, severe obesity, and codependency. These include dozens of recommended books, podcasts, websites, organizations, groups, movies, and provider directories related to healing childhood trauma and recovering from addiction and codependency.

## The Perspective I'm Writing From

I've written this book from the perspective of a trauma survivor who has experienced significant healing and recovery from Complex PTSD resulting in a substantial reduction in symptoms. This is primarily due to my utilizing trauma-informed body, brain, mind, and relational therapies and practices. It's also partly due to the personal development and recovery work I did (prior to knowing I had trauma) to achieve long-term recovery with codependency, alcohol, drugs, food, and severe obesity.

My intention for this book is to help survivors make sense of and find peace with why they've struggled or are currently struggling with food, weight, alcohol, drugs, relationships, or other common symptoms of complex PTSD. I also intend for it to be used as a guide and road map to help survivors heal their trauma and reach their recovery goals so they can go on to live a life they love.

Although I've done my best to minimize being repetitive, I've purposely reiterated specific experiences, perspectives, symptoms, or practices to emphasize what I've found essential to experience maximum healing and recovery from C-PTSD, addiction, obesity, and other common C-PTSD symptoms.

## If You Become Activated

Although my story doesn't include physical or sexual abuse, it does include being raised in a chaotic, dysfunctional, alcoholic home, as well as the story of my struggle and recovery with C-PTSD, food, weight, alcohol, drugs, and codependency. Therefore, if you become activated while reading it, please take care of yourself by taking a break, returning to it later, seeking the support of a trauma-informed coach or therapist, or skipping that section.

## Why This Book Provides Value Even If You Don't Have A History of Trauma or Addiction

Given that 12.6% of adults have experienced what is considered high levels of adversity or trauma during their childhood, and one in ten adults in the U.S. struggle with alcohol, drug, food addiction, or severe obesity, even if you don't personally struggle with these issues, you undoubtedly have survivors among your family, friends, or coworkers who do. Therefore, reading this book will help you better understand those who struggle with these issues. And when you're able to see those struggling with addiction and obesity with empathy and compassion, they'll feel seen, heard, and understood, which can give them a much better chance of being open to getting the support they need to recover.

Another benefit of reading this book for those without trauma or addiction histories is that a big part of healing trauma and recovering from addiction involves implementing self-care practices and learning essential life skills that can improve anyone's life.

## How This Book Provides Value For Those In Recovery From Addiction

Since addiction is not the core problem but instead is a survivor's best attempt at finding a solution to regulate or numb the pain of unresolved trauma, even if the addictive behavior has stopped, if the underlying trauma is not healed, survivors often switch to more acceptable addictions such as work, or screen time, or continue to exhibit other common trauma symptoms. These can include difficulty with close personal or professional relationships, depression, anxiety, attention, unexplained chronic illness, or chronic pain. Therefore, reading this book will help heal the underlying trauma that had driven your addiction and help you resolve existing or prevent future C-PTSD-related negative health and social. outcomes.

## How to Get the Most Out Of This Book

One of the most important lessons I've learned on this journey is that the degree of healing a trauma survivor achieves is directly related to their ability to make sense of what happened to them, understand how it shaped who they became, and do so with self-compassion. For this reason, I recommend reading this book from the beginning to the end rather than skipping around or skipping over chapters.

By doing so, you'll absorb the key insights and lessons I share as I make sense of my story. Since survivor stories typically share similar themes, learning how I've made sense of my story will more than likely make it much easier for you to make sense of your own. And once you can make sense of your story and can do so from a place of self-compassion, you're halfway home toward healing your trauma.

## Terminology

Throughout this book, I refer to complex PTSD as childhood trauma, trauma, complex post-traumatic stress disorder, or C-PTSD interchangeably. I refer to those who have suffered from the long-term effects of childhood adversity or childhood trauma as survivors or trauma survivors interchangeably. I use the term addiction interchangeably to refer to substance or behavioral addictions unless stated otherwise.

## It's Not Your Fault, You're Not Alone & You Can Heal

If you had a difficult childhood and you're struggling with substances, obesity, relationships, anxiety, or depression, the first thing I want you to know is it's not your fault. None of us asked to be traumatized as children, so remember, it's not your fault.

The second thing you should know is you're not alone. Over one in ten Americans have experienced high levels of adversity as children. Additionally, one in ten adults in the U.S. suffers from a substance use disorder and/or severe obesity. Due to shame, family secrets, and social taboos, most people are uncomfortable disclosing the adversity they experienced as children or how they struggle with substances or obesity. Just remember, you're not alone.

And the third thing you should know is you can heal. As you'll read in the following pages, my story is a testament that when you're willing to face that the adversity you experienced growing up caused you to develop complex PTSD, and you use the right trauma-oriented therapies and recovery-oriented practices, you can heal and go on to live a life you love

# PART I

---

# WHAT HAPPENED TO ME

# CHAPTER 1

---

# I NEVER KNEW IT
# WAS TRAUMA

## 2017: AGE 57

*What do you mean I have trauma?* I thought while reeling from the stark realization that for over thirty years, I'd missed seeing that childhood trauma had been the root cause of my most difficult struggles.

As I continued to listen to *The Body Keeps the Score: Brain Mind and Body In The Healing of Trauma,* it felt as if I'd stumbled upon a sort of holy grail that page after page revealed to me, in hard-core science, answers to why I'd struggled in so many ways for so long.

Until then, I'd thought the only way a person could be considered a childhood trauma survivor was if they'd been sexually or physically abused or had some other horrific things happen to them. Since I'd never had any of these experiences, I never thought that my most difficult struggles could be related to childhood trauma.

Yet after several hours of binge-listening to trauma expert and psychiatrist Bessel van der Kolk's *The Body Keeps the Score:,* I knew I'd been wrong. As I continued listening, I was riveted by what I was learning from the many peer-reviewed neuroscience research studies that proved how kids' brains were significantly changed by being exposed to toxic levels of adversity while growing up.

When I came across an image of an fMRI brain scan revealing how the brains of traumatized children have entire areas that don't function properly due to ongoing adversity, there was no way I could deny it.

According to Van der Kolk, I didn't need to experience sexual or physical abuse to experience trauma as a child. Being raised by an anxious, depressed, shaming, alcoholic mother and witnessing ongoing emotional and occasional physical abuse between my parents was more than enough toxic stress to traumatize my brain, body, and mind.

At first, I was shocked. How could more than thirty years of personal growth, thousands of dollars, and countless hours spent trying to heal my struggles with anxiety, addiction, obesity, relationships, and self-esteem fail to reveal childhood trauma as a possible cause?

Why hadn't the many therapists or psychiatrists I'd seen over the years (all of whom knew my history) ever suggested that my symptoms were classic signs of complex post-traumatic stress disorder and that I needed trauma-based therapies to fully heal?

Although it was maddening to realize that the mental health community had utterly failed me, I suddenly noticed a new feeling wash over me: relief.

Relief to finally have an answer to why I had been and was still struggling in so many ways. Constantly searching for over three decades to find ways to relieve my anxiety, addictions, and issues with self-esteem, weight, and relationships had been exhausting. The idea that maybe, just maybe, childhood trauma was behind at least some of these struggles and that new evidence-based trauma treatments and practices could help me heal and find sustainable relief gave me enormous hope.

I certainly knew before reading *The Body Keeps the Score* that I'd been negatively impacted on an emotional level by growing up in a chaotic, alcoholic home. I'd spent quite a few years doing intense healing work through therapy and getting sober in Alcoholics Anonymous in 1987. I'd also done a lot of healing work in Codependents Anonymous and Adult Children of Alcoholics. Plus, over the past thirty years, I'd always been involved with some type of personal growth support group, been in therapy, or learned about new ways to heal and grow through the many self-help books I'd read.

Before reading *The Body Keeps the Score*, I thought childhood trauma only impacted a person emotionally and that talk therapy and maybe antidepressants would be enough to heal or manage it. I had no idea that childhood trauma also changes a child's developing brain, body, sense of self, and worldview, and without intervention, these changes can last a lifetime.

As I continued listening, more puzzle pieces of my life began to fall into place. When I learned that childhood trauma impacts parts of the brain responsible for emotional regulation, impulse control, and attention, I thought, *Oh my God! No wonder I was such a worrier, had difficulty in school, and struggled with binge eating, drinking, and smoking marijuana while lacking the ability to moderate or stop.*

As I got further into the book, I noticed feeling like my life was finally starting to make sense. On the one hand, it was calming and comforting. Yet on the other, I found myself having more and more questions that I felt an urgent need to get answers for.

I wanted to understand how my childhood experiences had turned into a childhood form of PTSD. I also wanted to understand how this form of PTSD worked and, most importantly, what I needed to do to heal.

To gain this level of understanding, I knew I needed to revisit what had happened to me growing up. But this time, I needed to do so through the lens of childhood trauma.

# CHAPTER 2

---

# TRAPPED IN THE FAMILY FROM HELL & SAVED BY FOOD

1963

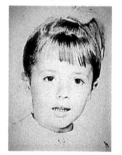

AGE 4

"I wanna go with Mommy! Please let me go, please!" I pleaded. "I'll be good, I promise. Please!"

"No, honey," Dad said. "Mommy has a lot to get done today and needs to go to the store alone. Don't worry though. She'll be back soon."

All I knew was I wanted my mommy, and she was leaving. My heart sank as I heard her car door shut and the car start. I knew it meant no amount of pleading or bargaining would help. I wasn't going to get to go with my Mom, and that made me really, really sad.

As she pulled out of the driveway in our light-blue 1962 Dodge station wagon and waved goodbye, there I was, looking on behind the screen door, with tears streaming down my face while my Dad held me. As the station wagon drove away and I lost sight of my Mom, I began crying even harder. "Mommy, mommy, mommy!"

As I continued to cry, I heard my Dad say, "Don't cry. She'll be back before you know it," as if that was supposed to make me feel better. But it didn't help. I didn't like being with my Dad when I felt sad like this because he never made me feel better. What I really needed was my Mom, but she was gone.

Once she was out of sight, Dad promptly put me down and made his way down the hallway to the den to finish watching the game on TV. I kept looking out the screen door, hoping Mom would change her mind and come back for me. As the minutes dragged on, I grew tired of standing, so I sat my weary, dejected self down next to the screen door. That way I could stay on the lookout just in case her station wagon pulled into the driveway.

A few minutes later, Dad came back through the living room and seemed surprised to find me sitting next to the screen door. Looking down at me, he said with a judgmental tone, "Are you still crying?"

I nodded as I looked up, revealing my red-nosed, puffy, teary-eyed face. He paused, seeming perplexed, then turned toward me and said optimistically, "I know. How about we walk down to the liquor store and get you a grape popsicle? I bet that would make you feel better."

At first, I didn't care so much about a stupid popsicle. I just wanted my Mom. But when I thought about the sweet, delicious grape flavor and the refreshing icy texture that only a grape popsicle can deliver, I had a change of heart.

"Okay, when can we go? Can we go now?" I asked.

"Sure, let's go," he replied.

So off we headed to the corner store.

As I began anticipating having my popsicle in just a few short minutes, a rush of excitement filled my body, and waves of joy washed over me. As we entered the store, I watched as my Dad headed straight for the freezer for my popsicle. Once he had it in hand, he made a beeline toward the counter to pay the clerk. Before the clerk could ring us up, Dad grabbed a Milky Way bar for himself and tossed it on the counter next to my popsicle.

I then heard the clerk say, "Okay, it's five for the popsicle and ten for the Milky Way. So that'll be a total of fifteen cents, please."

Dad tossed a quarter on the counter and pocketed the change. Finally, he handed me my grape popsicle with a small white napkin.

As we exited the store and I began taking in the first few bites of my frozen treat, I was giddy with delight. Somehow this frozen purple concoction magically transported me to a world where sweetness and joy seemed to live all the time. As we headed home, I skipped along the sidewalk in glee with my popsicle in hand. The world of despair I'd known just a few minutes earlier had become a distant memory. Like a miracle, suddenly, all was well in my world.

Over time, when I knew Mom was going to leave for the store without me, I would ask Dad for my popsicle in advance. Knowing I'd be getting one of my all-time favorite treats when she left seemed to snap me right out of my grief. The unspoken deal with my Dad was that I wouldn't make him uncomfortable with my tears if he rewarded me with a popsicle. At the time, it seemed like a great deal.

I soon discovered how a big stack of Oreos, a large bowl of chocolate chip ice cream, or eating handful after handful of Cap'n Crunch cereal straight out of the box could lift my spirits and take away the pain I was facing for at least a few glorious moments.

## When I Sensed Trouble Brewing At Home

The first inkling I had that there was trouble between my parents was when I was around five or six. It started when I noticed my Mom being angry with my Dad more often. She gave him terrible looks. It was like she was seething at him. Over time her grievances never got resolved, so they just kept building.

Her biggest grievance was my Dad's unwillingness to talk with her to resolve their conflicts. Dad's way of dealing with conflict with Mom was to give her the silent treatment, be sarcastic, or just leave. All I knew was I hated it when they got this way with each other.

As a little girl, I felt like I couldn't be okay unless my parents were okay. Since it seemed they weren't okay more and more often, I felt sad, disappointed, and frustrated. I just wanted my parents to get along so we could be a happy family.

Dad coped by eating. He gained and lost 20 to 40 pounds throughout my childhood. His idea of a big treat was to say, "Hey, kids! Wanna go to Baskin-Robbins for a banana split? Or let's go to Denny's for a short stack of pancakes." Of course, the answer was a big yes every time!

## Dad Disappears For A Month

When I was six, I began hearing Mom crying a lot behind her closed bedroom door. I felt really sad to know she was so upset. Yet I was also confused about what had made her so sad. I came to find out that my Dad had left. He'd left no note, no clues, no money. Just radio silence. My Mom was completely dependent on my Dad financially and emotionally, making his sudden disappearance devastating for her.

A few weeks after his disappearance, one of his coworkers from the restaurant he tended bar at called my Mom to inform her he'd been having an affair with a waitress. The coworker said it had been going on for a while, and they'd taken off on a European vacation.

Mom was devastated. She told my sister and me he was on a business trip. Luckily, we were too young to put together why Dad was really gone.

Mom had her mother come out from Massachusetts to help. About a month later, Dad came back. He blamed the affair and the trip on temporary insanity and asked Mom to take him back. I don't know if she believed him. What I do know is she took him back.

My guess is she took him back because, as a stay-at-home mom, she didn't feel financially capable of taking care of herself, much less two little girls. In the sixties, a woman was expected to be financially dependent on her husband. However, I think Mom was more than financially dependent on him. She was also emotionally dependent, especially for approval—which she rarely got.

Instead of giving her the approval she craved, he made mean, insensitive, put-down remarks about her abilities, her looks, and her friends. He even told her that her nose was too big and it made her unattractive. It apparently was such an issue that she had plastic surgery to fix it when my sister and I were really young.

## Happy-Go-Lucky

Mom used to say I was happy-go-lucky. Even today my default mode is to be optimistic and easygoing. My sister was the complete opposite. She, like our Mom, openly expressed her anger and dissatisfaction. I hated it when she and Mom got into angry, negative moods. I couldn't understand why they couldn't be happy like I was. I got so angry with them when they often ruined what could have been a perfectly fun day or family outing with their negativity.

Today I know that underneath that happy-go-lucky, almost always-smiling exterior was often a sad, disappointed, and frustrated little girl who desperately wanted a peaceful, happy family. On some level, I must have thought if I kept smiling and stayed as optimistic as possible, that it would somehow rub off on my sister and parents so we could become what I'd always longed for: a loving, happy family.

On another level, the happy-go-lucky Mary was the perfect persona for me to take on because she protected me from fully feeling the sadness, anger, and disappointment of witnessing the chronic tension between my parents.

## Gaining Weight and Getting Bullied

By the time I was about six, I was obviously gaining weight. As a six-year-old little girl, I didn't notice I was overeating. I just ate whenever I felt like it and thought it was normal. At first, my Mom seemed to think it was just a chubby phase. Then she said I had big bones. But it didn't turn out that way. Much to my dismay, I would continue gaining weight and struggle with food and weight issues into adulthood.

I was in second grade when the teasing and bullying started. I already felt ashamed of my body due to being one of the only chubby kids in school.

It was so humiliating to be called fatso or hear the boys yelling, "Hey, hey, hey, Fat Albert," at me. When the boys called me these terrible names, I felt like I was disgusting and unworthy to the core. I just wanted to hide and never go back to school.

As the bullying continued, I felt worse and worse about who I was. I figured there must be something terribly wrong with me if I was so repulsive that kids felt the need to be so mean to me.

I came home from school several times crying and told my Mom about the bullying. Although she was kind and empathetic, her only solution was that I should say to myself, "Sticks and stones may break my bones, but names can never hurt me."

The truth was those names did hurt me. They hurt me more than I'd ever been hurt before. Yet all she could offer me was a stupid platitude!

This left me afraid of the abuse continuing and inept for being unable to shake off my anxiety by using her stupid platitude. What I really needed was for my Mom or Dad to protect me by showing up at the principal's office and demanding that the abuse stop. Sadly, this never happened.

Once I realized there was nothing I could do to stop the bullies, my anxiety about having to go to school went through the roof. Going to school became an emotional minefield for me. As soon as I set foot on the school grounds, I would obsessively scan my environment to see where the bullies were. I tried to take routes to the cafeteria or recess that prevented them from seeing and taunting me. Eventually, they would find me, and the abuse would start once again. From that point on, I grew to hate school.

## Starting Catholic School

Before I began fourth grade, my parents and several Catholic families on my block decided to enroll their kids in Catholic grade school.

At first, I was excited to transfer to a new school because it meant I no longer had to attend catechism (a Catholic religion class for public school kids), which I'd been going to every Saturday morning since first grade. I also hoped the bullying would stop since my new school would have all new kids. But I had no such luck. Much to my dismay, the bullying continued.

The only thing I could do to protect myself was to always be on the lookout for the kids I knew would shame me about my weight, then avoid them like the plague. Even though I tried to avoid them, the fear of future abuse continually occupied my thoughts even when I wasn't at school.

7—When using food to cope becomes a weight problem

## Mom's Drinking Problem Begins to Show

Before my Dad left for Europe with his mistress, I remember hearing my Mom laughing a lot when talking with neighbors, her family, or friends on the phone. But afterward, I heard her crying behind her closed bedroom door a lot more often than I heard her laughing. As a little girl, I didn't know what was going on other than my Mom was sad. Since she was sad, I felt sad.

When I was about eight, I noticed something different about my Mom's demeanor after arriving home from a night out with my Dad. She seemed buzzed like she'd had too much to drink.

The first time I saw her like this, I thought it was funny because she seemed more loving and affectionate toward my sister and me. But as the months rolled by and it became a regular thing, it began to scare me. I didn't know what was happening other than when my Mom came home drunk; the Mom I knew was gone. She'd been replaced by a syrupy, overly affectionate, drunk woman.

I remember a few times when my Mom was so drunk that my Dad had to carry her into the house from the car. I knew there was definitely something not right for her to be that drunk. All I remember is being really scared, hating it, and wanting it to stop. I was also totally embarrassed, knowing the babysitter saw her that drunk.

After a year or so, I noticed a new pattern when she arrived home after being out with my Dad. Instead of being in a syrupy, affectionate mood, she was angry and belligerent with my Dad. Once this pattern started, it continued. Over the course of a year or so, my Dad got fed up with dealing with her anger or being embarrassed by her when she was drunk and stopped taking her out.

## Mom's Descent Into Alcoholism, 1968: Age 9

Mom's daily drinking began when she became close friends with our neighbors, Lily and Moe. They were retirees who loved ringing each evening in with a five o'clock cocktail hour. Mom found comfort in sharing her marital woes with Lily. Eventually, she walked across the street to drink with her every day. Over time, the cocktail hour at Lily and Moe's got earlier and earlier.

8—Wearing an uncomfortably tight dress

This helped usher in Mom's descent into daily drinking. Having easy access to a friend who listened to her troubles and who, like her, enjoyed daily drinking made it more acceptable for her to get drunk every day. Once this pattern started, I frequently arrived home from school to find her pretty buzzed. This was when I knew I could no longer invite my friends over after school since there was no way I was going to take the chance of being embarrassed by my drunk Mom.

As Mom's drinking progressed, her attempts to hide it progressed too. Instead of drinking her Carlo Rossi Rose out of a wine glass, she poured it into a yellow coffee cup, thinking we wouldn't notice. It took only a second to smell it on her breath and see the red wine in her coffee cup to know what she was drinking.

She eventually began to hide her wine bottles. Sometimes I found them hidden in the back of my closet, the bottom of the clothes hamper, and in other weird places in the house and garage. Smelling alcohol on her breath, noticing her slurred speech, and seeing her stagger as she walked were all so sad, frightening, and overwhelming. All I knew was that it was horrible to witness my mother being slowly decimated by the disease of alcoholism.

Normally, a child would seek out the comfort of their mother when feeling this distraught and overwhelmed, but I lost this option since my Mom was the source of my distress. And given how stoic and emotionally shut down my Dad was, I never even considered looking to him for help. All I had was my nine-year-old self to deal with my sadness, fear, anger, and overwhelm.

## Coping with Mom's Drinking

My sister and I handled our distress about my Mom much differently. She let her anger out by telling my Mom how much she hated seeing her drunk. On the other hand, I stayed in my room alone, door closed, sitting in my beanbag chair, watching TV with a box of Cap'n Crunch cereal, eating handful after handful straight out of the box.

If my Mom caught me eating Cap'n Crunch in my room, she'd immediately confiscate it because we were only allowed to eat it with milk for breakfast. It was then that I knew I needed to figure out a way to ensure I wouldn't be interrupted while I eked out a few glorious moments of sweetness in my otherwise hellish home.

That's when I learned that if I sat on the floor against my bunk bed with the cereal box positioned flat on the floor to my right, I could slide it right under my bed and out of sight in a split second if my Mom entered my room. The good news was it worked like a charm. The bad news was that I began gaining weight faster than ever.

Although I hated gaining weight and feeling so much shame about my body, food was the only thing that got me through. Knowing that I could access a tastebud rush and a sugar high on demand gave me the strength to face the dark cloud continually hanging over my family.

## Thank God for the Families on Kerry Street

Up until I was about seven or eight, I could count on my Mom to be there to hold me when I cried or reassure me when I was upset. Before her drinking got really bad, she always made our birthdays and holidays special.

But once Mom's drinking had taken over, everything began to change. Instead of being there for me when I was upset, she would look to me to comfort her while she was drunk and upset with my dad.

9-Mom neglects to take care of my hair for my school photo.

Before her spiral into alcoholism, I loved going to family gatherings and going on fun family vacations. But once her drinking took over, most of the vacations we went on or gatherings we attended as a family would get cut short, canceled, or we'd have to tolerate being totally embarrassed by my drunk Mom.

This is what made living on Kerry Street such a saving grace for my sister and me. Our house was surrounded by six or seven middle-class, single-family homes. Most of our neighbors were young families with kids right around my sister and my age to play with. Since all the moms stayed home, they frequently hung out at each other's houses. In many ways, our block was like one big family.

We loved riding our bikes, roller skating, playing ping pong, softball, and hide-and-go-seek with our friends. In the summers, we enjoyed Fourth of July block parties and played with our friends all day long, not having to come home until the streetlights came on or when our moms called us in for dinner.

My sister and I were especially close to the Phipps family. They had eight kids and were Catholic too. During the summer, my sister and I were frequently invited to join them for trips to the beach, where we loved going in the water, bodysurfing, and lying out in the sun. Since their Dad was active military, we were invited to join them for several weeks in the summer when they rented beach houses in the San Diego area where he got stationed.

Most of the families on our block were Catholic, so many of us went to church together on Sundays. Just being able to walk outside, find someone to play with, and be welcomed into a family that felt safe and sane was a major refuge for me. I hate to think what would have become of me had I not had the village of Kerry Street to grow up in.

## Mom's Late-Night Drunken Tirades Begin

As time went by, Mom's drinking got worse. Once she was drunk, she proceeded to unload all of her anger and resentment toward Dad by yelling and screaming at him about how horrible he was for having an affair and not being willing to talk out their problems. It got to the point many nights where my sister and I couldn't sleep due to our Mom screaming at our Dad until three or four in the morning.

Even when Mom wasn't drunk, and we pulled it together to go somewhere as a family, it seemed to always be colored by a dark cloud of conflict. I remember sitting beside my sister so many times in the back seat of our 1965 white Chevy Impala, with my Dad driving and my Mom sitting in the passenger seat. Either Mom was pissed at Dad, or my sister was pissed at Mom about her drinking. My Dad always stayed silent, like he was in another world as he drove. I kept to myself while feeling deeply sad, angry, and disappointed that, once again, my crazy family had ruined what was supposed to have been a fun family outing.

## My Food & Weight Problems Escalate

Food filled the sad, empty space in my heart as I witnessed my mother sink deeper into her alcoholism. It also quelled the anxiety of having to deal with the chronic tension at home and the bullies at school.

By the time I was ten, I was a good 20 pounds overweight. At this point, Mom's concern about my weight grew more serious. That's when she began putting me on a series of diets. One of the first weight-loss programs she enrolled me in was Weight Watchers. When I walked into my first meeting and realized

I was the only child in the room, a wave of shame rippled through my body. I couldn't help but think; *There must be something seriously wrong with me to be the only kid here.*

On the way home from Weight Watchers, we stopped at the grocery store to stock up on the food that was allowed on my new diet. We purchased the only three frozen diet dinners that existed in 1970: Weight Watchers Salisbury steak, halibut, and cod. The only one I liked was the Salisbury steak. I hated fish but choked it down anyway because I was desperate to lose weight. We also picked up what would become my diet staples for many years to come: light cottage cheese, eggs, canned pineapple in juice, tuna fish in water, fruit, lean meats, veggies, and Fresca—the only diet soda available.

Eating these types of foods and sticking to my diet meant I was being "good." Eating the forbidden, fattening foods meant I was being "bad." Over my many years of dieting, it seemed that I just couldn't help but be bad when it came to the food I ended up eating. After so many years of feeling bad about myself for my food choices and bad about gaining so much weight, it became hard not to believe that I simply was bad.

## Mom Takes Away My Best Friend: Food

Weight Watchers was just one of a series of restrictive diets my Mom put me on in her attempt to help me lose weight. Losing access to freely eating whatever I wanted, whenever I wanted, was deeply upsetting. It meant losing my best friend. Food was the only thing that provided joy and comfort in an otherwise chaotic, depressing home. It was there for me when no one else was. Not only did I have to deal with not having the comfort of a safe, loving family, but I was also losing my best friend.

I was angry at my Mom for taking away something that made me feel better for at least a little while. I knew losing the freedom to soothe myself with food would be a major problem. It also felt unfair. After all, everyone else could still eat whatever they wanted. But not me. I felt like I was being punished for doing something wrong or being bad.

That was when I started sneaking food. Until then, I'd been freely eating whatever I wanted for several years. The problem with Mom putting the brakes on my food is she did nothing to address the emotional issues that drove my need to overeat. She wasn't psychologically aware enough to realize that my overeating was emotionally driven by the grief I was experiencing from losing her to the disease of alcoholism, as well as the hell of having to listen to her drunken tirades against my Dad. As a ten-year-old little girl, I obviously wasn't aware of this either!

Mom did mention that weight issues ran on Dad's side of the family. To her, weight issues were partly inherited and partly a "calories in, calories out" equation. From my perspective, food was my best friend. It brought me lots of joy, and it was always there. But now, it was being taken away from me suddenly and without any warning. Even worse, my feelings about losing this supportive friend weren't even considered. When I thought about it, *Of course I was upset.* Anyone would be upset if they had to face the prospect of losing their best friend.

Once my favorite foods became "the forbidden fattening foods" that I shouldn't have, it made me want them more. So off to the races I went, figuring out ways I could be with my forbidden friend, food again.

## My Secret Pancake Ritual

One of my all-time favorite foods was pancakes. When my Dad and I went to the hardware store for supplies for our regular home improvement projects, he often took me out to Denny's for breakfast on the way home. I loved sitting at the counter with him while we waited for our short stacks of pancakes to arrive. Taking in the first few bites of the fluffy buttermilk cakes with the perfect mix of whipped butter and maple syrup was pure heaven!

Mom occasionally treated us at home with a pancake breakfast. I frequently asked her if I could help her make them. She happily obliged and even showed me how to flip them in the pan. By the time I was about nine, I'd made pancakes so often with my Mom that I could make them all by myself with Bisquick.

That's when I began my secret pancake ritual. I would get up at six in the morning once a month or so when I was sure that everyone but our dog, Tippy, was asleep. I tiptoed around the kitchen, making sure not to rattle a pot or pan so I wouldn't wake anyone up. After the first batch was ready, I gave Tippy the first two since they never turned out that great. Then I ate the next six or seven with lots of butter and syrup. Tippy got the last couple as well.

I felt so nervous sneaking behind Mom's back because one time, she did catch me and got really mad. She said she didn't want me cooking by myself. She also didn't want me to eat pancakes because they weren't good for me. I knew that I couldn't get caught again, or I'd possibly risk saying goodbye to pancakes forever. But the craving was overwhelming, so I just had to.

To make sure I wouldn't get caught, I totally cleaned up my mess, opened all the windows to air out the kitchen, and sprayed air freshener so the pancake smell would be gone.

My secret pancake ritual was my way of treating myself with my buddy Tippy at my side. He never judged me, and we enjoyed many a pancake breakfast together.

## The Guilt-Shame-Binge Weight-Gain Cycle

Mom tried hiding food from me, yet I always seemed to find it. It seemed like within a couple of days of going grocery shopping, all the sweets and carbs would be gone. Not having access to sweets and carbs on demand made my cravings go through the roof. That was when I got creative and began baking with whatever ingredients I could find in the kitchen.

I got out the cookbooks and made cookies, cakes, pies, and cream puffs from scratch to satisfy my sweets and carb cravings. I also made every recipe off the Bisquick box, including coffee cake, strawberry shortcake, and of course, biscuits with lots of butter. At first, my family loved having such delicious treats around. That was until my weight reached another high, and I once again had outgrown my wardrobe.

I frequently binged to the point of being uncomfortably full. I often felt physically sick and sluggish from eating so much. I felt so guilty and ashamed for being so out of control with food. Although I knew it was something I wasn't supposed to do and that after the initial pleasure, I would feel bad about myself, but I couldn't stop. It got to the point where I was convinced there had to be something seriously wrong with me to keep doing this to myself.

As a child, I didn't know then that it wasn't my fault that I didn't get the support I needed to deal with my feelings in a healthy way. Instead, I blamed myself for lacking the ability to reign in the impulse to eat when I wasn't physically hungry. I also felt like my Mom and Dad were disappointed in me for not having the strength to overcome my food and weight issues. I also sensed they were ashamed to have an overweight daughter because, on some level, it reflected on them as parents.

I was caught in a vicious cycle. I gained weight and felt more shame and guilt. Then, the more shame and guilt I felt, the more I ate to numb the pain of the shame and guilt. Sadly, this cycle of guilt, shame, binge, and weight gain continued for decades.

## The Shame of Outgrowing My Clothes

Another issue that continually came up was the shame of outgrowing my clothes. From the time I was about six or seven, it seemed like every pair of shorts and pants got tighter and tighter until the seams split. Seeing yet another hole in my shorts or pants was so humiliating.

It was a constant reminder that my body and life were out of control. This was when I had to ask my Mom to get out the sewing machine to repair them. Of course, the problem wasn't the clothes. My body was expanding at a faster and faster rate due to my binge eating. And it was one more thing to feel shame about.

When I was about eleven, I learned how to sew with a needle and thread out of sheer need. I also had my Mom teach me how to use our Singer sewing machine, so I could repair my shorts and pants myself.

It was such a relief to be able to repair my clothes on our sewing machine because it meant I wouldn't have to face asking my Mom to sew them for me. The less she knew about how out of control my weight was, the better.

Due to how often I outgrew my clothes, my Mom and I frequently needed to go clothes shopping. This was always really stressful for me because it meant I couldn't hide my weight gain from her. She knew what size I'd worn from the last shopping trip, so going shopping again made it obvious how many sizes I'd jumped due to all the weight I'd gained. This frequently triggered her to put me on another diet!

By the time I was ten or eleven, Sears was the only store with clothes that fit me since they offered Chubby sizes for girls. At first, it was totally embarrassing to have to buy Chubby sizes. But at the same time, I was also grateful there was a line of clothes for girls my size because I had completely outgrown regular-size girls' clothes.

Once I hit size 16½—the largest size in the Chubby line—I panicked. I had no idea where to find clothes after I outgrew Chubby sizes. I did find some relief when I discovered Sears also had Husky sizes for heavyset boys. Since the Husky sizes were larger than Chubbies, I could wear them when I outgrew my Chubby-size clothes.

Besides Sears, there weren't any large-size clothes for girls in department stores in the early seventies. The only option with clothes after I outgrew the largest Husky size was to buy men's pants and hem the length, which was a big hassle and super embarrassing. Once I outgrew the Chubby and Husky sizes, I started wearing some of my Dad's corduroy pants and jeans.

## The Hell of Swimsuits and Shorts

Summers were especially difficult for me as an overweight kid because I had to face the horrible shame of being seen in shorts or a bathing suit. Capris weren't in fashion for girls in the sixties and seventies. This meant if I wanted to wear shorts, I had to expose my hideously fat, cellulite-ridden, shockingly white legs.

If I wanted to go swimming at the beach or at a pool, I had to expose even more of my body by wearing a bathing suit. Back then, one-piece suits didn't come with shorts covering the upper part of a girl's thighs. Since I carried most of my weight in my thighs, being seen in a one-piece bathing suit was absolutely mortifying.

To minimize the utter panic I felt from being seen in my bathing suit, I waited until as few people as possible would see me as I took off my cover-up and made a run for the water.

Sometimes it was just too painful to deal with the shame of knowing people would see and undoubtedly be repulsed by my fat body, so I would forgo going swimming and wearing shorts altogether. There were many summers when I wore long pants instead of shorts, even in the scorching heat, just to avoid feeling such horrible shame about my body.

I don't recall talking to my Mom about how bad I felt about my body. In my mind, it was my own fault that I was so heavy. I also knew talking to her could spur her into "fixing" my weight problem by putting me on another diet. Being put on a diet meant losing my best friend, food. Since food was the only thing that helped me cope, there was no way I was going to take that risk.

## Dad Tells the Truth about Mom's Drinking

After a few years of Mom's daily drinking and rage-filled attacks against my Dad, one day he took my sister and me aside to talk to us privately. We knew this had to be something big since he'd never done this before. Once he had us alone in the den, he said, "I want you to know that your mother is an alcoholic and that I'm going to do what I can to get her help."

For the first time, I saw my Dad shed a tear.

This was a big deal since Dad never talked about anything deeper than sports and current events.

My sister and I were about ten and eleven then. It felt really scary to know that Mom's drinking problem was this severe. Yet, at the same time, it wasn't something we were unaware of. Given that she had been drinking every day for several years, how often we saw her drunk, and how much rage and contempt she spewed toward our Dad while drunk, it was obvious that she had a serious drinking problem. Nonetheless, it was still really scary and sad to hear my Dad inform us that Mom was, in fact, an alcoholic. I also knew it must be pretty bad if he cried in front of us over it.

Although he did say he would try to get her help, I don't recall anything ever happening regarding her going to rehab or Alcoholics Anonymous. Her drinking just kept on going and getting worse. I do remember a neighbor taking my sister and me to an Alateen meeting (a support group for children of alcoholics) once. All I remember is that I was extremely uncomfortable being there, and I couldn't wait to go home. We never went back.

## The Dreaded Diet Police Arrives

When I was about ten, my grandmother on my Dad's side came out to take care of my sister and me when my parents went on a European vacation. One of the first things Gramma did when she arrived was put me on a diet! It was so hard for me to have this forced on me against my will. Although Mom had put me on a series of diets over the years, over time, her discipline waned. And once her drinking got really bad, she rarely held me accountable for staying on them. However, Gramma was a different story. She was extremely strict, and I felt like I couldn't get away with anything!

Everyone on my Dad's side of the family struggled with weight. Therefore, my grandmother was quite comfortable taking on the role of putting family members on diets. Sadly, my Dad's Dad died of a heart attack when he was just fifty-nine years old, presumably due to him weighing over 300 pounds and being a smoker. My Dad had less trouble with weight than his parents and brother, but he still struggled.

Needless to say, there were a lot of issues around food and being overweight with my grandmother. I think that's why she was so determined to get me to lose at least 10 pounds while on her watch.

10—My Gramma, AKA The Diet Police & I

Even though Gramma was the official diet police, she also loved to bake. One day I arrived home from school and was greeted by the heavenly scent of freshly baked oatmeal raisin cookies and coffee cake. I asked Gramma if I could have a cookie, and she sternly said, "Oh, no, Mary. You can't have any cookies or coffee cake. You're on a diet."

My heart immediately sank. I was so sad and angry about her being the one to take care of us. I couldn't wait for my parents to get home so I could finally get my life and my best friend, food, back.

## Mom's Interest in Self-Help Sparks My Interest in Helping Her

Although Mom's first choice for coping with stress was alcohol, she also found a modicum of relief by reading self-help books. Some of her favorites were *How to Be Your Own Best Friend*, Wayne Dyer's, *Your Erroneous Zones*, and the *Between Parent and Child* and *Between Parent and Teenager* series. She also loved Reverend Terry Cole-Whittaker, who had a TV ministry that aired on Sundays. Together we'd laugh out loud while Terry joked about the plight of the average American housewife by combining comedy and self-help under the guise of religion.

Mom's interest in self-help books was what sparked my interest in personal growth. When I'd see her books lying around the house, I'd secretly read them. It felt so good to read books about creating positive changes in your life and understanding what drove certain behaviors or insecurities. In a way, reading those self-help books was like tapping into the wisdom and guidance of a healthy parent I so desperately needed.

Living with all the craziness at home naturally prompted me to begin a search for ways to make it stop. It was then I had a brilliant idea: *Why not take the wisdom of Mom's self-help books and see how I can help her resolve her conflicts with my Dad.*

Although I went on to become a life coach in my thirties, the truth was my coaching practice started when I was eleven with my first client, my Mom. My typical session with her looked like me sitting at the kitchen table with Dyer's *Your Erroneous Zones* book open and in hand. I would scan through it to find the most relevant lesson I thought would help her with her latest drama with my Dad. Once I found the chapter that provided the best solution, I dog-eared the relevant pages and underlined the content I thought would help her.

As Mom entered the kitchen carrying her yellow, wine-filled coffee cup while taking a drag off her Kool menthol cigarette, I would say, "Hey, Mom. Wayne Dyer says the best way to handle conflict is to use 'I' statements versus 'you' statements."

She would typically respond by saying, "Oh, really?" in her Boston accent. I would then attempt to coach her by saying, "Maybe if you try using 'I' statements with Dad, he might not feel so attacked when you bring stuff up. He might be more open to talking to you."

She always seemed open to my reading Dyer's or other self-help authors' words of wisdom and having someone to talk about her troubles with. That was when I got the green light and began reading out loud to Mom entire chapters from any self-help books I found.

Over time, we got through every chapter in Dyer's book and many of her other self-help books during our coaching sessions. Even though my attempts to help her with the wisdom from these books never helped in any significant way, it felt good to at least be able to take some kind of action to give me some hope that maybe it could stop the insanity.

The truth was I just wanted my Mom back. I also wanted my parents to get along, so we could have a peaceful, loving home and family. I didn't know then that, as an alcoholic with a broken marriage, she needed a lot more help than an eleven-year-old child with a self-help book could offer.

Over time, Mom got used to the emotional support I provided for her chronic depression and frustration over her relationship with my Dad. When I tried to take some space from her or call her out on her stuff, she would shame me and say I was selfish and that she didn't raise me to be that way. I now see she was manipulating me through guilt and shame, but as a child, I didn't know any better. So rather than feeling selfish or like a horrible daughter, I caved into meeting her needs.

I felt responsible for her feelings and well-being because she said I was. I believed what my parents told me was the truth. After all, who else would I believe? Little did I know that believing I was responsible for other people's feelings would set me up for a lot of pain and struggle in future relationships.

## At What Age Do Adults Go Crazy?

By the time I was just eleven or twelve, I'd acquired a basic understanding of emotional health through reading my mother's self-help books. During this time, I noticed a distinct difference between the emotional health and behavior of the kids vs. that of the adults I was around. It seemed like the kids I hung out with were pretty stable and relatively normal from an emotional and behavioral standpoint. Yet, I saw a completely different picture after witnessing all the alcoholic drama and craziness with my Mom and her adult family members and friends.

One day I thought, *I bet as kids, my Mom, her sisters, and her friends were normal, just like my sister, my friends, and I are.* This, in turn, begged the question: *I wonder how old they were when they went crazy?* This then begged a more disturbing question; *I wonder how old I'll be when I go crazy?*

Given the environment I was living in, being depressed, enraged, drunk, or doing crazy things was so ubiquitous with the adults I was around that I thought this automatically happened to all humans at a certain age.

## The Hell of Waiting for the Hell to Start

By the time I was fourteen, Mom's alcoholism had progressed to the point where she would launch into a full-on rage attack toward my Dad several times a week. Sometimes it happened twice a week, sometimes four times a week. You never knew how many times or what night of the week she would erupt. The one thing that was predictable was when her tirades would start: the moment my Dad arrived home from work.

Since Dad was a bartender, he didn't get home from the night shift until about two-thirty in the morning. This gave my Mom the entire day to drink and stew over how pissed off she was at him. By the time he arrived home, she was drunk out of her mind and ready to let him have it.

By this time, Dad had put a lock on their bedroom door so he could sleep without worrying that my drunk mother would come in and scream at him, slap him, or shake him to wake him up if he ignored her.

Since my bedroom was next to our front door, I would often wake up when I heard my Dad letting himself in. If my Mom hadn't passed out by then and she heard him arrive home, that would be the moment that would trigger her to go into another drunken, rage-filled attack toward him.

It was during these tenuous few moments each night, while I listened to my Dad carefully unlock the front door, that a surge of adrenaline would fill my body. I knew that if the insanity was going to start with my Mom, this was the moment it would begin. If Mom was asleep or passed out, we were safe. But if she was awake or if hearing my Dad letting himself in woke her up, all hell would break loose.

Each night as I lay in bed listening as my Dad attempted to unlock the front door as quietly as he possibly could, I was also listening for any sounds indicating that my Mom was awake in the living room or kitchen. My hope and prayer was that she'd already passed out and wouldn't hear him so I could go back to sleep. Sometimes my prayers were answered, and there wouldn't be a drunken tirade that night. But more often than not, my Dad's arrival home made just enough noise to alert my semi-awake, drunk mother to begin right where she'd left off from her last rage-filled tirade.

If my Mom happened to be awake, my Dad would have to make a run for their bedroom and quickly lock the door behind him to get away from her. But, even if he had made it past her and was safely behind the locked bedroom door, it wouldn't stop my Mom. She simply delivered her attacks by raging at him while simultaneously banging on the outside of the locked bedroom door.

Once I knew Mom was on the warpath, I desperately tried anything I could think of to not have to hear her raging at my Dad. Frustratingly, nothing seemed to work. Not playing music with the volume turned all the way up while wearing my stereo headphones, not earplugs, not pillows, and not my stuffed animals placed against my ears.

I just had to lie there in the dark and listen to the venom, the rage, the contempt, and the constant banging outside the locked bedroom door for hours. Day after day, week after week, and year after year, I just had to lie there and take it.

I couldn't understand why she kept doing this to us. Didn't she even care about the hell she was putting us through? Didn't she care that my sister and I had to get up for school at six-thirty and that it was already four in the morning?

I had nowhere to go and no one to call. It got to the point where I felt like I was trapped. Trapped in the family from hell.

On nights when Dad had tolerated her verbal abuse and rage for hours and couldn't take it anymore, I would hear him unlock the bedroom door and make a run for his car to get a hotel for the rest of the night. He had to be superfast in his exit to avoid my Mom because she would chase after him while trying to get a slap or two in before he got out the front door and into the car. Once in it, he had to rush to lock all the doors so she couldn't get in. I knew he was gone when I heard the screeching of the tires as he sped off into the night.

After more than eight years of tolerating listening to my mother's late-night, drunken rage-filled attacks on my Dad, I was so sick and tired of her insanity; I felt like the only hope it would stop was if my Mom would just die. I felt terrible guilt for wishing my mother dead. But at the same time, I was reaching a breaking point. I just couldn't take one more day of tolerating her insanity.

## Drunk-Dialing, Suicide Hotlines, and 5150s

Another coping mechanism Mom used was drinking and dialing. When drunk, she'd call neighbors, family members, and friends all over the country. She called anyone who would listen to how depressed she was over her life and marriage.

Eventually, she burned out her relatives and our neighbors with her frequent calls while drunk. That was when she resorted to the suicide hotlines. I don't think she really wanted to kill herself. I believe she was just desperate to connect with anybody who would listen. A few times, she did get 5150ed, where she was put in a psych ward on a seventy-two-hour hold. She apparently didn't like getting locked up in psych wards, so she stopped calling the suicide hotlines.

## When the Child Becomes the Parent

By the time I was fourteen, it wasn't unusual for my Mom to go through an entire gallon of Carlo Rossi Rose wine per day. She frequently wanted to talk with me about how depressed she was about her life and marriage. I tried to help by listening to her and offering advice from the self-help books I had been studying. In a very real way, I was her therapist, life coach, and best friend.

I didn't know that she was parentifying me. I know now that she was looking to me for emotional support that should have come from a spouse, therapist, or another adult. My needs didn't get met because she had reversed our roles. Instead of being there for me as a mother, she looked to me to mother her. All I knew was that I wanted my Mom back and hoped I could help her by talking to her about ways to solve her problems.

It seemed that no matter what self-help book I read to her, how often I tried to talk to her about handling her problems with my Dad, or how often I tried to console her or cheer her up, she never seemed to get better.

## Attempting to Save the Holidays

14— 225lbs.
1st year of high school

The holiday season always escalated my mother's depression and rage toward my Dad. When she went into a drunken tirade during the holidays, it wasn't unusual for Dad to get fed up and leave the night before a major holiday or on the actual holiday itself.

Over time, since Dad knew Mom would get extra crazy around Thanksgiving and Christmas, he would head her off by leaving the night before the holiday whether she was drunk or not. When he started making a habit of leaving us on these major holidays, I was devastated because I felt like it ruined what was supposed to be one of the most joy-filled days of the year. Yet, after it became a regular thing, I shifted into trying to save the holiday by attempting to cheer up my Mom and sister.

Once I knew my Dad would definitely not be around for the holiday, I sprang into action and announced to my Mom and sister, "Who cares if Dad is gone? We don't need him! We're going to have a great holiday either way!"

At the time, I may have convinced myself that my attempt to save the holiday somehow helped. But in my heart, I was sad and angry that one more time, my parents couldn't pull it together for even one day out of the year to give my sister and me a decent holiday without their toxic drama.

Over time I was relieved that my Dad would be gone on the holidays because it meant I wouldn't have to endure another holiday witnessing my drunk mother raging at him. Mom would still get drunk, but instead of going on a rampage toward my Dad, she would get depressed and nostalgic for the holidays of her youth. To avoid being around her, I holed up in my room with all my favorite holiday foods and binge-watched *I Love Lucy* and *The Twilight Zone* holiday marathons.

## The Dream: Discovering My Sexuality, 1973: Age 14

One morning while still in a semi-dreaming state, I found myself reviewing a dream I'd just had. All I knew was that I was really turned on. In fact, I felt more alive and turned on than I'd ever been before. As I lay alone in my dark room in a totally blissful state and continued to mine my memory for more details, clearer images suddenly appeared in my mind. I could see that I was in a dimly lit room, totally naked, and in what seemed to be a steamy love scene. I then noticed that I was fully engaged in a passionate kiss. I began asking myself, *Who am I kissing?* I continued to play the scene repeatedly, hoping for my lover's identity to be revealed. Frustratingly, no one appeared.

Throughout the rest of the day, I slipped back into reviewing the blissful, erotic scene from my dream. Toward the end of the day, just when I was ready to give up searching my unconscious for who my elusive lover was, an image began to take shape. Suddenly, a beautiful woman with blonde hair appeared. As I replayed the scene of us fully embraced in a passionate kiss, I was transported to a world of erotic bliss I'd never even known existed.

As I began to come down from this intoxicating experience, I realized that I was face to face with an alarming fact: I had just had one of the most thrilling sexual experiences of my life. And it was with a woman!

*What does this mean?* I asked myself. *Am I a lesbian? Oh my God, no. Please, no. I can't be a lesbian!*

The idea of being a lesbian completely horrified me. After all, I was Catholic, and it was a sin to be gay. Plus, I could go to hell! Also, what would my friends and family think? In the days and weeks ahead, as I recalled the dream—which I frequently did, the stark reality of what it meant was, frustratingly, a huge buzzkill.

Over the following weeks and months, I convinced myself that my hot, steamy dream was just a dream and didn't have to mean anything about my sexual orientation. Thankfully, I was able to let my worry about it go, at least for a time.

Fast forward one year later. I was fifteen, and it was the first day of my sophomore year. It was also the first time I laid eyes on Sophia.

She was in my first-period class and sat one row to the left and three seats ahead of me. She was a gorgeous Italian girl with dark-brown, shoulder-length hair, big brown eyes, and a gorgeous smile. I was instantly smitten.

Now my attraction to girls was something more than an erotic experience I could write off as just a dream. My attraction was now in living color, in the flesh every morning at 8:28 a.m. in my first-period class.

I couldn't get her out of my mind. Just hearing her say hi to me while passing in the hall would make my day! If by chance, she didn't acknowledge me while we caught eyes, I was crushed. While in a full-blown obsession, I looked up her home address in the student directory and plotted out my route on my Thomas Brothers map so I could drive by her house. As I nervously pulled onto her street, I slunk down in my seat while passing her house to hide my identity just in case she was outside. The last thing I wanted to experience was the humiliation of being caught in a drive-by.

Sophia was the first in a string of several crushes I had on female classmates, friends, and teachers during my high school years. Mind you, this was happening in 1974. Nixon had just resigned as president, and the Stonewall riots had just happened a few years before, in 1969. The gay rights movement was in its infancy and virtually unknown to me. There weren't any gay centers or support groups back then.

There was hardly anything on the news about the gay movement except Anita Bryant, an anti-gay activist spewing homophobic rhetoric wherever she could. It was definitely not an okay time to be an out lesbian. When I was younger, I remember Mom telling me to watch out for creepy lesbians, or what she would call "manly" women, who might try to put the moves on me.

I told no one. The last thing I wanted to be was a creepy lesbian! All I knew was that it totally sucked to have one more thing to feel deep shame about.

It was so hard not being able to talk to anyone about being gay. I felt like there was nobody else like me. There were no gay or lesbian characters on TV, in movies, or in magazines. No gay centers and no internet. Just gay bars. The problem was that I couldn't get in until I was twenty-one. I still had six long years to go for that.

## When the Alcoholic Is Driving the Car

One night when I was fifteen, I called my Mom to pick my sister and me up from our high school football game. We usually called our Dad, but he was working that night. After waiting almost an hour for what was usually a twenty-minute drive, I finally saw our 1974 Ford Country Squire station wagon pull into the practically empty football stadium parking lot.

As soon as I opened the car door to get in, I heard oldies music on the AM radio and caught a whiff of cigarette smoke mixed with the scent of alcohol.

I then heard Mom greet us, "Hi kids" with a slight slur.

As I turned to make eye contact with her, I saw the glazed-over look in her eyes, coupled with an all too familiar creepy, drunk, but "trying to look sober" expression on her face. At that moment, I knew. Mom was seriously drunk and was going to attempt to drive us home.

*Ugh!* I thought. *Why is this happening to me? I am so freakin' sick of this shit.* I sighed.

Immediately, my sister and I scrambled to put our seatbelts on, figuring in a worst-case scenario, if she flipped the car, at least we wouldn't be thrown from it.

As she began driving down Bristol Street—a four-lane road on our four-mile ride home—she began swerving between lanes. I said to her nervously, "Mom, be careful. You're swerving!"

She replied with an annoyed tone, "No, I'm not. I'm fine!"

A few minutes later, I noticed right outside my passenger-side window that she was way too close to the cars parked on the side of the road. I warned her again with an even louder, nervous tone, "Mom, you're too close to the parked cars. Be careful!"

She replied again annoyingly, "No, I'm not. I'm fine!"

When I heard metal on metal and felt the car's vibration making contact with several of the parked cars right outside my window. I panicked and yelled, "Mom, you just hit those parked cars!"

She responded, "I did not!"

Amazingly, she just continued driving as if nothing had happened! Even my sister told her that she had hit the cars, and she still wouldn't admit it. At that point, I was so anxious and terrified that my drunk mom was going to kill us that all I could do was pray that we would all make it home alive!

Thank God it was only a few more miles, and we made it home okay. Once home, all I could think about was how I couldn't wait to turn sixteen and get my driver's license so I would never have to risk my life again with my drunk mother behind the wheel.

## Free At Last — Getting My Driver's License

I was so excited to get my driver's license that I got my dad to drive me to the DMV on my sixteenth birthday. Getting my license meant I no longer had to put my life at risk by depending on my drunk mother to drive me to and from events. It also meant that when my mom was drunk and crazy, I could leave.  Given how long I'd felt trapped in the family from hell, finally being able to escape the insanity was a huge deal.

I also loved the feeling of freedom that having access to the family car gave me.  When I was driving alone or with my friends, I no longer had to play by my parent's rules.  I could go anywhere and do anything I wanted.  Not long after I'd gotten my license, I discovered the thrill of speeding, pulling reckless stunts in empty parking lots, and occasionally even racing other cars!  All I knew was that it was exciting and loads of fun, and I didn't see much harm in it.

I learned rather quickly that the local police didn't appreciate my reckless driving one bit. Within just one year of getting my driver's license, I had gotten three speeding tickets. Even worse, I received a letter from the DMV informing me that my license would be suspended if I got one more ticket.

 Just when I thought it couldn't get any worse, since I was on my dad's auto insurance policy, he was not happy about how much his bill had gone up because of my three tickets.  He warned me that I would have to pay for my own policy if I got one more ticket.  Given that I had no way of paying for my own insurance, I knew I had a decision to make.

Fortunately, I valued the freedom driving afforded me more than the high of being a reckless driver and was able to restrain my impulse to speed or engage in other reckless behavior while behind the wheel and avoided any further tickets.  Interestingly, it would be another forty years before I would learn why I felt such an intense need to be so reckless.

## Discovering Mom's Traumatic Past

When I was sixteen, my sister told me she'd overheard a phone conversation with Mom telling a relative how she'd gotten pregnant and given her baby daughter up for adoption about a year before she married my Dad.

We were stunned! We had a half-sister we'd never known about. Eventually, we told my mom we learned about the baby she'd given up for adoption and were able to talk about it with her. My sister and I wanted her to know that we didn't judge her for getting pregnant or giving the baby up for adoption. We just wanted her to know that we loved her no matter what.

As the years went by, more of the story came out about what had happened to my mom.  She'd been dating the same guy for about three years when she became pregnant. Her boyfriend wanted to marry her, but my grandparents didn't approve of him for two reasons: one, they didn't think he would be a good provider because he didn't make a good enough wage, and two, he wasn't Catholic.

Since my grandparents were devout Catholics and wanted to avoid the shame of the Church and the neighbors knowing that my mom had become pregnant outside of marriage, they flew her from their home in Massachusetts to a home for unwed mothers in California.  Once she gave birth to the baby, she was to give her up for adoption.

As planned, my mom had the baby in California and did a private adoption. Around six months later, she met my dad. Since the adoption wasn't yet final, in one last attempt to keep her baby, mom asked dad if he would accept the baby and raise her as his own. He told her he wasn't comfortable raising her little girl as his own since he felt she would continually remind my mom of her relationship with the baby's father.

My mom had no way of providing for her baby, and her parents hadn't offered to help raise her. So, she had no option but to let the baby be adopted.  Tragically, she never saw her again. My Mom and Dad married a few months later.

After hearing about my mom having to give up her daughter and the pain and shame she must have gone through, I had a much deeper level of compassion for her. Things started to make sense as to why she drank the way she did and why she may have been so angry with my dad.

Times were much different in 1956 for unmarried, pregnant women who were Catholic than they are today. I can't even imagine how painful the guilt and shame must have been for my mom when she was exposed as a woman who'd had sex before marriage and had become pregnant. I also can't imagine the grief of losing your firstborn child, not because you wanted to give her up but because of the pressure to do so due to the shame and stigma of having a baby out of wedlock.

## Dumping Out Mom's Alcohol

Although I had compassion for my mom's tragic past, I had reached the point after tolerating her insanity for a good seven years, where I couldn't take another night of her being drunk and keeping me up screaming at my dad into the wee hours.

It was only four in the afternoon, and I could tell she already had a decent buzz going. I knew if she continued to drink, she would get crazy drunk and pull the same old all-night tirade.

In an attempt to prevent another night of dealing with her insanity, I decided to dump her remaining stash of beer down the kitchen sink.

I went into the refrigerator, grabbed two six-packs of her tall Brew 102s, and began pouring them down the drain. While in the middle of doing so, she walked into the kitchen and went berserk. She started screaming at me, "Don't you touch my beer!"

I replied, "Mom, I'm not going to deal with you being drunk out of your mind again tonight!" Although I had already dumped seven of the twelve beers, I saw there were still five unopened beers in the plastic ring that held the six-pack together. Suddenly, my mom attempted to grab the beers away from me. As we both tried to take possession of the beer, I decided to move the altercation toward the front door because I thought I'd have a better chance of dumping the beer if I took them outside.

There my mom and I were, scuffling over her remaining beer in the entryway of our house. Suddenly, my mom slipped on a throw rug and fell to the floor. She immediately started screaming that she'd broken her ankle and it was all my fault.

My dad took her to the emergency room, where the doctor confirmed she indeed had broken her ankle. She arrived home with a cast and crutches. I felt horribly guilty. Yet, at the same time, I knew on some level that she was just as at fault as I was—if not more so.

16-After losing 80lbs over the summer

Interestingly enough, she couldn't drive due to her ankle being in a cast, so she couldn't buy her alcohol. As a result, my mom stopped drinking for two weeks for the first time since I was seven years old. Sadly, it didn't last, but I did cherish having my mom back for this brief window of time.

## Finally, Losing the Weight Over the Summer

After the many diets I went on over the years, I finally had some success through a medically supervised weight-loss program when I was fifteen. It consisted of a five-hundred-calorie, high-protein diet and a weekly HCG shot. I lost about 80 pounds over the summer after my first year in high school.

In the fall of my sophomore year, I went back to high school weighing in at 145 pounds. I loved feeling better about my appearance and being able to wear clothes that I really loved. But I must say it was disconcerting to suddenly have boys be interested in me when they hadn't given me the time of day the year before. It made me angry that their interest was solely based on the size of my body.

In time, I noticed that the boys weren't the only ones who showed more interest in me as a thin student. I was even able to gain the approval of the popular girls as well. It did feel good to be showered with so much approval and feel part of the "in" crowd.

Yet, in the back of my mind, I knew my new friends' approval was conditional. If I fell below their weight standard, it would be just a matter of time before I would be shunned once again. Who knew that the number on my bathroom scale could wield so much power to gain access to the upper echelon of the boys and girls in my sophomore class?

Even though it was a relief to get a handle on my weight over the summer, Mom's drunken tirades against my dad were as crazy as ever. I was so miserable living in the insanity of my family that I was hoping for anything to bring me some relief.

Little did I know, relief was just around the corner.

# CHAPTER 3

---

# FALLING IN LOVE
# WITH ALCOHOL &
# MARIJUANA

## 1975: AGE 16

**Initiation**

As soon as we walked in the door of the party, the scent of marijuana, coupled with the sound of super-loud music, hit me. As I looked around the dimly lit room, all I saw was a sea of teenagers. What really surprised me was that practically all of them were holding beers. While taking another glance across the room, I noticed a joint being passed among the partygoers as well. I thought, *Wow, Natalie must have some really cool parents!*

But after taking in the sights of this party for a few more minutes, I realized that I hadn't seen one parent since we'd arrived. As we made our way through the kitchen, attempting to locate Natalie, it soon became apparent that there was no adult supervision whatsoever at this party.

When my childhood friend Lynn invited me up to Big Bear to hit the slopes and join her at her friend Natalie's birthday party, I thought the party would be at Natalie's house with her parents and maybe a few of her friends. But this was an entirely different party than I'd expected. As I settled into the reality that I was at a party with fifty or more beer-drinking and marijuana-smoking teenagers, with no adults in sight, I thought, *Wow, this is totally awesome.* I absolutely loved being surrounded by kids my age and having the freedom to do whatever we wanted.

After milling through several more rooms filled with teenage partygoers, we finally spotted Natalie. Once we connected and Lynn introduced us, Natalie graciously offered us a beer. I'd never drank an entire beer before. I'd tried a few sips of my mom and dad's beers and remembered not liking its taste at all. So, at first, I wasn't sure that I could even drink a beer. But after seeing everyone else having so much fun, I certainly didn't want to miss out. So, I went ahead and accepted Natalie's offer.

Once I cracked it open and took my first sip, I was immediately reminded of how much I hated the taste. But I decided to soldier on and drink it down anyway, to see how it would make me feel. About halfway through, I noticed this strange, tingly sense of well-being ripple through my body. I thought, *Wow, this feels really good!* Then after a few more sips, I felt even better. Since I knew I wanted to keep this wonderful feeling going, I got about the business of finding myself another drink. I tried to find something other than beer but had no luck, so I settled for another beer.

I figured that if I chugged the second beer down really fast, I could minimize the time I'd have to suffer through the horrid taste. So off to chugging I went. Within a few minutes after downing it, I began to experience a level of euphoria that I'd never even known existed. It was like a "Where have you been all my life?" kind of moment.

Suddenly, I was tapped in, tuned in, and turned on—and loving every minute of it! I'd had no idea drinking could feel so good and be so much fun. As the party continued and the beer and marijuana flowed, I felt like I'd finally found what I'd been missing. Discovering that just a few beers and a hit or two off a joint could transport me to such a state of joy and bliss was mind-blowing.

Once I knew what I'd been missing, there was no going back. I simply had to get that feeling back. After I got home, the idea of going back up to Big Bear to visit Lynn and have another amazing time partying began to occupy more and more of my thoughts. I turned those thoughts into reality by finding a way to get up there as often as I possibly could. Once I arrived, Lynn and I always figured out a way to score some alcohol and marijuana through the various people she knew. And once again, the party was on, and I loved every minute of it.

Looking back, my first experiences with alcohol and marijuana were very much like falling in love. I was smitten and couldn't wait to be with my new love. But instead of a person, it was alcohol and marijuana that I couldn't stop thinking about and couldn't wait to be with. The truth was I was falling in love with alcohol and marijuana.

## Meeting My New Party Buddies

I got a part-time job as an usher at a local movie theater during this same period. That's where I met Mindy and Mandy, who would become my closest friends as well as my best party buddies. I soon discovered that they also loved drinking, getting high, and going to parties. Until then, Lynn—who lived over a hundred miles away in Big Bear—was the only person I'd found to drink and get high with. I was so excited to find some local friends I could also have fun partying with.

Although the three of us talked about how fun it would be to party together, we had a problem: I was only sixteen, and they were just eighteen, and none of us had fake IDs, so we couldn't buy alcohol.

When we started brainstorming about how we could score some alcohol and marijuana, I remembered how Mindy talked a lot about how much fun she had partying with her two older brothers, Nick and Harry, who shared an apartment. We knew they had parties on a regular basis, so we decided that getting them to invite all three of us to their parties was the best shot we had at being able to party together.

Within a few weeks, Mindy told Mandy and me that her brothers were fine with us attending a party they were hosting that Saturday night. After having an amazing time and hitting it off with Mindy's brothers, we started getting regular party invitations. Within a few months, we became part of Nick and Harry's regular party gang.

## The Party Oasis

Practically every weekend, and even on some weeknights, Mindy, Mandy, and I made our way over to Nick and Harry's to party the night away. When we weren't there, we'd find another one of Mindy's friends to party with. We somehow found somewhere to party a good two or three times a week. Given that beer was the most available alcoholic beverage at these parties, it didn't take long for me to get past my distaste for it and come to love it.

Cracking open my first beer of the evening and guzzling down my first few sips delivered an intense rush of relief, coupled with the anticipatory delight of knowing that I was just a few beers away from arriving in the land of joy and bliss, where excitement was around every corner, and where the fun never ended.

As the night progressed and the beers and weed flowed, the party would kick into a whole new level of wild and crazy fun. Before long, we were arm and arm, cigarettes and beers in hand, singing along to the hits of the seventies while dancing the night away. As the hours rolled by and more friends arrived, the party would shift into an even higher level of joy and bliss. And for one more glorious night, a wild and crazy time was had by all.

Partying with my friends made me feel like my life could actually be fun. Having a safe place to go, where I felt I belonged, was pure heaven. It felt so good to finally relax and take a break from the insanity I'd faced at home all week.

Within a year, we became such regulars at Nick and Harry's that it felt like we'd become part of a family. It was like having a home away from home. It was definitely an oasis from the insanity I'd been dealing with at my house.

Given how severe my mom's alcoholism was, it may seem strange that I would have even considered drinking. It wasn't that I didn't think or have concerns about becoming an alcoholic because I did. But the incredible feeling of well-being and joy alcohol gave me, coupled with the powerful sense of connection and relief it provided, overpowered any rational concern about the risk I was taking.

In my mind, drinking and getting high with my friends was pure heaven. There was no way I was going to give that up.

## My Partying Almost Cost Me My High School Diploma

One of the problems with my new party lifestyle was that I needed to get up for school by six-thirty in the morning to be in class by eight. Given my friends and I were getting drunk and loaded and staying out late several nights a week (including school nights), the combination of sleep deprivation and hangovers began taking their toll on my schoolwork, attendance, and grades.

At first, my mom had concerns about my drinking and staying out late. At one point, she even told me that alcoholism ran in families and that I was vulnerable to it. She, of course, wasn't referring to her own drinking since she didn't think she was an alcoholic. But she said we had family members who were. She attempted to give me curfews, but I rarely complied. And she was too busy with her own drinking and drama to hold me accountable. I was never grounded or given consequences for not obeying her rules. As a result, I just drank and used and came and went as I pleased.

Even before I started drinking and smoking marijuana, I was never a great student. I typically averaged a few As, a few Bs, and a few Cs. But once I started drinking, smoking marijuana, and staying out way past my bedtime, I could barely stay awake in class, much less get my homework in. Consequently, by the end of my junior year, I'd failed my algebra II and chemistry classes.

This was a big deal because my high school had a policy that wouldn't allow students to come back the following year if they got any Fs unless they made up the classes in summer school. Since the following year was my senior year, there was no way I was going to transfer to a public school! The only way I could get back in was to retake chemistry and algebra during the summer.

I begrudgingly enrolled in summer school to make those classes up. This meant I had to be in school eight hours a day for about six weeks straight! It was like a full-time job. It was painful, yet I knew I wanted to at least graduate from the high school I'd already spent three years attending.

Even though I was spending eight hours a day in summer school, totally immersed in chemistry and algebra, I was still barely passing the tests (which I'm sure was due to still not being able to resist partying). This was when my parents agreed to get me a tutor. Thankfully, I barely slid by with a D in each class, which was just enough to get back in to finish out my senior year.

## Still Teetering on the Edge of Graduating from High School

The relief I felt from dodging the bullet from being let back into my high school for my final year came to a screeching halt when I got called into the dean's office halfway through the year.

The meeting was to inform me that due to my missing twenty days of school, along with my grades being rather poor, I might not have enough credits to graduate. The dean told me to stay laser-focused on my studies to improve my grades. He also said that I couldn't miss any more school days if I wanted to have the best chance of graduating.

This was highly distressing news after the hell I'd gone through with summer school just to make it back into my school. Yet, I couldn't deny that my partying and new love of snow skiing were clearly taking their toll on my ability to make it through high school. So, I did the best I could in my classes despite my budding addiction to alcohol, marijuana, and skiing.

One day about six weeks before graduation, I was relieved to receive a letter from my school informing my parents and me what we needed to do to prepare for my graduation ceremony. It covered cap and gown rental information and the date, time, and location of the ceremony. Once I read through the letter and took the time to think it through, my relief turned to doubt about whether the letter was a confirmation that I'd qualified to graduate. I couldn't help but wonder if the letter had been automatically sent to every senior whether they had enough credits to graduate or not.

Since I hadn't heard back from the dean who warned me about my credits, it seemed even more plausible that the letter was a mistake. On top of that, I was pretty sure my final grades were not going to be high enough for me to qualify for a diploma.

At this point, I wasn't sure what to do. My grandmother had already purchased her plane ticket to fly all the way out from Massachusetts for my graduation, so I felt stuck. I had too much shame about it to tell my parents, and there was no way I would bring it to the attention of the school. So, I decided to keep it to myself and just show up for my graduation ceremony.

On graduation day, I showed up in my cap and gown, and my parents, sister, her boyfriend, my grandmother, and my party girlfriends were all in attendance. I was so thrilled to finally be done with school! We all went out for dinner afterward, and after that, Mindy and Mandy took me out to celebrate by doing what we loved to do the most: getting as drunk and loaded as we possibly could.

What I initially found distressing at the graduation ceremony was that the diploma holder they gave me was empty. At first, I thought, *Oh my God. I was right. I really didn't graduate.* But then I noticed that none of the other students had diplomas in their diploma holders either.

We were told we needed to stop by the school to pick up the actual diploma a couple of weeks after the ceremony. Since I seriously still believed it was possible that there'd been a mistake and that I hadn't technically graduated, I decided to forgo going to the school to pick up my diploma. I wasn't ready to deal with the possible humiliation of getting the news that there'd been a mistake and that I really hadn't graduated. I had so much shame that this could be a possibility that I didn't even tell my parents or friends about it.

It wasn't until over a decade later, when I was sober, that I decided I needed to close this chapter of my life. I knew I needed to get okay with and accept myself whether I was a high school graduate or not. Given I had done two solid years of recovery work in AA, thankfully, I was ready to face the monster.

I was twenty-nine when I decided it was time to find out if I was a high school graduate or not. As I picked up the phone and nervously dialed the school's phone number, I kept saying to myself over and over again, *you're ok whether you graduated or not.* I reassured myself if I hadn't graduated, I would simply take the GED.

Once I heard the school pick up, I explained I'd "forgotten" to pick up my diploma and asked the clerk if she could check their records to see if it was on file. She asked me to hold while she searched the school files. I nervously waited on hold for what seemed like forever. When the clerk finally returned to the call, she informed me that they did indeed have a diploma on file for me! As I let the news sink in, a tsunami of relief and joy washed over me!

Finally, I faced the monster, and it was over! That same day, I drove down to the school and finally picked up my twelve-year-old diploma. I don't believe I would have had the courage to face the truth of whether I'd graduated or not unless I'd found recovery.

I still have that diploma hanging on my office wall today!

## Opting Out of College

Given how much hell I went through just trying to graduate from high school, the idea of going to college was out of the question. I just needed a break from the whole school thing. It was such a relief knowing that I could party with my friends without the pressure of having to show up for classes, study, and make decent grades.

I didn't get much pressure from my parents to attend college either. After all, Dad had dropped out of high school and had gotten a full-time job when he was sixteen. My mom graduated from high school but never attended college. My dad didn't see the value in college. In his mind, it was like, Why bother going to college? Just go out and get a good job or start your own business and make your own way in life.

## Mom's Behavior Starts Getting Really Out There

By the time I was seventeen, my mother's behavior while drunk was more than crazy. It had moved into becoming rather bizarre.

During this time, my dad owned his own cocktail lounge. One of the food items he offered his customers were knackwurst sandwiches. Since he had limited refrigeration space at the bar, he used our home freezer to store some of his inventory.

Mom was sick of his knackwursts taking up so much space in our freezer. She nagged him for months to take them to the bar, to no avail. One day she finally reached the end of her rope and decided to take matters into her own hands. She not only removed the offending wieners from the freezer but decided to teach my dad a lesson.

When I looked out the front window onto the front lawn of our house, I couldn't believe what I was seeing. *What the hell are all these frozen knackwursts doing strewn all over our front yard?* I thought. I then walked into the kitchen to find my drunk mother removing the remaining knackwursts from the freezer.

Suddenly, I see my dad making a run for it down the hallway toward the front door to escape my mom's wrath. As I turned around, I saw my mom run after him, armed with the remaining frozen wieners. She chased him straight out the front door into the broad daylight of our front yard, screaming about what a no-good loser he was while hurling the remaining wieners at him as he attempted to take cover in his truck.

Once he was safely locked inside, she began hurling the wieners at the truck's windows. Hearing the frozen wieners hit the glass with such force was like hearing a large rock hitting a windshield. As I continued to watch the scene play out, I couldn't help but question if my mom was actually trying to break the windows or if she was just blowing off steam. I winced each time I heard another knackwurst hit the windshield, fearing the glass would crack or even completely shatter in on my dad while he sat in the cab of the truck.

Finally, dad started the engine to begin his escape. As I watched him pull out of the driveway, I saw five or six wieners slide off the windshield and onto the street while hearing my mom scream, "Get out of my house and take your damn knackwursts with you!"

I finally saw my dad speed away down the street, barely escaping injury or a cracked windshield.

Once again, I was totally embarrassed, knowing that at least one neighbor had to have caught a glimpse of the latest alcoholic drama being played out in the Giuliani's' front yard.

## Dad Files for Separation & Moves Out

Finally, after twenty years of marriage, Dad had enough of Mom's insanity and decided to file for separation. He moved out within a few weeks.

My sister and I were actually relieved. At last, this war between my parents was going to end! That was the good news. The bad news was this left my sister and me to deal with our out-of-control, crazy, alcoholic mom. This was when her drinking and behavior got even crazier.

Since my dad no longer lived with us, Mom had zero accountability. This meant she could hit the bars. One night a bar in Anaheim called me to say my mom was drunk, creating a scene, and was too drunk to drive. They asked me if I would come to pick her up, which I reluctantly did.

She often would stay at the bars until closing and sometimes even bring drunk men home with her to continue the party. It frightened my sister and me to know that some strange, drunk man could be arriving at our home at one or two in the morning with our mom after we'd gone to bed.

Who's to say what these men could have done to us or our mom, given that she could have easily been passed out. One of them could have visited my or my sister's bedrooms. Thank God they never did. Yet just wondering who mom was allowing into the house after we were in bed was very unsettling.

## Dad Files for Divorce

When I turned eighteen, Dad had Mom served with divorce papers on Valentine's Day. I don't know if he requested the divorce papers be delivered that specific day or if it was a karmic coincidence. Frankly, I wouldn't be surprised, given the hell my mother put him through for over a decade.

Within about a year, the house was listed for sale and had sold, the divorce was final, and it was time for my dad, mom, sister, and I to all forge ahead with lives of our own.

Sadly, we weren't a close-knit family. Instead of being a pillar of support for each other, we each found ways to get our needs met outside of our family. My dad had his girlfriend, my sister had her boyfriend, my mom had her alcohol, and I had my party buddies, my food, alcohol, and marijuana. What we didn't have was each other.

## Moving Out of the Family From Hell & Getting A Full-Time Job

While working at the movie theater, one of my coworkers, who also had a full-time job at Children's Hospital of Orange County, told me about an available full-time position in the hospital's business office. So, I got my best interview outfit together, applied, and got the job. It was perfect timing since it gave me the full-time income I needed to afford the rent for an apartment.

Since we couldn't afford to get places on our own, my sister and I decided to rent an apartment together in Anaheim. Although it was heaven not having to live in the insanity with my mom, dealing with a roommate, even if it was my sister, made it clear to me that I definitely needed to have my own place. After a year of living together, my sister decided to move out with her boyfriend. It was then I knew it was time for me to get my own place.

I found a cute little 1920s studio bungalow that had a Murphy bed and a clawfoot tub in Old Towne Orange. The rent was only two hundred and twenty-five dollars a month and was just a mile away from my work at Children's Hospital. I was twenty years old and absolutely loved having my own place.

# 1980: AGE 21

## Hitting the Gay Bars

Turning twenty-one was a major milestone for me. It wasn't because I could legally buy alcohol since I'd had access to a daily supply of beer through my friends for a good three years. It was because I could finally get into the gay bars— and getting into the bars meant I could maybe even find a girlfriend.

The lesbian bar nearest to where I lived was called the *Happy Hour*. It was about a twenty-minute drive from my studio apartment. Being at the *Happy Hour* made me feel like I was normal. It felt so freeing to be in a place where there were women just like me and where it was safe to be my authentic lesbian self.

Within a few short months, I made a new set of lesbian friends who liked to party as much as I did. We hit all the gay bars and gay pride festivals throughout Southern California. It was a total blast and, in many ways, was like a rebirth!

Even though coming out was awesome, my drinking, food, and weight were seriously out of control. At twenty-two, I weighed over 270 pounds. I was drinking a twelve-pack of beer per day and usually more on the weekends. I also smoked marijuana and cigarettes daily and occasionally partook in other party drugs. I tried to quit drinking a few times on my own but couldn't get even one day off alcohol. The pull toward drinking was so intense and overwhelming that I felt powerless to resist it.

I had so much shame about my drinking that I went to different liquor stores each day to avoid the embarrassment of buying my daily twelve-pack from the same clerk. I'm sure the clerks all knew I was an alcoholic, but my shame was too intense to make it obvious.

I'd also tried to lose weight without success. I finally just gave up and ate, drank, and smoked how I wanted to. I felt deep guilt and shame for not having the inner strength and resolve to control myself around drugs, alcohol, and food. But it was too hard, if not impossible, to stop or control it. So, I just let it have its way with me.

I hated myself for drinking the way I did and for the horrible hangovers I subjected myself to. I found myself stuck in a self-destructive spiral that kept spinning, leaving me feeling utterly powerless to do anything about it.

My drinking and using not only impacted my self-esteem and weight. It also affected my work. I was an insurance biller at Children's Hospital during this time. My pattern with employers was rather predictable. By about the third-year mark, my lack of productivity and tendency to call in sick on Mondays with hangovers would catch up with me, and I could tell I was about to be written up or fired. To avoid losing my job, I would find another one before it happened. As a result, I worked at several local hospitals billing insurance during my drinking career.

## Coming Out to My Family

I met my first girlfriend at the *Happy Hour* when I was twenty-three. After being together for about a year, we decided to move in together. Since I wasn't willing to lie to my mom about my partner being just my roommate, I knew it was time for me to come out.

My mom's initial reaction to learning I was a lesbian was to cry. Since my dad had wanted a son, she thought it was his fault for encouraging me to embrace my tomboyish energy. Of course, he hadn't needed to convince me to embrace being a tomboy. It was just who I was.

My mom also shared her concerns that embracing a lesbian lifestyle would set me up for a really tough life. What's interesting about this perception is that the toughest life in my mind would have been to deny my true self.

Once I came out and felt more comfortable talking openly about my lifestyle in front of her, she would say things like, "I know you've come out, but do you need to talk about being gay so much?" Or "I just don't like that word, *lesbian*. Do you have to use that word?"

The fact that the word *lesbian*, which embodied who I was, was so distasteful to her that she couldn't stand to even hear it left me feeling, one more time, that it wasn't okay to be who I was.

Another sign that she wasn't thrilled with my lifestyle would come out in the types of questions she'd inevitably ask when I'd go through a breakup and was single.

"Have you thought about dating guys now that you're single?" she'd ask. When I'd reply, "No, Mom, I'm gay," she would say, "Why don't you just give it a try?" When I finally got sick of her nagging me to date guys, I would reply, "Have you thought about dating women? Why don't you just give it a try?" Turning the tables on her seemed to make her finally get it, to where she finally stopped trying to get me to date men.

When I came out to my sister, she said she didn't agree with it but still loved me. I knew my dad knew I was gay because I knew my sister had told him, but he never acknowledged it openly. He didn't reject my partner and me at holiday gatherings either. It was more or less like a "don't ask, don't tell" environment.

Although my parents and sister did the best they could to be open and accepting when I came out, sadly, I was still left feeling on some level that it just wasn't okay with them to be who I was.

## The Trauma of Living in a Homophobic Culture

In the years after coming out to my family, my sexual orientation seemed to be, for the most part, not a big issue. It wasn't like my family was thrilled with it. It was more like they tolerated it. The environments I still had the most difficulty being out were at work and with people I didn't know well.

Being an out gay, lesbian, bi, or trans person in the 1980s was a whole different reality than it is in 2022.

Just until a few years ago, before gay marriage became legal in 2015, I would frequently be at work or at a straight social function, where the conversation would frequently reach the point where I would be asked questions such as:

- Do you have a boyfriend?
- Are you married?
- Are you in a relationship?
- Do you have children?
- Where is your husband?

Once I'd get these types of questions, I'd immediately tense up since I needed to decide on the spot whether I needed to lie, tell the truth, or avoid the question. In a split second, I'd have to decide if the person was safe and if telling the truth would affect my job, family, or career.

Going through this kind of stress simply to answer basic questions about my relationship or family status every time I started to get to know a new person was a major deal! Coming out meant risking losing your job, children, or even your family back then. Unless I felt safe, which was typically only with other gay people or known gay-friendly people, I kept my sexual orientation hidden.

One time, when I was twenty-three, I was caught off guard when my girlfriend surprised me by sending flowers to my work for my birthday. Feeling pressured by coworkers to reveal who they were from, I lied and said they were from a boyfriend. After going through the stress of keeping the charade up about my partner's gender, I decided at subsequent jobs that it would be much less stressful to simply lie and say I was single, even if I was in a long-term relationship with a woman.

I didn't realize how damaging and isolating it was to hide who I was at work and with people I didn't feel safe coming out to. Keeping the real me hidden required me to avoid sharing anything that really mattered to me.

Whenever I was asked how my weekends, holidays, or vacations went by my co-workers, I would give the same generic answer: "It was good." Or "I spent it with friends or my family." Or I would quickly change the subject to deflect the focus from being on my personal life.

This kept my relationships at work extremely shallow and left me feeling sad that I lacked the same kind of connection and camaraderie that my coworkers had with each other.

# CHAPTER 4

---

# GETTING SOBER: MY TICKET OUT OF HELL & INTO HEALING AND RECOVERY

## 1987: AGE 27

27—300lbs. Mom & I. This is what untreated complex PTSD looks like.

What began as a teenage girl wanting to have fun and party with her friends turned into a decade of battling a serious, life-threatening drug and alcohol addiction.

It was 1987. I was twenty-seven, and my daily drinking and using had progressed to the point where they no longer produced the joy and bliss on demand like they did when I was sixteen. Instead, they functioned more like medication I needed to take to take the edge off of how crappy I felt.

To see where I was headed, all I needed to do was look at the disaster my mom's life had become. She'd lost her marriage, family, health, friends, and self-respect, and she was getting worse by the month. I knew if I continued, I would end up just like her. In a weird sort of way, she inspired me to get sober. There was no way I wanted to end up like her: a very sad, lonely alcoholic.

It had gotten to the point where I drank just so I could feel functional enough to do the minimum tasks of life. I remember looking at the eighteen beers in the refrigerator that I knew I had to drink to get where I needed to be and thinking, *Man, I hate that I have to drink this many beers to get the buzz I want.* Yet I knew if I switched to hard liquor, I would get too drunk too soon and get way out of control and sloppy. I didn't like being that kind of a drunk, so I would soldier on and not even feel a buzz until my eighth or ninth beer.

The party with booze and marijuana had ended a few short years after it started. Basically, the only thing drinking and using accomplished was to help me feel less crappy.

The other downfall of my need to drink so much beer was that it only added to my serious weight problem. By the time I was ready to get sober, my weight had shot up to around 300lbs. This only added to the mountain of shame I already had about not being able to control my drinking and using.

Even though the hangovers were hell, and I hated what alcohol and marijuana were doing to me, I still struggled with whether I even wanted to quit. It seemed like drinking and getting high were the only things I had to take the edge off of how crappy I felt.

The other thing that made the idea of quitting so hard was that I thought I'd be giving up the ability to ever have fun again. Since drinking and getting high were the only ways I thought I could have fun, the idea of living without alcohol or marijuana felt like I'd be signing up for a totally dull, depressing existence. This made me question if quitting was even worth it.

I was in a catch-22. Drinking and using made my life a living hell. Yet the only way I thought I could find relief from my living hell and have any hope for enjoying my life was by drinking and using.

## Hitting Bottom

I was strangely proud of the fact that I wasn't in denial about being an alcoholic. My denial was about believing my life was manageable. My philosophy about my alcoholism was rather cavalier; I simply told myself I would ride it as long as I could.

My bottom finally found me while in the midst of a horrific two-day hangover. I was sick as a dog and flat-out hated myself for not being able to quit, and for the hell I kept putting myself through with alcohol.

After ten years of daily drinking, smoking, using, binge eating, and weighing over 300lbs, I'd finally ridden it as long as I could. I'd had enough. I was sick of feeling like crap all the time, hating myself, hating my life, and knowing all along I was killing myself.

There's a passage from the Big Book of Alcoholics Anonymous (the main text of the program) that states when an alcoholic has hit or is nearing their bottom, they'll often experience:

*Pitiful and incomprehensible demoralization.*

Yep, that would describe me that weekend. Thank God I'd hit bottom. I couldn't do it anymore. I was ready. Ready to do anything to stop the nightmare of my life.

I was ready to get sober.

## My First AA Meeting

Since we both had failed numerous times trying to quit drinking and using on our own, my girlfriend and I decided to give Alcoholics Anonymous a try. Thankfully, we'd heard about gay AA meetings and found one on a Tuesday night in Orange County.

The name of the AA club where the meetings were held was somewhat uncomfortable for me. It was called *Alcoholic Services for Homosexuals*, or *ASH* for short. It seemed like it should have been called Alcoholic Services for Gays and Lesbians since that would have been a more politically correct way to refer to the gay and lesbian community in the 80s. My discomfort with the term homosexual was due to it being the predominant word used by homophobic groups, religions, and organizations to spew anti-gay rhetoric.

ASH was located in a sleazy, old strip mall next to a pizza place. The funny thing is that it was almost directly across the street from the *Happy Hour* lesbian bar where I'd been a regular for the past six years.

The front door of ASH had a purposeful lack of signage. Unless you knew what the letters stood for, you wouldn't know what ASH was. When I walked in, the scent of stale cigarette smoke hit me. It was dark and dingy, and the vibe reminded me of some of the gay dive bars I'd gone to. There was a coffee bar to the right, where you could buy soft drinks, snacks, and cigarettes. Next to the coffee bar was a small area with some worn-out donated couches and a coffee table where members could hang out.

At the front of the room was a small stage, a podium, and two large hanging scrolls of the Twelve Steps and the Twelve Traditions of AA. In between the scrolls was a small black sign with tacky, off-center letters that spelled out the club's full name, *Alcoholic Services for Homosexuals*. On the wall behind the podium was a framed photo of Bill Wilson, the co-founder of AA, along with a few framed AA sayings: "Keep Coming Back" and "One Day at a Time." When I looked up at the scrolls and the framed AA sayings, I couldn't help but notice the cigarette smoke-stained popcorn ceiling above them.

In front of the stage, eight rectangular folding tables had been arranged to form a large square. About sixty metal folding chairs surrounded the tables for members to sit at while attending the club's various Twelve-Step meetings. It was as if this beaten and battered AA club was a mirror reflection of the beaten and battered souls of its recovering gay and lesbian members.

My first AA meeting was a Tuesday-night women's book study. There were about fifteen women there that night. In this type of meeting, each member reads a paragraph from the *Twelve and Twelve* (short for AA's *Twelve Steps and Twelve Traditions* book). The language in it was really old school. It was written somewhere between the thirties and forties and hadn't been revised much. They did refer to God a bit more than I was comfortable with. I was hoping that these God references didn't mean I needed to "get religion" to get sober since I'd let go of my affiliation with religion back in my teens and had no interest whatsoever in taking it back up.

As the meeting progressed, I was amazed when one of the women mentioned she had seven days of sobriety. Then another one shared that she had ninety days, and some even had a year or more! Given I hadn't been able to stay sober for even one day, hearing several women share that they'd found a way to stop drinking blew my mind. Suddenly, I thought, *If these women could stop drinking, then maybe I could too.*

Thoughts began flooding my mind about what getting sober could mean for me; *Oh my God, maybe I could get my life back. And maybe I could even make something of myself!* The feeling of inspiration that I could actually quit drinking and what that could mean for my future was a hope I'd never experienced before. It was exhilarating!

This was what one AA meeting did for me! Needless to say, I went back, and after a couple of months, lots of meetings, and a few starts and stops, I was able to put together over twelve years of consistent sobriety.

Sadly, my girlfriend had a more difficult time staying sober. Within a few months, it became clear she would not be pursuing a sober lifestyle. I certainly knew I couldn't stay with her if she continued to drink because it would put my sobriety at risk. This was when I knew I had to make the very difficult decision to let go of the relationship.

I was twenty-seven years old when I walked into the doors of ASH, and I can honestly say that AA and ASH saved my life. AA provided the hope, structure, support, and a community of lesbian and gay sober members to connect and have fun with so I didn't have to go back to drinking. It also opened the door to a new kind of spirituality I'd never even known existed.

## How Alcoholics Anonymous Helped Me Get & Stay Sober

In AA, you get to choose your own Higher Power. Unlike Catholicism, you're asked to find a power greater than yourself. It doesn't matter what it is as long as it's not you. I chose AA as my higher power since it was the only thing that was ever successful at helping me get and stay sober.

I was told in AA that you had to be willing to go to any lengths to stay sober. Since I never wanted to go back to the hell I came from as a practicing alcoholic, I took it very seriously—as if my life depended on it because it did. I did what I was told. I made a lot of AA friends, worked the Steps, and went to lots of meetings. It required a complete lifestyle change. But I was desperate. I knew I was miserable and dying, so I was ready to do whatever it took to stay sober.

As the days, weeks, and months went by, my confidence in my ability to stay sober grew. I picked up thirty, sixty, and ninety-day sobriety chips. I started learning all kinds of new ways to think about life, face challenges, and manage my life in healthy ways. It was so wonderful to finally be sober, not have hangovers, see my life getting better, and have a supportive community be there for me. It was incredibly healing, and it felt so good!

It's as if I didn't know what I was missing because I'd never had this kind of love and acceptance before. Since my family was so dysfunctional, I'd never learned healthy ways to deal with conflict or be in mutually supportive relationships. I didn't feel safe talking about my feelings with my family. But in AA, I felt safe to share about anything since I knew I would be accepted.

The stories I heard from fellow alcoholics at AA meetings ranged from losing marriages and jobs to resorting to prostitution, going to prison, being thrown in psych wards, and beyond. They made me feel that I was okay and would be accepted no matter what I'd done while I was drinking.

Nobody judged anyone else when they shared the crazy things they'd done during their drinking careers. In fact, it seemed that most members could laugh at themselves for all the drama and craziness that had gone down when they were in their addiction. Often during meetings, the whole room would erupt into hysterical laughter at some of the crazy stories that were shared.

It was so freeing to feel safe to share anything at meetings. Hearing so much laughter in AA gave me hope that I could actually have fun being sober. I thrived in this environment. Everything began turning around in my life. I made a lot of close, sober girlfriends. It was like a new, healthy, sober family had started forming in my life!

## The Value of AA Sponsorship

After my first year of sobriety, I had worked the first three Steps but felt stuck on Step Four. This Step asks you to take a fearless moral inventory of your life. Since I was so resistant to doing this step, it was obvious I needed help. This was when I decided to get a sponsor. I hadn't wanted to get a sponsor when I first got sober since it meant being accountable. Yet, at the same time, I'd heard at meetings that if you're serious about staying sober, you really need to work with a sponsor.

I met Rosalee at a Tuesday-night women's meeting in Tustin. She was about fifty and had a kind, motherly vibe about her. She had ten years of sobriety, and to me, having ten years was like being a sobriety rock star! After attending the meeting for about a month and being impressed by what she shared, I asked her to be my sponsor. Thankfully, she agreed.

She worked with her sponsees by having them over one night a week for dinner. Monday was designated as my night. During our visits, I shared how I was doing on my Steps and my overall sober life, and she gave me her support and guidance.

If I was going through relationship issues, she'd say, "Honey, you're going to be in a lot of different relationships in your sobriety. You're learning what you like and what you don't like. So what do you like, and what don't you like about this person?" Another thing she would say when I was struggling with something was, "Honey, we have options when we're sober. When we're not sober, we only have one option, and that option is to drink. So, let's take a look at your options!" The way she reframed things just made life seem better somehow. She was like the wise (sober) mother figure I'd never had but always wanted.

For the first year in AA, I was terrified to share, so I hid out at speaker meetings where I knew I couldn't be called on. When I shared this with Rosalie, she suggested a way to overcome my fear was to go to discussion meetings, raise my hand, and when called on, simply say, "I promised my sponsor I would raise my hand and share at meetings." And that would be all I would share. Although it initially seemed like a silly thing to say, my fellow AA members loved it, and it helped me overcome my fear by giving me a safe sharing experience. As a result, I began to share on a regular basis, resulting in many members approaching me afterward, thanking me for sharing since they'd had similar experiences.

When I struggled to make new friends in AA, Rosalie suggested I invite members to go for coffee after meetings. When I shared with her I was too uncomfortable to ask a member out for coffee, she suggested I walk up to them, introduce myself and simply state that I promised my sponsor that I would reach out to fellow members and invite them for coffee after the meeting. Although I was still extremely uncomfortable reaching out to a complete stranger, especially in this way, I was always met with kind responses and ended up making some wonderful new friends.

## Sharing My Secrets

Although the main reason I sought out the support of a sponsor was to help me complete Step Four and Five, I still found myself reluctant to start writing my inventory. Just the idea of having to face and disclose all the stuff I did when I was drinking was really scary.

Step Five says you have to share your inventory with another alcoholic. If you have a sponsor, it means you share it with them. That meant I had to share it with Rosalee.

Being vulnerable by exposing the secrets of my past was something I had avoided at all costs up until that point. But now that I was sober and wanted to stay that way, I became willing. I reckoned if facing my past and sharing it with my sponsor meant I'd have a better chance of staying sober than I was all in.

The beauty of having a sponsor is they nudge you to work on your Steps, especially if you don't want to. Thankfully, Rosalee kept nudging me. It took me six months, but I eventually got my fourth step inventory done.

It was now time to share it with Rosalee. Although the thought of sharing it with her terrified me, I knew I needed to bite the bullet and do it if I wanted to give myself the best chance at staying sober. So, I set up a time to meet with her after our regular Monday-night dinner the following week.

Once we'd finished dinner, Rosalee invited me into her den and closed the door. As I looked up at her and nervously began to share my inventory, I was comforted by the kindness and compassion I felt through the loving expression on her face as she met my gaze. I knew I was safe. Finally, after being on edge all day while anticipating this very moment, feeling safe with Rosalie helped my body and mind relax.

After half an hour or so of going through the various items from my inventory, I finally got down to the last few, which were the scariest ones for me to share. As I looked up at Rosalee, I noticed she didn't even raise an eyebrow over what I was sharing. *Thank God*, I thought. *Maybe my stuff isn't that bad after all.* I felt totally relieved.

As we wrapped up, Rosalee acknowledged my courage in being willing to be vulnerable, and she reassured me that everything I'd shared with her was extremely common. She told me I needn't feel ashamed. She also said that as long as I'd learned the lessons those experiences were meant to teach me and was no longer engaging in them, they'd served their purpose as my perfect teachers.

The relief I felt while driving home that night was palpable. It was like a natural high. I felt so proud of myself for walking through my fear and finding that once I was on the other side of it, it wasn't so bad.

Going through Steps Four and Five helped me realize that I'd never been the bad person I'd thought I was. It helped me see that I'm pretty normal after all. I'm so grateful to Rosalee for nudging me to get through these steps because if she hadn't, I would have missed out on one of the most significant healing experiences of my life.

## How AA Helped Save My Life

I know today that had I not fully thrown myself into my recovery, asked Rosalee to be my sponsor, or if I hadn't developed close friendships with AA members, I likely would not have gotten or stayed sober. The truth is, not everyone gets to experience the gift of sobriety.

Sobriety requires a complete change of lifestyle. I found my first year to be the most difficult. You have to let go of your drinking and using friends, the bars, and anything that could pose a potential risk to your sobriety. You also have to go through every holiday, every celebration, and every tragedy the first time sober.

When you give up your primary source of fun and soothing (alcohol, drugs, and your party buddies), you either replace them with healthy alternatives, like personal growth, spirituality, healthy activities, and sober friends, or you relapse. Thankfully, I was ready to make a major change in my life.

A strong Twelve-Step program is designed to help you use the fellowship and the tools in AA to cope with the ups and downs of life instead of using alcohol or drugs.

My sponsor and the close friendships I developed with fellow sober lesbians were what soothed me the most and prevented me from relapsing during the rough patches of my early recovery.

One time I heard an AA "old-timer" say that "AA does for us slowly what alcohol did for us quickly." I thought that was such an elegant way to capture the essence of how AA works.

I learned that I needed to stay committed to not drinking no matter what and trust the process while I learned how to use my new sober support system instead of my drug of choice. I was told if I kept working the program, that my life would get better. But that it would be a slow process.

This is why it was critical that I was totally committed to working my program. Just like the saying in AA goes, "You must be willing to go to any lengths to stay sober." Thank God I took this advice!

Getting sober was truly the hardest thing I've ever done. It's also the greatest gift I've ever received since it literally gave me my life back! Given that I was the kind of alcoholic who couldn't stay sober even one day until I went to AA, I'm here to say that if I can get sober, anyone can!

## Codependency and Family-of-Origin Recovery

Although AA saved my life by helping me get sober, I found that I needed more than just AA for my healing and recovery. I was also drawn to explore other personal and spiritual growth genres outside the program.

After about two years of continuous sobriety, I started exploring different personal development programs and authors. Some of my early favorites were Claudia Black, who wrote a book about adult children of alcoholics, *It Will Never Happen to Me*. I also loved Melody Beattie's *Codependent No More: How to Stop Controlling Others and Start Caring for Yourself*.

Reading these books on adult children of alcoholics and recovering from codependency opened my eyes to realizing that my mom got what she wanted by using guilt and shame to manipulate me. Learning this prompted me to explore CoDA (Co-Dependents Anonymous) and ACA (Adult Children of Alcoholics) meetings. It was perfect timing because I was still struggling with my mom's alcoholic drama. She would call me several times a day to complain about how depressed she was or guilt me for not visiting her more. She sometimes even called me when she was drunk at two or three o'clock in the morning.

After attending ACA and CoDA meetings and hearing similar stories from other members, I came to the realization that my mom's attempts to manipulate me with guilt and shame and her drunken phone calls were no longer acceptable behaviors, and I didn't have to tolerate them any longer.

CoDA opened my eyes to the fact that it was actually okay and that I wasn't a bad or a selfish daughter if I told my mother I would no longer tolerate her abusive and dysfunctional behavior.

It took several years of working on healing my codependency issues to see significant progress in my relationship with my mom. It began with setting healthy boundaries with her. Over time she finally stopped the late-night drunken calls and the guilt tactics. I had to make it clear that if she continued calling me at all hours while she was drunk, I would no longer be available for phone calls or visits. In other words, she would lose me. I was no longer willing to sacrifice my sanity to engage in her insanity.

It eventually took changing my phone number and having a period of no contact with her for her to understand I was serious. I was so sick of putting up with her insanity for so long that I wasn't willing to let her violate my boundaries without her experiencing the consequences. She eventually got that my life had a new price of admission. That price was respecting my boundaries. It took several years of her testing my new boundaries, but eventually, all of these behaviors stopped. Apparently, she valued seeing and speaking to me more than she valued guilting me and calling me when she was drunk.

By setting boundaries with my mom, I risked losing her. If she decided not to respect my boundaries, I needed to be ready to let her go and not see or speak to her any longer. I know this may seem severe to some people, especially when dealing with a parent or family member.

What I've learned from this experience is that I'm not willing to be abused emotionally, physically, spiritually, or financially by anyone. And yes, someone calling you several times a day when you've asked them to stop or calling you when they're drunk and using manipulation to guilt and shame you is emotional abuse.

I'm not willing to tolerate this behavior because it doesn't serve anyone to allow myself to be abused. If I continually allow myself to be abused, I'll eventually get so miserable that I'll relapse and begin drinking, using, smoking, and overeating. The only path this leads to is death. I'm not willing to die to let someone else abuse me.

Some other issues began popping up that required me to set more boundaries and say no to my mom. Since she'd had three DUIs and lost her driver's license, she'd call me for rides even though she could take the bus. As a codependent in recovery, I learned to say, "No, Mom. I won't be able to drive you to the store. You'll need to take the bus."

It was a miracle for me to say no and not feel guilty about it. When she would attempt to guilt me for being a selfish daughter for not driving her, I would readily come back with, "Mom, I've told you that if you try to manipulate me with guilt, I won't speak to you at all." It felt so good to finally have a way to protect myself from allowing her insanity into my life.

Even though she'd stopped calling me while she was drunk, she still had a ton of drama going on in her life. She frequently lost jobs and apartments and needed help moving. She also began calling the suicide hotline again, leading her to be put on seventy-two-hour holds at the local psych hospital. Since she had given the psych hospital my number, I would be the one to get the call to go to pick her up when the hold was over.

Like when she would call these hotlines when I was a child, I don't believe she ever wanted or planned to kill herself. What she really wanted was to be able to drink and be soothed by anyone who would listen to her woes.

Getting into recovery with codependency taught me that I deserve to care for myself by setting healthy boundaries with my mom. Although it took several years to have the courage to communicate and enforce these boundaries, doing so improved the quality of my life immeasurably.

Changing the rules on what I accepted and how I interacted with my family was extremely uncomfortable at first, but once I was willing to feel the fear and do it anyway, my life transformed in every way.

After experiencing so much growth through my CoDA work, I realized that I no longer needed to be a victim of my relationships. Instead, I could rise above my past by proactively choosing healthy, life-affirming relationships over dysfunctional ones. I knew it was time for me to define what I wanted in my relationships versus letting others determine what they wanted from me.

## Going to Therapy with My Mother

At one point, I thought it would be helpful to do a therapy session with my mom to see if a nonbiased therapist could help us create a healthier relationship. At the time, Mom complained that I'd erected emotional walls and didn't spend enough time with her.

She was right about the emotional walls. I had good reason to do so because I knew interacting with her was toxic for me. If I backed down on my boundaries, I knew it would give her free reign to blame, shame, and drain me. After all the work I'd done in CoDA, I wasn't willing to allow myself to be abused by her ever again.

Although I did see therapy as an attempt at having a healthier relationship with my mom, when I got honest with myself, I had to admit that one of my ulterior motives was my hope that she'd make a special connection with the therapist and get the help she needed to get sober. I'm sure, on some level, I was hanging on to the hope that once she got sober, she could finally be there for me.

I offered to pay for the session, so my mom agreed to join me. After speaking with us for fifteen minutes, the therapist asked to speak with my mother one-on-one. Then, about ten minutes later, she asked to talk with me one-on-one. As I sat across from her, she said, "Mary, after speaking to your mother and observing her interact with you, I have to be upfront with you and share that she's operating on an emotional level of a five to six year old child. I don't want to sugarcoat this since I want you to know the truth. Your mother can't be what you need her to be for you, and I'm sorry to say that she will never be able to. The truth is, she's never coming back."

At first, I was shocked to hear her say this about my Mom since I naively felt there was hope for her if she would only do the work to quit drinking. I guess the little girl in me thought with the right help, she could pull her life together and create a happy life for herself like I had after I quit drinking. And once she was sober, I hoped she could finally be the mom I needed her to be for me.

But once the therapist shared her assessment of my mom's emotional health with me, my hope shifted. I realized that I had no control over what my mother would do about her drinking. The basic message from the therapist was that my mother's emotional state was so intractably regressed that she would never have the ability to be there for me whether she was sober or not. In other words, she was never coming back to be the mother I needed.

This realization made me grieve not only for the mother who hadn't been there for me from when I was a young child but also for the nurturing, emotionally healthy mother I'd hoped for had she gotten sober.

Although it was extremely painful to face this reality about my mom, the silver lining was that giving up hope for the mother I wanted freed me up to accept the mother I had.

All any of us want is to be accepted for who we are, warts and all. This is not to say that my acceptance of her continuing to drink meant that I would suddenly start hanging out with her or tolerate any bad behavior. I was still fully committed to honoring and protecting myself with healthy boundaries. My acceptance of her "as is" simply meant that I committed to embracing a mindfulness practice of letting go of my attachment to her being any different than she was.

## The Fallout With My Dad

During this time, my girlfriend and I enrolled in a weekend gay and lesbian personal growth course. During the course, we were given a process designed to bring some completion to our relationship with our parents. The assignment was to write letters to our parents regarding how we felt about our relationship and what, if anything, we wanted to be different about it. We were then told to actually send the letters.

As I contemplated writing my dad's letter, I remembered how uncomfortable I felt sharing my feelings with him. Yet I also knew that if there was a chance to be closer to him, I needed to discuss some of the issues in our relationship that I wasn't okay with.

I started my dad's letter with my intention, which was to have a closer relationship with him. I then explained to do so, we needed to discuss some of the things that had happened over the years that I felt incomplete about.

I began by sharing how hurt I was that he abandoned and betrayed our family by going to Europe with his mistress and then continuing the affair for many years afterward.

I also shared how hurt I felt by his frequent put-downs about my weight.

I finished by sharing how sad I felt when he wasn't supportive when I shared my goal of pursuing a career as a singer. Instead of championing me and being a pillar of support, he instead said I should just get a job since I'd never be able to make enough money as a singer.

Although I was extremely uncomfortable bringing up these topics, I also (naively) trusted the workshop leader's guidance that sending my letter would help me have a closer relationship with him. Once I'd completed my letter, I nervously addressed an envelope and mailed it to him.

After about a week, I got up the courage to call my dad to follow up on the letter and his thoughts. When he answered, I asked, "Did you get my letter?"

He said, "Yes."

"Okay, so what did you think?" I asked.

"I think it's a piece of shit. I think you've been brainwashed by the AA meetings you've been going to!" He responds.

I shockingly respond, "Dad, the entire reason I wrote you this letter is so we can have a closer relationship. But to do so, we need to clear things up that are getting in the way of it."

I attempted to present a quick recap of the letter, briefly mentioning being hurt about his ongoing affair, putting me down about my weight, and not supporting me when I wanted to pursue a singing career.

"What do you mean I didn't support you? He replied in his defense. "I always paid the bills and gave you spending money." "As far as your singing goes, I have friends that could have gotten you an introduction to Sinatra, but the truth is, you don't have what it takes to be a singer." He then put the final nail in the coffin by saying: "You're not my daughter. I don't want to hear from you anymore."

At this point, I was so hurt and angry that all I could do was say, "Fuck you!" And I hung up on him.

As I sat back in my chair, in utter shock over what had just transpired, all I could do was sob. I then thought, *How could he be so mean and insensitive? All I wanted to do was be closer to him! Now we're further apart than ever!* Not only had he invalidated the entire letter and viciously attacked me for what I addressed in it, but he also explicitly disowned me!

After this falling out, we were estranged for about three years. I didn't go to holiday gatherings, birthdays, Father's Day, or anything he would be at.

Three years later, my sister called and said she'd spoken with him and that he would be open to seeing me during the holidays. She asked if I would be open to joining him and his partner, along with her and her husband, for Christmas Eve dinner in Palm Springs. Although I was super nervous about accepting the invitation, I agreed to go.

After a two-hour drive on Christmas Eve, I arrived at the Italian restaurant in Palm Springs for our holiday dinner. As I entered the restaurant, I immediately saw my dad, his partner, my sister, and her husband at a nearby table. As soon as I sat down at the table, I could tell my dad and his partner had drank quite a bit of wine by noticing the empty carafe and the half-empty one next to it.

After about forty-five minutes of small talk, my dad turned to me and casually said, "Gee, Mary. You've been able to quit drinking and smoking, but when it comes to your weight, what have you gained, about 80 pounds since I last saw you?"

I was so incredibly shocked and hurt that he'd made such an insensitive remark about my weight that I immediately got up and ran to the bathroom in tears. My sister followed me and attempted to console me, saying, "Oh my God! I can't believe he said that! I'm going to talk to him about this! This was not okay!"

It did feel good to have my big sister be there for me. But I just needed to keep on crying. This was supposed to be the reunion after a three-year estrangement, and he said what?

Strangely enough, when I returned to the dinner table, my dad didn't even seem to realize he'd done anything wrong or had offended me! Instead of confronting him at the table, I pushed through, had a few bites of my lasagna, got a to-go container, and left early.

My sister did follow through by confronting him later that evening, and my dad called me the next day to apologize for what he'd said. I accepted his apology with a big dose of caution. I knew he would have to do some major internal work to stop his mean-spirited remarks. And I knew that it wasn't going to happen, at least in this lifetime. As I suspected, even after the apology and the three-year estrangement, he still couldn't help himself from making gay slurs or making ignorant, insensitive remarks about the nature of addiction in front of me.

After going through this experience, I've realized that some people are just not emotionally aware or healthy enough to be able to filter what comes out of their mouths. Once I got clarity about this, I learned to limit my contact with my dad to just a few times per year. If he makes insensitive comments when I do see him, I just consider the source and don't personalize it. I view him as a crazy old man with no clue about people's feelings. I now can see his behavior for what it is: a reflection of his own unhealed wounds and a lack of emotional awareness.

## Food and Body Issue Recovery

Food was the first substance I found to soothe myself. In a very real way, it was my best friend. It was there to soothe me when I felt sad, lonely, angry, ashamed, tired, frustrated, or enraged. It was also there to help me celebrate the good stuff too, like birthdays, holidays, and vacations. Unlike my mom and dad, food was a reliable friend who was always there to soften my pain and comfort me.

My affair with food became a love/hate relationship when becoming overweight attracted negative attention. On the one hand, food was my emotional saving grace. But on the other, it caused me deep shame for not having the strength to reign in my eating and being so fat. Yet, at the same time, I felt utterly powerless to stop myself from binge eating. So, one more time, I felt trapped, alone, and powerless in a dynamic that was hurting me.

One of the books that helped me with my eating and body issues in my early recovery was *Feeding the Hungry Heart: The Experience of Compulsive Eating* by Geneen Roth. I also attended many Overeaters Anonymous (OA) meetings to get the support I needed to find healing and recovery from my food addiction and weight issues. I also went to many seminars, workshops, retreats, and anything else that resonated with me to heal my relationship with food, weight, and my body.

I found that food functioned like an anti-anxiety medication for me. Whenever I felt anxious, food calmed me down. It also soothed me whenever I felt alone, sad, or angry. Whenever I felt uncomfortable feelings, I ate. I discovered that a big part of why I ate was that I didn't know how to get my basic needs met. In OA, I learned that if I used healthier communication to ask for what I wanted or set healthy boundaries with people, I had less anxiety, anger, frustration, and sadness, which in turn decreased my need to soothe myself with food.

By attending regular OA meetings, I made a lot of like-minded friends, which in and of itself was a healthy way to be soothed. In addition, I learned how to design a self-loving food and exercise plan. As a result of all these changes, I began to lose weight. It was so exciting to not only be sober but to be losing weight and forging healthier relationships as well!

After two years of working an OA program, I lost 140 pounds and was finally down to a healthy weight. I was so excited to finally be able to wear regular clothes. It also felt so good to feel good about my appearance. It was just so nice not to be embarrassed to be seen in public.

However, as most people know about weight loss, the initial weight loss is hard, but it's not as hard as keeping it off for the long term. I found that my weight fluctuations acted like an emotional barometer indicating the level of stress or emotional pain I was experiencing during a specific period of time.

I believe the primary reason I was able to stay sober and experience so much success losing weight in OA was that I intentionally surrounded myself with a close group of lesbian friends who were all sober in AA. Many of my AA friends were also working an OA program too. Since we were all committed to our recovery and our health and wellness on emotional, spiritual, and physical levels, we naturally supported each other. I also felt completely safe with my recovery friends because we were all in the same boat.

One of the most positive things I did for my health, weight, and well-being in my early recovery was taking up bicycling with my AA and OA recovery girlfriends. We got together and rode every weekend. We challenged ourselves to do longer and longer bike rides. Eventually, we got up to doing thirty-mile rides on a regular basis. One time we even rode from Orange County to San Diego and then took the train back.

We also hiked or walked, then went out for a fun lunch on the weekends. It felt amazing to feel so good in my body, and it was so exhilarating to be accomplishing such life-enhancing goals! It was an incredible time of growth for me on every level.

## Exploring the Law of Attraction and Metaphysics

A new philosophy I discovered in my late twenties was the Church of Religious Science in Huntington Beach. My girlfriend & I were referred to this church by a recovery counselor who said it was gay-friendly, and there were quite a few people in recovery who attended services. The church was based on the Science of Mind philosophy. I loved how the congregation was a mix of all types of people, including out gays and lesbians. In 1987, seeing gay and lesbian couples holding hands at church was a big deal!

I was completely blown away by how different this church was from any Catholic Mass I'd been to. The central message was, "Change your thinking, change your life." The teachings were aligned with the Law of Attraction philosophy. The funny thing about this church is that it was the same church that Terry Cole-Whittaker, the reverend my mom and I had enjoyed watching in my early teens, hailed from.

I loved the idea that you could change your life by changing your mindset and that there was a benevolent force that would align with you when you did so. I also loved that the church members had a prosperity consciousness too. It was much more metaphysically based than the Bible-based Catholic Church I'd been brought up with.

I totally fell in love with the church and its awe-inspiring philosophy. It was more like going to a motivational seminar than a church. They also had a few affinity groups within the church. One of these was a Friday night gay and lesbian support group I attended regularly. I was thrilled to find a safe space to connect with gay and lesbian friends who were also into personal and spiritual growth.

The church also invited thought leaders aligned with their philosophy to visit and hold workshops. One such leader was Wayne Dyer. This was the same author of the book *Your Erroneous Zones* that my mom and I read back in the seventies. Dyer ended up becoming a favorite author of mine.

Louise Hay was also a Religious Science minister and was just getting started back then. I loved reading her book *Heal Your Body* and learning how my mind, body, and spirit were connected. I thoroughly enjoyed learning about these philosophies and meeting such life-affirming, spiritually oriented people. It was like I was on this incredible spiritual odyssey where I was becoming more and more confident that I really could create the life of my dreams!

In the mid-nineties, I was introduced to another teacher, Esther Hicks, who taught the Abraham Law of Attraction philosophy. I became an instant fan and began learning about the Law of Attraction through listening to her huge catalog of audio programs.

Due to my work, I spent a lot of time driving, so I always made sure I had an Abraham tape or CD playing while on the road. My car became a rolling classroom where I completely immersed myself in learning how to apply Abraham's Law of Attraction processes to manifest what I desired in my day-to-day life. It was so exciting witnessing my life change as I honed my Law of Attraction skills.

## Pursuing Singing & Playing Guitar

In 1988, I ran into an old drinking friend at ASH, Mary Von. We'd previously partied together in the lesbian bars, where we used to talk about loving music and wanting to be singers. But it never went beyond talk because we were too busy drinking to do anything about it. Now that we were both sober, she invited me to start hanging out with her to practice our singing together.

It was like a dream come true to have a positive, sober friend to sing with. Mary Von was a huge influence in helping me take my singing and music seriously for the first time. She had about as much sobriety as I did and already had put a singing act together. She was even getting paid to play at restaurants and coffeehouses. Seeing her pursue a career in music inspired me to do the same.

I'd taken guitar lessons for about a year when I was seventeen. I learned how to play basic chords and could play a handful of songs. However, once I got seriously into my drinking, I'd let singing and playing guitar go.

30—3 years sober & 140lbs lighter from my OA recovery. Performing at the 1990 Orange County gay pride festival.

It was so much fun getting back into it in sobriety. I also discovered how healing it was for me to be able to pick up my guitar and sing when I was dealing with difficult feelings. It was also a perfect vehicle for my authentic self-expression. Reconnecting with singing and music was one of many gifts I would receive from getting sober.

My first public performance was at a talent show that ASH put on. It was the perfect place for me to be vulnerable for the first time with my music. I knew I would be loved no matter how much I sucked because I was with my gay and lesbian recovery homies! I was super nervous about performing publicly for the first time, so I made sure I practiced the three songs I planned to perform at least fifty times each.

Finally, the day came for me to make my debut performance. I was so nervous. I vividly remember my voice and fingers shaking while performing in front of the eighty-member audience. The good news is that it went reasonably well, given it was my first public performance. It was so wonderful to experience everyone at ASH being so supportive and complimentary of my singing. It was also exhilarating to walk through such a major fear and come out of it feeling so wonderful.

After that performance, a few of my fellow recovering lesbian musicians—who had also performed in the ASH talent show—decided it would be easier for us to get more gigs if we formed a troupe and booked all of our acts under one name. Given we were all lesbian musicians, we decided to call ourselves Dykes on Mics. We ended up booking gigs all over Southern California and played at various women's bookstores, gay and lesbian festivals, and various events. It was so fun, and it felt so great to be part of a group of recovering lesbian musicians.

## Becoming a Songwriter

One of my musician friends, Chris Rose, seemed to always show up at our gigs with a new song she'd written. One night I asked her what her process was for writing songs, and thankfully, she agreed to meet with me to show me how.

As a result of her support, I turned a lot of my journaling into song lyrics. I then played around on my guitar to find the chords and a melody that best delivered the feeling I wanted the song to convey. I naturally gravitated to writing songs about my recovery and transformational journey.

Becoming a songwriter also gave me the hope of having a better chance at launching a successful career in music since I was now both a singer and a songwriter. It was an exciting time to be pursuing my musical ambitions. I was twenty-nine and making my dreams come true. It felt amazing.

## Getting My Musical Act Together

After watching what Mary Von had put together to become a professional singer and guitar player, I knew if I was going to get serious about pursuing a career in music, I would need to commit to mastering my craft. This meant I needed to put together a solo act. So, I practiced my singing and guitar playing every day until I reached my goal of being able to perform forty-five cover songs by heart.

Within one year, I'd put together an entire solo act. The forty-five songs I knew by heart were enough to fill three forty-five-minute sets. I also recorded a demo tape and had a bio printed, which I used to get gigs. Over the next few years, I would go on to play at several coffeehouses, cafes, weddings, parties, gay pride festivals, lesbian bookstores, on KPFK radio, and anywhere they let me.

## Recording My First Album of Original Songs

By 1992 I'd written thirteen original songs about my journey of recovery and transformation. I was able to get my songs recorded with the help of a musician friend who had a home recording studio. I named the album *I'm Showin up for My Dream*. I found a designer to create the cover, had one hundred copies made on cassette, and sold them at my gigs.

Twenty-seven years later, in 2019, I followed Wayne Dyer's lead and decided that I wasn't going to die with my music still in me. So, I had my 1992 analog cassette album transferred to a digital format so it could be listened to on streaming platforms like Spotify, iTunes, Amazon Music, iHeart Radio, and Google Music.

I'm Showin Up For My Dream

1992 cassette cover for the album of original songs I recorded.

My intention in getting my songs out there on a global scale is to inspire and uplift people in recovery, survivors, aspiring singers, and artists of all kinds to know that sharing their voices with the world matters. The entire album can be accessed by searching for *Mary Giuliani; I'm Showin up For My Dream* on all the major streaming platforms such as Amazon Music, ITunes and Spotify.

What's so interesting about listening to these songs today is recognizing that every single one of them is about my trauma-healing and recovery journey. Since I had no idea I was dealing with trauma, I described them as songs about my healing, recovery, and transformational journey.

I'm so grateful I could get these songs written and recorded since they capture what I was going through in my early recovery when I was struggling to find myself and the love and connection I longed for in relationships.

Although I had some of the most phenomenal experiences of my life singing, playing, and writing songs, and it was a pivotal part of my initial journey of healing and recovery, I found that my passion for pursuing a career in music waned over time. I was much more drawn to helping people heal, grow, and live lives they love than I was to singing, writing songs, and performing for audiences.

I knew if I wanted to change my focus to pursuing a career in personal development, I would need to chart a whole new course to figure out how to make it happen.

# CHAPTER 5

---

# CAREER, MONEY, & SELF-ESTEEM RECOVERY

### 1992: AGE 33

At thirty-three, I was five years sober and desperately unhappy with my work as an insurance biller. Looking back, I was never really happy billing insurance for a living. But before I'd gotten sober, I felt lucky that I even had this job and income level, given I had no college education. Before my recovery, I never even dreamed or believed I could do anything else.

But once I was sober and had done quite a bit of personal and spiritual growth work, I wasn't the same person I'd been five years earlier. My life had completely transformed.

I was sober, I'd quit smoking, I'd lost 140lbs, and I was maintaining a healthy weight. I was also in a relationship with a woman I loved and had a wonderful circle of close sober friends

I'd been studying the law of attraction philosophy, which is all about learning how to manifest your desires. With all of this growth under my belt, I saw my desire for more meaningful work as the perfect opportunity to put what I'd learned to the test.

## The Search for Meaningful Work

Once I was clear that I wasn't going to pursue a career in music, I shifted to focusing on how I could find work that was aligned with more of who I'd become. I started journaling to get ideas on combining some of the skills I'd gained from insurance billing with my love for personal growth.

I also realized that if I was going to explore more entrepreneurial ways to make a living, I might need to let go of depending on the salary I made from my insurance billing job. So, my first priority was to minimize my expenses so I wouldn't need as much money to live on while I got my new career off the ground. While I still had it, I used my full-time income to pay off my debt. The only expenses I had left were basic needs like food, housing, insurance, gas, and entertainment.

While deciding what industry to target for jobs, I thought it would be helpful to at least get my foot in the door in the personal-growth field. So, I cold-called therapists and practitioners who advertised in local holistic and new-age magazines to see if they needed any administrative help. I got a part-time administrative job with a therapist who held inner-child seminars.

That was when I gave notice at my insurance billing job. I also still had a few music gigs that produced some income. It was so wonderful to no longer have to tolerate the soul-sucking insurance billing job. However, the income from the therapist and my music gigs were not quite enough to cover my expenses. This prompted me to look for additional work.

While searching the want ads, I saw an ad for a commission-only sales position with a women's networking organization that had chapters in Orange County and Los Angeles. The job was cold-calling women business owners throughout Southern California and selling them a business networking membership that allowed them to attend dinner meetings, network with other entrepreneurs, and develop referral relationships to grow their businesses. It also involved selling advertising to the members in the organization's directory.

I got the interview and was offered the job. It required me to drive seventy miles one way into West Los Angeles from Orange County five days a week for training that would last several months. Also, since it was a commission-only job, I wouldn't get paid a dime unless I sold a membership or an ad. I decided to take a risk and went for it.

It was so hard being in sales for the first year. So much rejection and so much pressure to sell!

Fortunately, my partner at the time had many years of sales experience in her background and was a great pillar of support for me. I cried many a tear for the first two years of my sales career!

The upside to my new job was that it required me to learn some extremely beneficial sales and marketing skills. It also required I attend business networking events where I was surrounded by powerful women business owners creating their own destinies as entrepreneurs. Little did I know that gaining sales and marketing experience and being inspired by so many powerful women entrepreneurs would provide the exact keys I needed to unlock my future success.

## Birth of the Entrepreneur, 1992: Age 33

After selling memberships and advertising for the women's business network for about a year, I noticed while cold-calling gay and lesbian advertisers that although they showed little interest in joining a straight woman's networking group, many stated if we offered gay and lesbian chapters, they would join. I brought up the idea to the owner of my company, hoping she would be open to launching gay and lesbian chapters, but she declined.

After seeing my company had no interest in serving the gay and lesbian community, I decided to ask Ron, a gay coworker of mine, to join me as a business partner so we could start our own networking organization for gay, lesbian, and gay-friendly entrepreneurs. He accepted, and in 1992, we began planning the launch of our own gay and lesbian business networking organization.

Since Ron lived in Hollywood and I lived in Orange County, we met halfway at a coffee shop once a week to lay out the vision, action plan, and division of labor for executing our business plan. I was thirty-two, and it was so exciting to be a partner in my first company!

We got busy selling memberships, setting up a solid infrastructure for the organization, and promoting the network. We launched the business with our first networking meeting at Ozz Dance Club & Lounge, a gay and lesbian venue in Orange County. There were fifty-five people at our first networking meeting. It was so exhilarating to see what we'd created out of nothing but our vision and commitment to taking action to bring it into existence!

Within the first two years, we had six chapters and over three hundred members in the network. What was remarkable about it was that I could live off our company's income without needing another job. On top of that, our business continued to grow each year, allowing me to live a very comfortable lifestyle for another nine years.

Our company's success just didn't fall into our laps. We worked our butts off to launch and grow the network. The funny thing about working to grow my own company was that the work didn't feel the same as when I was working to grow someone else's business. When it's your baby, you're fully invested.

You're excited to see it grow and blossom. You still get tired, but it's a good tired.

At one point, I was contacted by a journalist from The Orange County Register who was writing a story about opportunities opening up for gay and lesbian professionals in our county. I invited her to one

GAY HURDLES EASE

**Making strides**

Opportunities are growing for gays and lesbians in O.C. workplaces
AT WORK ■ PAGE 6

Mary Graham (cq.) 43
at a meeting of the
Community Business
Network, an
organization of gay
and gay-friendly
business people

36 years old, 1995- Photo of me on the front page of the business section of The Orange County Register leading a meeting at my lesbian, gay and gay-friendly business networking organization.

of my networking meetings to meet my members. She took many photos, including those of me leading the meeting. Little did I know that within a few weeks, one of the photos she took of me leading my networking event would appear on the front page of the business section of the paper with the title "Gay Hurdles Ease." It felt amazing not only to have my picture and an article about my company featured in my local paper but also to be acknowledged for my contribution to the gay and lesbian business community.

Ron and I continued working as partners for about two years and then decided to split the business in half. I took the Orange County, Long Beach, and Inland Empire chapters, and he took the Los Angeles, San Fernando Valley, and South Bay chapters. It was a tough split, but it was necessary because we were on a totally different page with each of our visions for the network.

Sadly, a few years after we split the business, he informed me he was HIV+ and, within a few months, died of AIDS. Since there was no one to run his chapters, he asked me if I could step in and run them right before he passed, which I agreed to do.

At the peak of the business, I had nine chapters and six hundred members in Southern California. After being in business for three years, I had three full-time employees and a beautiful office and was making more money than I'd ever made.

When I looked back on where I'd been just five years earlier—a practicing alcoholic who got drunk and high every day, weighed over 300 pounds, lived paycheck to paycheck, and hated her life—I was beyond thrilled.

It was truly astounding to see how much I'd been able to accomplish in such a short period of time.

## The Key Pillars of My Success

Looking back, I know that if I hadn't gotten sober, none of this would have happened. Also, if I hadn't invested in my personal and spiritual growth by taking personal development and business classes, going to retreats, reading books, listening to tapes and CDs, and attending different Twelve-Step groups, it wouldn't have happened.

It also wouldn't have happened if I hadn't stepped out of my comfort zone by quitting a job I hated and taking the commission-only sales job. After all, that's where I met my future business partner and got inspired to start my own gay and lesbian business network.

The point here is that if you're serious about following your dreams, you have to be willing to step out of your comfort zone and take risks on a regular basis.

I worked on one area of growth at a time. Obviously, I had to get sober first for anything else to happen. Then I joined OA and got into recovery with my food and weight. Once I got a foothold with my food and weight issues, I quit smoking. The next area I focused on was learning how to forge healthy relationships by getting into recovery with codependency. And last, I actively sought out and found a career that was a better fit for who I'd become.

Taking incremental steps helped bolster my confidence, abilities, and courage to transform the next area of my life. Getting sober and making all of these changes were the most challenging things I'd ever done. Yet, getting past these major hurdles gave me the solid foundation I needed to unlock my potential.

## Becoming a Life Coach

One night in 1994, I met a life coach at one of my business networking meetings. I'd never heard of life coaching before and asked him what a life coach was. He said life coaching is about helping a person identify their core values and then helping them be true to themselves by setting value-based goals for the main areas of their life. It also involves helping clients identify and overcome the obstacles that get in their way and assisting them with finding the motivation and specific steps they need to take to reach their goals.

This was exactly the training I'd wanted to find years earlier after getting sober! I just didn't know it existed. I immediately knew that becoming a life coach would be the perfect path to help me acquire the skills I needed to become what I'd wanted to pursue since my early recovery: a personal-growth workshop facilitator, motivational speaker, and author.

In fact, one of the reasons I was motivated to start the business network in the first place was because I saw how it could provide the platform I needed to promote my future work in personal development.

Since coaching was perfectly aligned with the vision I had for my life, I dove headfirst into getting trained as a coach by enrolling at the Coaches Training Institute (CTI)—one of the most respected coach training programs in the field.

I loved my coach training program because the curriculum was perfectly aligned with my passion for personal growth. It was also exciting to see how I could use my new coaching skills to help the clients in my networking organization grow their businesses and experience more meaning and purpose in their lives.

The nine-month CTI coach certification program I'd enrolled in was extremely rigorous and required we prove our competency as coaches through various checkpoints throughout the program and through an in-person, videotaped final exam. This exam was written and oral, which meant we had to demonstrate we were competent coaches by doing a coaching session with one of the founders. Thank God I passed and received my first formal designation as a CPPC- Certified Professional, Personal Coach.

I started promoting myself as a business coach to the small business owners in my business network. Within a relatively short period of time, I built a substantial client base as a business coach. Within five years, I had accrued the required training and the number of hours working with clients to receive my Master Certified Coach-MCC (the highest designation you can achieve) from the International Coach Federation, the organization that sets standards and ethics for the coaching industry.

This was a big deal since it takes a significant amount of education, training, and hours of coaching experience to be eligible for the Master Certified Coach designation.

After working with business coaching clients for several years, it became clear that I was more interested in helping people grow on a personal level versus being solely focused on helping people grow their businesses. This prompted me to shift my marketing to attract more personal development oriented clients instead of business coaching clients. Sadly, once I began working with more clients who wanted to work on personal development, I started experiencing more anxiety instead of more satisfaction and fulfillment with my practice.

I couldn't seem to shake feeling responsible for my client's well-being and outcomes. When things weren't going well for a client, I often felt like it was my fault and that maybe I just didn't have what it took to be a competent coach. What was really strange about this dynamic was that I knew on a cognitive level that I was a good coach and wasn't responsible for client outcomes. Nonetheless, I still found myself getting triggered into some pretty intense anxiety and shame while working with clients.

Over the course of several years, I tried everything I knew to overcome these triggers. But the anxiety

I experienced while working with my coaching clients was just too overwhelming. This prompted me to put my individual coaching practice on hold and offer group coaching and workshops instead. It would be another seventeen years before I would discover why working with personal development oriented coaching clients was so triggering for me.

## H.A.L.T.

By the time I'd been in business for five years, the day-to-day stress was grueling and began taking its toll on me. I managed the sales and operations side of the company from nine to five, Monday through Friday. I also facilitated all eight monthly dinner networking meetings. This required that I drive to eight locations throughout Southern California during rush-hour traffic two to three times a week. I also managed several full-time employees and held a few monthly seminars. This meant I was working sixty-five to eighty hours a week.

One thing they talk about in AA is the need to be careful about the level of stress you put yourself under because it can undermine your sobriety and cause a relapse. I started seeing the external signs of stress appear on my bathroom scale. Over five years, I gained back thirty of the 140 pounds I'd lost through my OA program. It didn't help that I was served a full-course meal during my dinner networking meetings three times a week.

Before my weight gain, I'd been able to forgo the dessert that came with the meals and was able to purposely eat smaller portions at my networking meetings. However, once the stress got to a certain point, I couldn't seem to resist the desserts and the larger portions instead of using healthier ways to soothe myself.

An acronym I learned in AA is HALT. The idea behind HALT is that when a sober alcoholic becomes too hungry, angry, lonely, or tired, they put themselves at high risk for relapse. Part of working a strong AA program is finding ways to manage HALT symptoms through various self-care practices. Although I was doing as much as possible to get the support I needed, achieving a work/life balance seemed to continually elude me. I'd definitely hit the tired part of HALT.

## Anxiety Recovery, 1996: Age 37

In 1996 I was nine and a half years sober and a year into a serious relationship with a woman I loved. We'd just bought our first home together. From the outside looking in, life was really good. I felt like I was living the American dream! In many ways, I was like a phoenix that had risen from the ashes, yet I was still struggling in other ways.

The biggest issue I struggled with was the chronic worry about my business. I worried about sales, expenses, client retention, how to produce large enough events, and client and employee issues. It got to the point where it seemed like it didn't even matter what the topic of worry was. My brain just seemed to have a need to be worrying about something.

For many years, I thought my struggle with worrying was just another unhealed emotional wound I could tackle as I'd done with so many other problems I'd overcome. But this constant worry thing was really getting to me. I'd wake up and immediately find something to worry about. I remember jokingly referring to it as my worry du jour.

Sometimes it was so bad that I would stay stuck ruminating on a worry for an entire weekend. It was exhausting. Given that I'm an external processor, it was also exhausting for my partner to have to listen to me constantly ruminating and needing to process my worries with her.

When I reflected on my history, my worrying didn't begin when I went into business for myself. In school, I frequently ruminated about getting my homework done in time or not being ready for a test. In my friendships, I worried about whether someone was upset or judging me. In my romantic relationships, I obsessed over whether my partner was upset with me or, worse, going to leave me. When I was an employee, I dwelled on whether my boss thought I was doing a good enough job and whether I would be put on probation or, worse, be fired.

At the time, I discovered that practically all my friends in recovery were on one antidepressant medication or another. This made me wonder if there might be something going on in my brain chemistry that medication could help. So I made an appointment with a psychiatrist.

After my initial appointment, I was diagnosed with generalized anxiety disorder and dysthymia (a persistent, low-grade form of depression), and the psychiatrist prescribed an SSRI antidepressant.

I noticed that the constant ruminating decreased within a week of taking the medication. Within a month, it was practically gone. I was like a new person! It was a true miracle. Finally, I'd found relief from this chronic anxiety and rumination! My only regret was that I hadn't gotten on an SSRI twenty years sooner.

## The Stress of Being an Entrepreneur

Although the relief from the anxiety through my new meds was astounding, I still struggled with the chronic stress of running my business. Facilitating the eight monthly networking meetings was the fun and easy part for me. The grueling part was the pressure to produce eight well-attended monthly networking meetings and make at least $20,000 in sales every month to cover my expenses.

If I didn't make my nut ($20k in sales each month), I was losing money. The idea of not only making zero profit but having to pay money after working my butt off just to stay in business was horrifying.

Running my business felt like having to keep eight plates spinning simultaneously just to pull off a decent month. Once I'd had a successful month, I was faced with the daunting task of pulling it off for the next month and the next. If the attendance became too low too often at any particular chapter, I risked having to close it, which meant refund requests from members and a permanent financial hit to the company.

My ultimate goal was to find a general manager to run the networking organization and manage the staff so I could pursue being a motivational speaker, seminar leader, and author. I kept thinking that if I could just find the right strategy or hire the right people, there would be more ease and flow, and the pieces would fall into place. However, the ease and flow I longed for just kept eluding me.

My mantra then was, "Failure is not an option." That's how committed I was to make my business successful. In my mind, the only thing worse than my business failing was having to get a real job. Although I was proud of my resolve to be strong and soldier on, I've since learned that sometimes it's better to cut your losses and move on after a certain amount of time when the costs outweigh the potential gains.

In hindsight, the biggest lesson I learned from this experience is that nothing is worth ruining your health, family, or recovery over. But back then, I wasn't going to quit. So, I kept trying new strategies and new staff. And on and on and on it went, month after month, year after year. I was burning out. My burnout affected my relationship as well. My partner got sick of hearing me talking about how stressed out I was all the time and suggested I get a regular job.

What nonentrepreneurial types don't know is that suggesting that a freedom-seeking entrepreneur get a job is like suggesting they give up on their dream and give up on themselves. I was having none of my partner's "just go get a job" business. The truth was, I was burned out. But I couldn't—or wouldn't—quit on myself or the business I'd poured my blood, sweat, and tears into for over six years.

CHAPTER 6

_____

# RELAPSE & RECOVERY 2.0 LESSONS FROM THE EDGE

## 1999: AGE 40

### Relationship Crisis

About three years into my relationship, I started smelling alcohol on my partner's breath when she returned home from visiting with her dad. This was extremely upsetting for me because we agreed that we wouldn't include alcohol in our relationship before we started dating. She understood that it was a requirement for me due to my commitment to my recovery. She'd been completely okay with it and even liked the idea of an alcohol-free relationship because she felt it was a healthier way to live.

When I initially confronted her about smelling alcohol on her breath, she said I was mistaken. But eventually, she admitted she'd lied and said she'd changed her mind about staying sober. She informed me she wanted to be a social drinker and felt she shouldn't have to stay sober just because I was.

This was devastating news for me. I knew I couldn't be with an active drinker and stay sober, and I told her that. But she insisted that she should be able to drink just like some of her friends who had recovering spouses were able to. The message I got from her was that it was my problem if I didn't like her drinking; therefore, I was the one who needed to deal with it.

We ended up going to therapy over it. I was hoping the therapist would have some concern and support me in protecting my sobriety by telling my partner it was her choice if she wanted to drink but that she would need to move out, as I'd suggested. Instead, the therapist thought I should allow my partner to drink while living with me and use the experience for a therapeutic journey into healing some childhood issues I had with my mother's alcoholism. Naively, I agreed.

I clearly didn't feel that the therapist supported me in protecting my recovery in that session. All I can say is I had no idea what I was setting myself up for by allowing my partner to drink while continuing to live with me.

### The Insanity of the First Drink

After seeing that my partner wasn't backing off on insisting that she be able to drink while living with me, the thought occurred to me that if I could be a social drinker and we could drink together, then maybe we could stay together.

I then began to question whether I still was an alcoholic. When I looked at my life, it looked completely normal. I was a healthy thirty-nine-year-old woman. I had a partner I loved and was maintaining a healthy weight. I had a lovely home, a thriving business, and great friends. I was even growing my retirement account!

I'd overcome many struggles with alcohol, drugs, cigarettes, weight, money, self-esteem, and codependency. Given I'd done so much emotional healing over the previous twelve years, I reasoned it was entirely possible that many of the emotional wounds that had driven me to drink could have healed.

Even some of the teachers I took classes from at the Church of Religious Science said that someone with a drinking problem could become a normal drinker with the right amount of spiritual and emotional healing. This led me to question the validity of the "once an alcoholic, always an alcoholic" philosophy.

I reasoned that the only way I could find out if I was still an alcoholic was by experimenting with alcohol. If I could be a social drinker, the experiment would have worked, and my partner and I could stay together. If it turned out that I couldn't be a social drinker, then the experiment failed. I would simply go back to AA and get sober again as I had before. I didn't think about what would happen if the experiment failed, and my attempt to get sober again in AA didn't go well. I naively thought getting sober again wouldn't be that difficult since I'd proven to myself I'd been successful in doing so before.

In AA, this line of thinking is known as the insanity of the first drink. I justified drinking as a way to save my relationship. I convinced myself it was risk-free because if it didn't work, I told myself I could always go back to AA and get sober as I'd done before. I had no idea what kind of hell would break loose from this decision.

## The First Drink

I discussed my idea of experimenting with drinking to see if I could be a normal drinker with my partner. She readily agreed to try it out with me. So, in December 1999, we decided we would go out for dinner at Coco's restaurant and share some wine with dinner.

When the waitress arrived at the table, we gave her our dinner order, which included a carafe of Chablis. Once the wine arrived, my partner and I held our wine glasses up for a toast and took our first sips together as a couple.

Experiencing the first taste of alcohol after twelve years of sobriety was rather anticlimactic. It was white wine, and I'd never been a big wine fan. Beer was more my thing. But since my partner liked wine and I wanted our first drink together to be something special, we had wine.

Throughout dinner, we finished the wine and went home. I remember feeling buzzed, but it wasn't an over-the-top experience. The jury was still out over how this new drinking version of Mary would fare.

When I look back, what I find surprising about my first drink after twelve years of sobriety is that I didn't have any guilt, regret, or fear over what could happen after taking such a major risk.

I realize now that I had so thoroughly convinced myself I would be okay no matter what happened that it seemed to shield me from any concern other than hoping my experiment could save my relationship.

## Relapse

It didn't seem like I was getting out of control the first couple of times my partner and I drank together. But within a few days, I was bringing beer home to drink. Within a week, I'd become a daily drinker. Within a few weeks, I was back to drinking a twelve-pack of beer per day like I had before I'd gotten sober.

The only problem was my partner wanted to be with a social drinker, and how I drank made her very uncomfortable. My experiment taught me that I couldn't be a social drinker even after twelve years of sobriety. If I learned anything from this relapse, it's that I would never be able to control my drinking once I started. The only solution for me was abstinence.

Not only was I drinking every day, but I was also compelled to take up smoking cigarettes and marijuana every day too. On top of that, between all the extra calories from my daily beer consumption and my increased appetite from smoking marijuana, I also started gaining weight.

Making just one decision to pick up a drink single-handedly created a domino effect. While caught in the insanity of relapse, I felt like a helpless witness as I watched my life and relationship begin to burn down around me. A few weeks after relapsing, I tried to get sober again by going back to AA, but the obsession to drink was full-blown. I would go to a meeting, but then I'd stop at the liquor store for beer on the way home.

At this point, I knew I was in major trouble. Plus, my partner was more distant than ever now that she'd seen how I drank. It seemed like there was no hope for our relationship to survive. I couldn't handle being a social drinker, and she wasn't willing to stop drinking.

Given the circumstances, the tension between us just kept on building. One night when I'd been drinking, I asked my partner if she would sit down to discuss the issues in our relationship. She immediately said that she wasn't willing to talk. I then asked her when she would be willing to set up a time to talk, and she wouldn't commit to a day or a time. I told her that if she continued to stonewall me, I couldn't be in the relationship any longer. After seeing she still wasn't willing to let me know when we could talk, I angrily stormed into my office, typed up and printed out a notice that the relationship was over, and gave her a sixty-day notice to move out.

## Breakup, 2000 Age: 41

We agreed to do a therapy session to "complete" the relationship. However, in my heart, I regretted breaking up with her and really wanted to work it out. Therefore, I hoped this therapy session would be more of a reconciliation session than one for completion.

I told the therapist and my partner that I regretted breaking up with her and apologized. I also shared that I really wanted to work it out. However, when the therapist asked my partner if she wanted to continue in therapy to save the relationship, she simply said no.

I was devastated. I burst into tears, abruptly left the office, ran down the stairs to the parking lot, and got in my car. I was so upset that I couldn't even drive, so I sat there for a good thirty minutes and just sobbed. I had no idea how unprepared I'd been for her to say that she no longer wanted to be in a relationship with me.

Another part of me was shocked. I remember thinking, *How do you spend almost four years building a life together, declaring your love for each other, buying a home together, and then suddenly think, 'You know, on second thought, I really value being able to drink over being with the woman I said I loved.* All I could say was, "Wow."

I was devastated. I experienced some of the worst emotional pain I think I'd ever gone through. The next couple of years were some of the worst years of my life.

After we split up, I went back to Alcoholics Anonymous, attempting to get sober several times. Sadly, the obsession to drink was more intense than ever, and even though I went to regular AA meetings, I kept relapsing.

## My Motorhome Adventure

After breaking up, my ex and I decided to sell the house and split the profit. Once the house was sold, I needed to figure out where I wanted to live. I knew I didn't want to rent, yet I hadn't made enough money on the house to buy another one. While looking at my options, I recalled an article in TIME Magazine about how life coach Thomas Leonard (considered the father of the life coaching movement) lived in his motorhome and worked with clients over his cell phone.

I was so inspired by the article that I decided I wanted to be a mobile coach and entrepreneur. All I needed was a motorhome, a cell phone, and a laptop, and I was in business. So, I sold all my possessions, bought a 1995 thirty-five-foot Class A motorhome, and took off with my two cats, Magic and Mocha, with my 15-foot turquoise Jeep Cherokee in tow.

At this point, my business network and coaching business was nine years old and had been slowly dying due to my burnout and relapse. Consequently, the income from it was minimal. I had a bit of money left in savings after buying the motorhome with the money from the house, but I'd need more income within a year or so.

During this period, I desperately tried to get sober but failed miserably. I would go back to AA and get two weeks of sobriety, then relapse, get another three weeks, then relapse, then get another two weeks, then relapse. I went in and out of relapse for two and a half years. It was so mortifying to raise my hand one more time as a newcomer at my AA meetings. This was in front of many friends I'd initially gotten sober with over a decade earlier!

It was such a bizarre experience to have been such a health nut for over twelve years—no alcohol, cigarettes, or drugs, and lots of healthy food, regular exercise, and personal growth—to become a sedentary, mindless drunk again. It was so freaking weird! I felt like I was in two parallel universes at the same time. One was an enlightened spiritual universe, and the other a dark, depressing, no-hope, pit-of-hell universe. I'd lost my sobriety, my family, my home, my health, and my income. I'd never felt such sadness, pain, and utter despair before. It was a terrifying and dark time for me.

There's a saying that once you go to AA, it ruins your drinking. Boy is that the truth! Once you know you're self-destructing and on a path that will eventually kill you or land you in jail, it's very difficult to be in denial and have a great time as a party animal. I learned the hard way that relapse is no party. Instead, it's a living hell.

After more than two years, I couldn't take the chronic relapsing anymore, so I decided to ask my doctor for Antabuse. My first girlfriend had told me about it because her girlfriend had been sentenced to mandatory Antabuse after getting a certain number of DUIs. It works by making you violently ill if you ingest any amount of alcohol. Also, since it takes three to five days to leave your system, it stops you from impulsively picking up a drink.

Given you know you can't drink without getting violently ill, you simply won't do so because there's no reward. Since I knew I needed something more powerful than my own will to divert me from my insane obsession to drink, Antabuse became the perfect solution. My plan was to take it and go to regular AA meetings, get a sponsor, and get back into the rhythm and routine of sobriety without disrupting it by chronically relapsing.

Thank goodness it worked!  After living the motorhome dream (or nightmare) for two years, I was ready to let it go. I knew I needed stability to stay sober—and living in a motorhome is anything but stable! So, I ran an ad and sold it.

Next, I needed to find a job and a new place to live. I knew living in an environment with people who were either sober or didn't drink was really important for my sobriety. That was when I thought of my friend Sue. I'd known her for over a decade. Given she had long-term sobriety, was local, and lived alone in a large house, I decided to reach out to her. I told her about my relationship and relapse and said I was newly sober. I asked her if she was open to my two cats and me living with her temporarily until I could get a job and move out on my own.

Thank God she said yes. It was the beginning of the second round of my sobriety. I moved in with Sue in September 2002, when I was just two weeks sober. I haven't had the need to pick up a drink since. My "temporary" stay with my sober friend Sue turned into an extraordinary four-year journey of recovery and transformation for me. We had so much fun as sober roommates. We started a wonderful weekly sacred-circle meeting and invited other women in recovery to attend. It was a great experience and just what I needed to get back on track! I'll be forever grateful to Sue for being there for me when I really needed a friend.

## The Lessons My Relapse Taught Me

This new round of sobriety has given me many lessons that I didn't get in my first twelve years:

1. I can never drink alcohol again without my life burning down around me. Whenever I get the urge to drink, my mantra is, "Drinking equals dropping a nuclear bomb on my life!" It helps me to think the drink through by visualizing a mushroom cloud with everything I hold dear in it being blown to smithereens. This is hands down the best mantra I've ever used to shift myself out of a craving state!

2. I cannot be in a romantic relationship with anyone who drinks, uses drugs, or has unresolved issues with alcohol or drugs.

3. My sensitivity to stress is a significant limitation for me. I simply cannot afford to get too stressed out. No matter what's at stake—a business, a job, a relationship, money, or anything else—nothing is worth getting so stressed out that I end up drinking.

4. It's been humbling to recognize that I must take the disease of alcoholism very seriously and that if I don't take care of my sobriety, I'll set myself up for relapse.

The gift of this relapse is that I now know my limitations and vulnerabilities around alcohol and drugs and what I need to do to stay in long-term recovery.

## Switching from Being an Entrepreneur to Selling Advertising

Once I was sober, I needed to figure out what to do for income. I had only a few thousand dollars left from selling my house and motorhome. I no longer had any income from my business because I'd closed the last chapter of my business network a few months earlier and hadn't worked with any coaching clients for a while.

I needed stability more than anything else, so I decided I needed a real job instead of pursuing another business venture. This is a painfully hard decision for an entrepreneur, but I knew I had to minimize my stress level if I was committed to staying sober. Since starting a business is incredibly risky as well as highly stressful. I knew getting a job was the only sane option to protect my sobriety.

My next step was figuring out what I wanted to pursue in the job market. I contemplated what had worked best for me in my business regarding my skills, what had a sense of ease and flow to it, and what produced the most income. The clear answer was advertising sales. I sold display and listing ads in my business networking organization's monthly newsletter and annual membership directory. The advertising program also had the highest profit margin and the lowest fulfillment burden compared to my membership and coaching programs. Plus, I had a real talent for selling it.

That's when I decided that selling advertising would be the focus of my job search. I then asked myself, *What types of ads do businesses with advertising budgets need to run to survive and thrive in their markets? Where do I look when trying to find a company, like a plumber or a furniture store?* My immediate answer was, "The yellow pages, of course!" This was back in 2002 when the internet was just a few years old and hadn't made much of a dent in the yellow pages industry.

I started searching the want ads for advertising sales positions for yellow page publishers. I applied for positions I found with three different companies. I ended up getting interviews for all three. Then, to my surprise, I received job offers from all of them! I decided to go with the publisher that offered the best opportunity for income and the most stability and had the highest-quality product.

I was amazed that I could get this new job done in half the time compared to the stressful, grueling hours I'd had to put into running my own business. Selling yellow page ads was a piece of cake compared to running an entire company. Since I was paid a base salary plus commission as an outside sales rep, I could make my quota in twenty to thirty hours a week and still earn a full-time income!

Here I'd thought I was giving something up by settling for a "real job," but I actually enjoyed it more than running my own company. I loved that I didn't have to manage employees or run everything. I was also able to make more money while working far fewer hours than I had at the height of running my own company.

I also loved how valued I felt by my employer when they acknowledged my hard work. I won many sales contests and received several awards. I'd never won contests or awards with previous companies I worked for, so I totally loved it.

Another perk was that I could build back my savings, which gave me a sense of financial security that was very calming, especially since I hadn't felt financially secure in quite a few years due to my relapse.

It felt so good to finally get my life back on track again with my sobriety, work, income, and feeling at home with my friend Sue. I also loved having much more free time than I did when I ran my own business.

Now that my life was stable again, I knew it was time to figure out how I was going to lose the enormous amount of weight I'd gained during my two-and-a-half-year relapse.

# CHAPTER 7

---

# WEIGHT-LOSS SURGERY: SAVING MYSELF FROM A HIJACKED BRAIN

## 2002: AGE 42

Over about a six-year period before my relapse and breakup, I'd gained back about 50 of the 140 pounds I'd lost working an OA program. Part of what drove me to use food to cope was the stress of running my business. The other part was the stress of going through the last year of my relationship. But once I relapsed and started drinking a twelve-pack of beer or more per day, coupled with using food to cope with the grief of losing my relationship, I gained weight at a much more rapid rate. Sadly, over my two-and-a-half-year relapse, I gained an additional 90 pounds.

42—My top weight of 310lbs. This is what untreated C-PTSD looks like.

Once I was sober again, I made several attempts to lose weight, but I couldn't seem to overcome my cravings and stick to my food plan. Although I occasionally lost 10 or 15 pounds, it seemed like within a few short weeks, I wouldn't be able to overcome my cravings to eat and would put all the weight back on.

It was so demoralizing after working so hard in OA to lose 140 pounds, only to gain it all back and weigh over 300 pounds again. What was even worse was facing the daunting task of figuring out how I would lose it again.

Weighing over 300 pounds in my forties was a much different experience than in my twenties. Carrying so much extra weight at forty-two not only caused me to feel shame about my body. But it also made me worry about dropping dead of a heart attack or becoming diabetic, not to mention the many other health risks that go along with being severely obese.

The harsh reality I knew I needed to face after losing and gaining hundreds of pounds several times over thirty years was that every attempt I'd made to maintain a healthy weight for the long term had ultimately failed.

Even though I'd spent decades on personal development, seen many therapists, was on antidepressants, and had gone to hundreds of OA meetings, I still had no clue why I couldn't rein in my compulsive need to overeat. I felt utterly defeated. I knew I needed to do something completely different if I wanted to get a completely different result.

This was happening right around the time when Good Morning America-GMA weatherman Al Roker had undergone gastric bypass surgery and began dropping quite a bit of weight. As I tuned in to GMA every morning, I found his rapid weight loss inspiring.

I started researching the pros and cons of different weight-loss methods and surgeries. I compared the data with the results from a traditional diet, exercise, psychotherapy, and other solutions that had empirical evidence to support their effectiveness.

When I dug into the research, it became clear that for people who were 100 pounds or more overweight, gastric bypass surgery had the best long-term success rate at the ten-year mark than any other weight-loss surgery or method.

According to my research, in 2001, gastric bypass surgery patients could lose, on average, 80% of their excess weight and be able to keep 70% of that weight off. In contrast, those who were 100 pounds or more overweight and tried to lose weight with diet and exercise alone lost only 20% of their desired weight and could keep only 5% of it off.

After doing my due diligence, it became clear that gastric bypass surgery would give me the best chance to reach and maintain a healthy weight for the long term. So, I got about finding a reputable bariatric surgeon and had my surgery on August 23, 2002. The good news is I ended up losing 160 pounds within two years. The even better news is I've been able to keep this weight off for the past twenty years.

## Not Knowing Childhood Trauma Was Driving My Struggle With Food & Weight

When I had my weight-loss surgery in 2002, I had no idea the reason I felt so compelled to eat the way I did was because my brain and nervous system had been highjacked by childhood trauma.

It would be another fifteen years before I would learn that trauma had sensitized my stress-response system, making it highly reactive to stress triggers and causing me to suffer from significant impulse-control deficits. This created the perfect storm setting me up with overpowering cravings to eat to calm down my chronically hyperaroused brain while lacking the ability to resist them due to deficient impulse control.

Now that it has been almost twenty years since my surgery, I can say that having the surgery not only saved me from a highjacked brain and the immense suffering that goes along with it, but it may also have saved my life.

If I had not had the surgery and had continued to carry an extra 160 pounds for the past two decades, I undoubtedly would be suffering today from at least a few more common illnesses, that accompany severe obesity, such as diabetes, chronic pain, and sleep apnea. Even before my surgery, when I was only forty-two and weighed 310 pounds, I was pre-diabetic, had high cholesterol, and experienced chronic knee and back pain.

In addition, the emotional toll that being severely obese took on me was, in many ways, as painful as the physical toll. The shame I had about being overweight fueled my social anxiety, making it difficult to form friendships or romantic relationships. This, in turn, drove my need to use food to cope with the pain of feeling so alone and unlovable.

## Physical & Emotional Health Improvements After My Weight Loss

Once I had the surgery and reached a healthy weight, my blood sugar, cholesterol, and other labs automatically decreased to normal levels. Also, the chronic back and knee pain I'd been dealing with for several years disappeared as well.

It was such a relief to be freed up from constantly thinking about how much I hated being overweight and feeling powerless to do anything about it. It was also wonderful to no longer worry about becoming diabetic, having a heart attack, or developing other health issues known to be caused by being severely overweight.

Maintaining a healthy weight meant I no longer dreaded walking long distances or participating in physical activities. In fact, since I wasn't so winded due to carrying so much extra weight, I embraced being physically active and grew to love it.

I felt a sense of healthy pride for finally ending the forty-year war I'd been in with food, weight, and my body. It felt wonderful to be able to shop anywhere for clothes and actually feel good about how I looked in them.

The most amazing gift of all was finally reaching my goal where issues around food, weight, and my body had become what I had always dreamed of them becoming: non-issues. Before my surgery, it felt like I was constantly burdened with thoughts or feelings of shame, guilt, worry, or despair around food, weight, and my body. It was exhausting. I was so ready to be done with having to deal with thinking or stressing about food and weight issues.

Once I had the surgery, lost my weight, and had a food, exercise, and self-care plan in place that I could count on that worked, these draining thoughts that had been my constant companions finally left.

Once these stressful, draining thoughts about food, weight, and my body ceased, I noticed a more expansive energy open up for me. I felt a natural pull to focus on life-enhancing projects, such as helping others overcome their struggle with trauma, addiction, obesity, and relationships. It feels so good to finally be freed up to focus on what I love the most, finding ways to grow and evolve into the highest version of myself, and helping others to do so as well.

## Structure & Accountability Have Been Key In My Reaching & Maintaining A Healthy Weight

A primary key to my success was deciding to implement food, exercise, and self-care plans from day one after having my surgery. I still use my plan today and continually fine-tune it to make sure I include foods, types of exercise, and self-care practices that I enjoy so that it's sustainable. I've included a more detailed version of this plan as well as how to develop your own plan in Part III.

## Finally Ending the War with Food, Weight, & My Body

I'm eternally grateful that I finally figured out a way to put my forty-year war with food, weight, and my body to rest. This is what's possible when you keep on keeping on and never give up. Had I given up, I would still be living in the hell of active food addiction and morbid obesity. This is why I consider having weight-loss surgery right up there with getting sober and healing my trauma as one of the most important turning points in my life and one of the best decisions I've ever made.

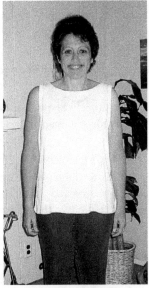

I do want to clarify that the reason I've shared about having weight-loss surgery is that it's been a critical part of my healing journey. However, this doesn't mean I recommend that anyone else get weight-loss surgery to address food or weight challenges. If you struggle with food and weight, choosing a program or method to solve these issues is a very personal journey—one you should take up with your doctor and family members.

In Chapter 33, "Food Addiction and Weight-Loss Recovery Options for Survivors," I share several resources I've used to find support and recovery on emotional, physical, and relational levels with food addiction and obesity. I also share a more detailed version of what I've done to maintain a healthy weight for the past twenty years.

44 — Two years after weight loss surgery and a 150lbs lighter.

# CHAPTER 8

---

# EMOTIONAL LIBERATION: HEALING SHAME & GUILT

## 2010: AGE 51

One day I noticed in my TiVo recordings an episode of Super Soul Sunday that featured Oprah interviewing Dr. Brené Brown. I'd never heard of Brown before, but since I typically enjoyed the kinds of people Oprah interviewed, I decided to go ahead and check it out. As soon as I began watching, I immediately noticed how much I resonated with Brown's message about how damaging unresolved shame is for a person's emotional, relational, and behavioral health.

Before watching her interview, I'd studied shame and was aware of what a destructive force it had been, and still was, in my life. Although I'd made some progress with healing shame, I also knew there were still issues with it holding me back.

While watching Oprah interview Brené, I thought, *Finally, someone is actually telling the truth about shame and vulnerability and doing it publicly!* It was so exciting to find someone who was not only writing about shame but also showing me how to resolve it within myself on a deeper level.

I intuitively knew that healing my remaining shame would free me up in a profound way, which is what made stumbling upon Brown's work so exciting. I hadn't been this excited about finding a possible solution to move my life forward in years! I remember being on a natural high while soaking up everything I could find in Brown's work.

I took to Google and discovered that Brown certified psychotherapists to facilitate her curriculum on healing shame and vulnerability through psychotherapist-led groups. While browsing the listings, I was excited to see two therapists who led groups in my area. What was so great about these groups was that they allowed only six to ten women, and the material was all written by Brown and included handouts and video clips from her. Plus, the groups had the interactive, experiential structure I was looking for.

I checked out both groups in my area and enrolled in one. I completed the first six-week group, then enrolled in the second therapist's group a few months later. I loved how the groups were totally safe because trained therapists led them. Getting to experience a safe group of women doing work based on Brown's teachings helped me take a significant leap forward in healing my shame.

Since shame is something everyone has and something you never completely get rid of, I learned the goal is to become more shame resilient. This means when you feel shame coming on, you have the awareness and tools to deal with and process it more rapidly. As a result, it doesn't paralyze you, wipe you out, or run you.

I could totally relate when I heard Brown mention shame is about the fear of disconnection. I knew that when I was experiencing shame, I definitely feared being cast out or disconnected due to how flawed and unworthy I felt.

I also loved learning from Brown how we get set up to feel shame due to the impossible number of expectations our families and culture put on us. In one example, Brown explains how body image and weight were shame triggers for 90% of the women she interviewed. Yet, if you look at the photoshopped images on the covers of magazines across America, they show fake, unattainable bodies. I was astounded that graphic designers actually edit images of body parts and combine them to make the person in the photo look perfect. This means we're often sold an image of what we should look like that's anatomically impossible!

## The Definition of Shame

The intensely painful feeling or experience of believing that we are flawed and therefore unworthy of love and belonging—Brené Brown, LCSW, Ph.D.

## The Difference Between Shame & Guilt

- Separating our behavior from the self is the difference between guilt and shame. Guilt says, "I did something bad," whereas shame says, "I'm a bad person."
- Shame is a global evaluation of the self that drives the belief of being a bad or fatally flawed person who is unworthy of love and belonging.
- We experience guilt when we act outside our values. E.g., We feel guilty when we've engaged in some behavior that we believe is morally wrong.

## Guilt Is Helpful

Guilt, although painful, is a helpful emotion because it alerts us to clean up our behavior, make amends where necessary, and do our best to learn the underlying lesson, so we don't have to repeat it. Once we've cleaned up the mistake that caused the guilt, we can use self-compassion and self-forgiveness to forgive ourselves.

However, long-held guilt isn't helpful because it eventually morphs into feeling unforgivable, which then morphs into shame. This is why learning the skill of self-forgiveness is so important.

## Shame Is Never Helpful

Shame is never helpful because it does nothing to move us in a positive direction. It destroys self-esteem and self-acceptance and is the core driver of addiction, depression, anxiety, anger, violence, relationship difficulties, perfectionism, and suicide.

## How Shame Drove My Career, Self-Image & Relationship Issues

As a result of digging into understanding shame and how it operated, I began to look at how it had been driving me in ways I hadn't been aware of until then. For example, when I was fifty-five, I felt fine about being out as a lesbian. However, I still struggled with fully coming out to people about my past struggles with addiction and my weight. If I came out about them, I feared I would be considered weak or a failure for even having struggled with these issues, even though I'd already overcome them.

That's when I had a major aha moment. I realized that toxic shame drove my need to hide this part of my past. Before this insight, to feel okay about who I was, I needed to be seen as strong and successful because, on a deeper level, I still believed I was weak and a failure.

## How Shame Had Been Driving My "Success at All Costs" Mindset

As I contemplated these insights, it finally made sense why I'd been so driven to be a strong, successful entrepreneur. It was all a way for me to make sure others never perceived me the way I still felt about myself, which was as being weak and a failure.

I couldn't be perceived as weak and a failure because it would trigger shame, the most painful emotion there is. Shame told me that my entire self was weak and a failure. This is why shame is so painful. When I believe that the entirety of who I am is weak and a failure, I can't help but feel unworthy of love and belonging. And feeling unworthy of love and belonging is one of the darkest and most painful states to be in. A state that most people avoid at all costs.

Having this insight helped me make sense of why I was so reluctant to share the gift of my story of recovering from alcohol, drug, and food addiction and severe obesity on a broader level for many, many years. If I did so, I would expose the part of me that still believed I was weak and a failure. Once people saw this part of me, I was convinced they would judge me. Just the idea of the shame I would feel by being judged and then shunned was too big of a risk to take. Instead, I stayed small and played it safe.

Becoming aware of how unhealed shame was holding me back in my life made me realize I needed to focus on healing my relationship with myself.

## Shame Is a Lie

After all the research and personal healing that I've done regarding shame, I know today that when you believe you're bad, less than, broken, stupid, ugly, weak, a failure, defective, undesirable, unlovable, or one of the many other thoughts preceding the feeling of shame, what you're believing is a lie. I'm not saying what you're feeling is a lie since feelings just are. We feel what we feel, and feelings are not lies. What I'm saying is what you believe about yourself is a lie.

Shame is a lie that has been perpetuated for eons upon children and adults alike. If we believe this lie, we feel fundamentally flawed and not worthy of the love and belonging that we assume normal or more together people (who we presume are perfect or problem-free) deserve.

Many of us have lived with shame for so long that we've never known any other way to relate to ourselves. Due to our shame, we dare not speak of the terrible flaws we believe we have with anyone. This is why many of us feel we're the only ones who feel as bad about ourselves as we do. This is how shame keeps us isolated and disconnected from others.

It's amazing to see what opens up for us when these deep, painful feelings of shame begin to heal, and we can embrace the whole, beautiful, imperfect, lovable person we've been all along. Once we embrace and accept the truth of who we are as perfectly imperfect beings, it's as if all the pieces that eluded us get freed up to fall into place and allow us to manifest the life we've always wanted.

## The Shame of Having Shame

One of the most challenging aspects of healing shame is that there's so much shame about having shame. Shame isn't an easy topic of discussion. If you think about it, when was the last time you were at a dinner party, and someone asked you, "So, tell me. How do you feel about shame?" The mere mention of it with folks not used to discussing it conjures up shameful feelings from their past that make them feel icky and would rather not be reminded of.

What I know about shame is that when we don't deal with our shame, our shame will deal with us. Shame deals with us by making the risk of vulnerability very difficult, if not impossible. It stunts our ability to form meaningful, intimate relationships with romantic partners, friends, and family members. It also hurts our ability to risk pursuing fulfilling businesses or careers.

It is well documented that the deep emotional pain of shame is a driving force behind all types of addictive and compulsive behaviors. When we are steeped in unbearable feelings of shame, we feel compelled to escape the pain at any cost. Unresolved shame keeps us hustling to feel worthy, good enough, acceptable, and lovable. Since shame won't ever allow us to be enough, we desperately hope that external approval and accomplishments will do the job.

Many of us buy into the myth that making more money, being perfect, looking perfect, acquiring more assets, or finding a romantic relationship will finally prove we are successful or acceptable. I certainly know I did.

For some, the only way to feel acceptable or worthy is by choosing a family role or career that involves rescuing or being of service to others. Some people believe that once they build a successful business or career, they'll finally experience a sense of being worthy of love and acceptance.

I can tell you from experience that no amount of external success or approval can deliver the internal feeling of being good enough, being lovable, or being accepted as is. It has to come from our relationship with ourselves versus what we accomplish or who accepts us. The work of healing shame is about understanding its nature and unraveling shame-based lies others have told us, which we internalize and then tell ourselves. To fully heal shame, we must come to a place where we can accept ourselves just as we are.

## Healing Shame

Healing shame is a process. It takes time. It's not a quick fix that can come from a book or weekend seminar. However, it is possible to heal one day at a time. I know because I have, and many others have as well. This means you can too.

My hope is that by sharing my story about healing shame, those who have been too uncomfortable to reach out for support can realize that they're not alone and begin their healing process.

When I first got in touch with my unhealed shame, I began studying everything I could about how to resolve it. As I began sharing more and more about my shame with my partner, in my groups, and with my therapist, I noticed a shift in me. When I shared parts of me that I was ashamed of with safe people and saw that they still loved me, my shame began to ease. I felt lighter emotionally, spiritually, and physically. I noticed I felt less concerned about what people thought of me—especially when I shared my vulnerable self.

I felt more willing to be vulnerable and put myself out there by sharing my shame with trusted friends. My self-compassion increased. My empathy for others increased. I noticed this incredible feeling of freedom from finally accepting myself as is come over me. Over time, I noticed this new feeling of being at peace with myself that I'd never felt before.

It wasn't until I learned about shame that I realized the reason I hadn't re-launched my coaching career sooner was because of my unhealed shame. Risking failure or being shamed or judged for launching my own brand was overwhelming, so I stayed small and played it safe and instead worked as a support person to promote other people's businesses and dreams. Healing shame has given me the gift of feeling safe to share who I am with the world.

## Learning Self-Forgiveness Is The First Step Toward Healing Shame

Through my deep dive into learning about healing shame and guilt, I discovered the first step involves resolving any lingering guilt you may have. The reason guilt must be handled before healing shame is that if you have unresolved guilt, you can't help but feel unforgivable. And when you feel unforgivable, you feel shame. Once we have forgiven ourselves, we are then ready to take on healing shame.

## Learning Self-Acceptance Heals Shame

One of the more eye-opening experiences I had during my healing shame and guilt journey was learning that working toward better self-esteem was actually counter-productive to healing shame. It was really surprising to learn that what heals shame is not high self-esteem but self-acceptance.

I define self-acceptance as accepting my whole self as is. The reason self-acceptance is key to healing shame is that it frees us up to focus on the goal of living a life that honors our core values versus endlessly chasing externally based self-esteem or self-worth goals. When we're focused on pursuing value-based goals, we naturally set ourselves up for a life focused on fulfillment and satisfaction.

## Why Working Toward Increasing Self-Esteem or Self-Worth Is Not Helpful

- Self-esteem and self-worth are subjective constructs that aren't real.  Since they are made up and typically shift with the tides of a person's successes or failures, they make you vulnerable to experiencing shame.
- Many people think if they just feel good enough about themselves, failing won't make them feel shame. However, since feeling good enough is a global evaluation of the self based on a subjective construct that isn't real, it's unattainable.
- Self-esteem is often based on appearance, feeling one up, and putting others down. This creates a false sense of confidence since experiencing failure brings on shame.

Ending the quest for better self-esteem has been a truly liberating experience.  Before I understood this concept, I'd deluded myself into believing that if I could just feel better about myself, I would finally experience the fulfillment I longed for. The truth was, I had my ladder up against the wrong wall. I had it up against the self-esteem wall when I would have been much better served to put it up against the self-acceptance wall.

## Why Self-Acceptance Is Necessary To Experience Fulfillment In Life

- Without self-acceptance, we can't fully experience a satisfying life because we'll be caught struggling to achieve higher self-esteem. Pursuing better self-esteem doesn't work because it does nothing to address improving specific areas of our lives.
- The wiser goal is to seek fulfillment, not self-esteem, because achieving fulfillment is attainable.
- The wisest way to judge how well we're doing in our overall lives is to focus on value-based behaviors and goals for the various areas of our life, e.g., work, romantic partner, health, friends, fun, etc.
- The irony of focusing on achieving self-acceptance and pursuing value-based goals is that better self-esteem is often a natural byproduct of doing so.

## How Healing Shame & Guilt Caused Major Breakthroughs in My Life

After being heavily steeped in healing shame and guilt over a three-year period, I had so many breakthroughs that my whole life began changing. The most significant breakthrough was that I stopped being attached to the good opinion of others. This was due to my finally figuring out how to accept myself as is. This was a HUGE miracle! As a result, I felt safe to speak up and share my opinion with my partner, family, and friends even when I knew I wouldn't get agreement from them.

I also had the courage to re-launch my coaching practice, launch my own website, as well as start a new weekly women's group focused on healing shame and guilt. I even began blogging and building my own social media following. It was as if this level of deep healing had given me the keys to let myself out of my shame-shackled prison so I could finally spread my wings and fly!

## How Healing Shame & Guilt Caused a Major Breakdown in My Relationship

Although I was basking in all of the positive changes from healing my shame and guilt, sadly, this new version of Mary caused tension in my romantic relationship. Before healing my shame and guilt, I automatically assumed that any problems in my relationship were because of me and that I needed to work on my issues to be a better partner. But afterward, I didn't automatically accept that I was the problem. I began standing up for myself more often, speaking my truth, and having stronger boundaries.

Although it was exhilarating to let go of so much toxic shame and start my own projects, it was also sad and stressful because of the tension it created in my relationship. It was a bittersweet time. On the one hand, I gained a whole new sense of my true self and purpose. But on the other, it felt like I was losing my partner, whom I loved and had spent many years building a life with.

**Note:** I provide all the steps I took to let go of and heal guilt and shame in Part III, The Trauma Healing & Recovery Journey, chapter 29, "Letting Go of Guilt and Shame."

# CHAPTER 9

---

# CHRONIC PAIN & MY MEDICAL MARIJUANA JOURNEY

## 2012: AGE 52

One day after returning home from a walk, I noticed a strange tingling sensation in my left foot. At first, I thought it was just my foot reacting to a new pair of shoes I'd worn that were too tight. However, the next day I noticed both of my feet tingling. This tingling feeling continued daily for a week. By the second week, the tingling morphed into an uncomfortable burning sensation on the bottoms of both feet.

I Googled my symptoms and found that they were consistent with a nerve condition called peripheral neuropathy. I learned it is most prevalent in people with diabetes, multiple sclerosis, muscular dystrophy, vitamin deficiencies or surpluses, chemotherapy patients, older people, and those with metal toxicity.

Within a few weeks, I saw my primary care physician, who diagnosed me with peripheral neuropathy and ordered the requisite blood work to determine its cause.

Within a week, I learned my blood work was normal, and I wasn't diabetic. My doctor then referred me to a neurologist, who did a brain MRI scan (to rule out multiple sclerosis) and nerve conduction studies on my limbs, ankles, and feet. It showed some minor nerve damage but nothing that should cause the type of pain I was experiencing.

Thankfully, the brain MRI came back normal, ruling out multiple sclerosis. The neurologist also ordered some blood work to see if there might be toxic levels of metal in my body causing the pain. It also came back negative. My official diagnosis from him was idiopathic peripheral neuropathy. *Idiopathic* means "unknown cause."

I found my pain was relieved only by lying back in a fully reclined position in my recliner, walking, or lying down on the floor or in bed.  Frustratingly, ibuprofen, Tylenol, and even opiates can't manage nerve pain.  I tried taking the most common meds prescribed for nerve pain, Lyrica and Gabapentin, but they didn't help either.

### Becoming a Disabled Person

Within a month, I could no longer sit in a regular chair or work at a desk because I couldn't tolerate sitting down with my feet on the floor for more than a minute without them beginning to burn. Even going to restaurants was uncomfortable unless we got a booth where I could put my feet up. If I couldn't elevate my feet within a few minutes of sitting in a regular chair, the burning would become unbearable, and I would have to get up and stay standing.

I ended up ordering a portable stool to elevate my feet. I took it to restaurants, the movies, seminars, and even parties. It was so scary and embarrassing watching myself become a disabled person.

I began noticing that the bottoms of my feet became more and more sensitive to touch, especially in the arch areas. Even applying lotion to them became intolerable. Just trying on shoes while shopping could trigger an hours-long flare-up of burning pain.

I couldn't wear my regular shoes or socks because my feet could no longer tolerate any tightness. I had to buy special nonrestrictive socks and shoes in larger sizes that were loose enough for my feet to tolerate.

My feet became so sensitive to touch that I couldn't even tolerate sheets or blankets touching the tops of my toes when I slept. The only solution was to sleep with my feet hanging off the end of the bed so nothing would touch my toes.

One day, to my horror, I noticed the same sensitivity I had in the arches of my feet had begun to happen with my palms and my lap. I would have to shoo my cat off my lap because I couldn't tolerate her being there without it triggering my feet to start burning. I couldn't even tolerate my partner's hand on my lap. It all started to become overwhelming.

At that point, I'd been dealing with the pain for over two years. I'd seen several top neurologists, and they still had no clue what was causing it. Being constantly tortured by this burning pain in my feet and then worrying about it spreading to my palms and legs began to take its toll on me.

I couldn't help but worry about what else I would have to endure or lose to this pain. I now could see why so many people with chronic pain turn to drugs and alcohol. Tragically, some even choose suicide as the only way out of the daily hell of their pain.

I discovered firsthand how chronic pain can rob your life force energy to the point where it's really difficult to feel even a fraction of the joy you once felt. As the months and then years rolled by, I felt trapped in my pain and powerless to do anything about it. Interestingly enough, it was similar to the feeling I had growing up with my mom's raging alcoholism. Back then, it was emotional pain. But this time, the pain was not only emotional but physical too.

## My Medical Marijuana Journey

One day I read an article in *O, The Oprah Magazine,* about how medical marijuana was especially effective at relieving nerve pain. Even though I hadn't smoked marijuana in over a decade and knew that I would be taking a significant risk by using it for my pain, I was so desperate for relief that I began giving it serious consideration.

Although I'd definitely been into marijuana when I was a partier, I wouldn't have described myself as a total stoner who smoked weed all day long. I'd been able to go without it if I had to, but I definitely couldn't go without alcohol. Alcohol was clearly my drug of choice. I knew I couldn't touch it without my life completely exploding. Given marijuana wasn't my main drug of choice, I reasoned it might be worth the risk of overusing it if it could relieve my pain.

I shared with my partner my thoughts about trying medical marijuana. Although she wasn't thrilled with the idea, she agreed that I deserved to find some relief and reluctantly supported me in trying it.

I went online to find a medical marijuana doctor to get the required recommendation to purchase the drug. Once I had my doctor's recommendation, I went to a local dispensary and bought my first supply of medical marijuana.

After smoking my first bowl, I noticed that it helped relieve the burning sensation in my feet immediately, which was really encouraging. But I also noticed how much I loved the feeling that marijuana gave me. After not having smoked any for over a decade, I'd forgotten how wonderfully sensual a marijuana high is.

I noticed colors looking more beautiful and vibrant, food tasting amazing, and music sounding incredible. Taking a shower while high took me to a whole other high in and of itself. I also noticed feeling much more connected to my body when high. In many ways, it reminded me of how I felt when I first started partying—a blissful state of being tapped in, tuned in and turned on, and loving every minute of it—at first, at least.

Given how much I enjoyed smoking again, I noticed I wanted to smoke even when I wasn't in pain. Hence, restricting myself to using it for just pain soon became impossible. That was when it became a problem for me and my relationship.

My partner wasn't okay with me being high around her. Frankly, I wasn't comfortable being high around her, either. Yet, at the same time, I was so sick of the chronic burning pain that having something that worked, even if the side effect was overusing it, seemed worth it to me at the time.

Also, due to the transformation I'd experienced in the previous three years with healing guilt and shame, there had been quite a bit of tension between my partner and me even before I started using marijuana. It was then I realized that I was using marijuana to medicate the pain of the tension between my partner and me, as well as my nerve pain.

## A Retreat to Vermont

In an effort to get some space from the tension I was experiencing with my partner and attain some perspective on my overall life, I booked myself for a weeklong retreat with Robert Fritz in Vermont. He's the author of one of my favorite books, *The Path of Least Resistance: Learning to Become the Creative Force in Your Own Life,* published in the nineties. The retreat's topic was learning to use his philosophy of *Creating* to manifest what you want in your personal and professional life with less effort.

Since I'd always wanted to attend one of Fritz's workshops and had also wanted to tour the beautiful state of Vermont, I decided to go for it. I loved traveling through the New England landscape and viewing the quaint Cape Cod-style architecture. I also thoroughly enjoyed a self-guided tour of several of the state's covered bridges.

The retreat was a perfect size, with fewer than twenty people, and held at Fritz's traditional New England farm. There were acres of rolling hills of green grass, giant trees, a classic New England-style main house, and an old barn that had been converted into a classroom. The Fritzes ended the retreat by offering us a traditional New England clambake, complete with Maine lobster, crab, and all the trimmings.

Strangely enough, I noticed that during my week in Vermont, the burning in my feet decreased by a good 70%. It was such a relief to experience a reprieve from the pain. It made me wonder what had contributed to this sudden reduction in my pain. At first, I thought it was obvious: I was in a beautiful state and at a wonderful retreat, which, in and of itself, was very calming and therapeutic. However, a few days into the retreat, it dawned on me that there was another aspect of being in Vermont that was different than being home. In Vermont, I didn't have to cope with the tension I had at home with my partner.

I couldn't help but wonder if the stress of my strained relationship was contributing to the pain. This was the first time I'd been away from my partner since the pain had started, so I couldn't say for sure. But given how much tension there was at home and noticing how my pain dramatically decreased while on my trip, I couldn't rule it out either.

## Finding Pain Relief Without Drugs

After I returned from my retreat, sadly, the pain in my feet returned. That was when it became clear that using marijuana to manage my pain would not be sustainable for me, my relationship, or my recovery. So, I kept searching for other pain management options.

One day, while seeing my therapist, Sharon, and sharing my frustration with managing my pain, she mentioned that she had a client who'd suffered from terrible back pain. After many years, she opted to have a spinal cord stimulator (SCS) implanted to manage her pain. Sharon told me it was a game-changer, and, as a result, she got her life back. Hearing this story gave me more hope than I'd ever had for finding a permanent solution to manage my pain.

I did a bunch of research on SCS and was happy to find a neurosurgeon who specialized in doing SCS implant surgery. I set up an appointment and showed up at his office with my five-inch, three-ring binder with my medical records from all the doctors I'd seen over the previous few years for my chronic nerve pain.

He diagnosed me with complex regional pain syndrome (CRPS) instead of peripheral neuropathy. He said CRPS is typically triggered by an injury. But since I had chronic burning pain and hypersensitivity issues with being touched on my feet, arches, toes, lap, and palms, he thought my symptoms were more consistent with CRPS.

He told me that the SCS was known to perform exceptionally well in stopping CRPS nerve pain and sensitivity. It was also known to help prevent nerve pain from moving up the legs or arms. At that point, I hadn't even known that this pain could do that! Needless to say, I was thrilled that I'd found something to not only stop my pain but also to stop it from spreading.

I got approval from my insurance, set up a surgery date, and had the SCS surgery. Although the post-op pain was some of the most horrible pain I've ever experienced, within about six weeks, I was able to get around.

Like the doctor had promised, the SCS delivered in relieving my foot pain. Within a month of using the SCS daily, the pain levels significantly decreased in my feet. To my surprise and delight, the pain level gradually decreased, and within a few months, it stopped without my even needing to continue using the device! It was as though the device itself had healed 90% of my condition. Miraculously, within a few more months, I no longer needed to use the device at all.

I'm thrilled to report that nine years after the surgery, my issues with nerve pain in my feet are 95% better than before. Also, the sensitivity in my lap area and palms are practically gone. I also no longer need to use my portable stool because I have no problem sitting in restaurants, movie theaters, or on airplanes. My life is totally manageable today. Although this nerve pain occasionally comes up, it's completely manageable and no longer rules my life. For this, I am eternally grateful.

## Time to Quit Smoking Marijuana

Once my back surgery healed and my SCS implant was handling my foot pain, it was time to quit smoking marijuana. I was a good two years into daily marijuana use by this point. My tolerance had built to the point where it took smoking a lot more to experience just a fraction of the high I'd gotten when I first started smoking.

Like alcohol, the bliss on demand I first experienced with marijuana became a distant memory. After only a few short weeks to a month of smoking weed throughout the day, the sensual high and bliss I'd experienced at first slowly faded to a mild buzz. I found that marijuana functioned more like a sedative than anything else for me. It relaxed me, and then it made me tired. Once the honeymoon was over, it became just another addiction I felt the compulsive need to engage in, even though I knew it was hurting me and my relationship.

And once the SCS implant managed my chronic pain, I could no longer justify my marijuana use. It was clearly time to quit. Plus, I'd promised my partner I would stop once I'd healed from my surgery. It was then that I began attending Marijuana Anonymous (MA) Twelve-Step meetings and sought support from Sharon, my therapist. Although the cravings were pretty intense, and it wasn't easy, I was finally able to quit.

## Becoming Disabled — The Wake-Up Call To Do It Now

Going through the experience of waking up one day with a slight tingling sensation in my feet, to it morphing into debilitating, burning nerve pain within a few months, was a major wake-up call for me. It taught me that you never know when in the blink of an eye, something can happen that can completely change your life to where you no longer have the ability to travel or do something you've always wanted to do.

After struggling for two years to find a solution to end my pain, I was faced with the possibility of never being able to sit on an airplane or travel again due to how debilitating it was to do so. Once I recovered from my back surgery to implant the spinal cord stimulator to manage my pain, I made a vow to myself that if I had the means and the time to do something I really wanted to do, I would say YES, and do it while I still could.

This is why when I got an email about the retreat in Vermont, a state I'd always wanted to see and with an author I'd always wanted to attend a seminar with, I booked my ticket and went. A few months later, when I found out a friend of mine was organizing a trip to Italy, a country I'd always wanted to see, I didn't hesitate to reserve my spot. I had incredible experiences on both trips and am so glad I followed through on my vow.

Giving myself permission to live my dreams now vs. waiting until I have more money saved or have officially "retired" has been a game changer for me. If there's a silver lining to going through my chronic pain experience, it's learning this lesson.

# CHAPTER 10

---

# FINDING MY VOICE, REINVENTING MY LIFE

## 2016: AGE 56

### Becoming An Author

During a session with my therapist, Sharon, she shared a story of how one of her clients—although severely disabled with multiple sclerosis (MS)—and unable to hold a pen to write, was able to write an inspirational book about his MS journey using Amazon's publishing platform. She also mentioned how well it was selling on Amazon and how gratifying it was for him to see the difference he was making by sharing his story.

56—Fourteen years after weight loss surgery and staying committed to a healthy food, exercise and self-care plan.

Hearing this story was a major inspiration for me. I remember thinking, *If this severely disabled kid, who couldn't walk or even hold a pen, could write a successful book to uplift and inspire others, then so could I.*

I had wanted to share my story of overcoming childhood adversity, addiction, and obesity for many years before hearing about Sharon's client's book. When I heard that this kid with MS had gone for it with his book, despite his many obstacles, it became clear that my excuses were up. It made me realize that the only thing holding me back was me. And the last thing I wanted was to be on my deathbed, regretting that I hadn't shared my story with the world. Little did I know that it would take a young man with MS who had the courage to share his story to motivate and inspire me to get off my butt to share mine.

Although the initial focus of this book didn't include the topic of childhood trauma since I still had another five years before I would discover I had been traumatized, it included my story of overcoming addiction, severe obesity, codependency, and shame and guilt.

When deciding who I thought would be the best person to reach out to for referrals to help me write my book, I thought of Cheryl Richardson since she was a fellow life coach and author of several New York Times bestsellers. I have also been following her career for twenty years. So, I decided to reach out to her through Facebook to see if she might have a referral for me for a good book coach or editor. Lo and behold, she referred me to her sister, Kerri Richardson, who is also a life coach and was Cheryl's editor for several of her bestselling books.

In June 2015, I hired Kerri to be my writing coach. I met with her weekly over the phone while working on the initial manuscript for this book. During this same time, I learned that her sister Cheryl Richardson and Reid Tracy, CEO of Hay House (a self-help book publisher), were offering a "Speak, Write, Promote" seminar for aspiring authors on an upcoming Holland Alaska cruise. Since I had always wanted to see Alaska and needed support to hone my writing skills, I eagerly signed up for the cruise and the seminar.

## Finding Myself Meant Losing My Relationship

Looking back, it makes sense why my romantic relationship had become so rocky. Over the previous three years, I'd done some major foundational work on healing guilt and shame. As a result, I made significant progress in strengthening my sense of self. I no longer deferred to my partner for being right regarding the issues in our relationship. I'd begun speaking my truth more and more, regardless of whether I thought my partner would agree with me.

Each of these things alone could shake the strongest of relationships. Then, when you throw in my bout with chronic pain, my marijuana relapse, and major back surgery to help relieve my pain, it's no wonder we reached a breaking point.

Although we did everything we could to save our relationship, we had to face the truth that we were no longer compatible as partners. It was then that we mutually agreed that it was time to end our relationship.

## Finding Relief for My Grief

Although I knew in my heart that the breakup with my partner needed to happen, it was still extremely painful. At the time, I hadn't put together that the deep sadness and grief I'd felt for the better part of a year was not only due to losing my current relationship. It also triggered the profound loss I hadn't processed from the ongoing emotional abandonment I experienced growing up in my dysfunctional family.

I saw my therapist every week, attended Twelve-Step meetings, and utilized the many tools and resources I'd developed over the years to navigate the deep emotional pain I was in. Yet the pain of losing my partner, who was essentially my family, left me heartbroken. As I struggled to cope, my mind began drifting into the fantasy of how wonderful it would be to get high.

I tried combatting my craving by telling myself, *Mary, you know once you start, you can't control your use, and you'll end up right where you did the last time you smoked.* Although I knew it was true, at the same time, I was in pain, and I felt deprived. It really bothered me that it seemed like everyone else could take the edge off by having a drink or getting high when they went through a breakup, but not me. It felt like it wasn't fair that I was left to suffer, and that made me really angry.

As I stewed in my anger, I thought, *I know I can't drink because it's not worth the hell that I know will break loose if I pick up a drink. But marijuana is different. I don't have to worry about getting a DUI or doing anything crazy. Plus, I'm single, so I don't have to worry about losing my relationship if I start smoking.*

As the ache of my heartbreak worsened, I reached a point where the pain became too much to bear, and in a moment of despair, I caved and said, "Fuck it, I don't care! I deserve to get relief just like everyone else does!" And, boom, that was it! Within a few minutes, I went online and found a local dispensary, and within an hour, I was high.

## Marijuana's Subtle Seductiveness

Although I somehow managed to quit every few months, there seemed to be a subtle seductiveness that kept luring me back to marijuana. After a year or so of being on and off with it, I realized that I kept going back to it because I had a deep desire to make it work in my life.

I thought that if I could figure out a way to be a social user, I could satisfy the part of me that felt deprived of getting to let loose at a party or take the edge off like it seemed everyone else was able to do.

Also, when I compared alcohol to marijuana, it seemed relatively benign and innocent. One of the things I loved about it was there were no hangovers. I also loved that I never had to worry about inappropriate behavior like I did when I was drunk. It was also much cheaper than booze.

I didn't feel the need to smoke cigarettes with marijuana or worry about having slurred speech or people smelling alcohol on my breath like I did with alcohol. I also didn't get the munchies with weed, so I didn't gain weight as I did with beer. The bottom line was marijuana was much, much less destructive than alcohol was for me.

## The Insidious Robber of Ambition and Dreams

As a regular marijuana smoker, the biggest problem I found was that it robbed me of having even an ounce of ambition. I simply had no energy to get into any kind of focus or creative flow whatsoever.

I started writing this book about six months before the end of my relationship. Once the relationship was over, and I'd become a daily marijuana smoker, having the ambition to sit down, focus, and write was simply impossible.

I told myself that I was putting my book on hold so I could heal the pain of my breakup. But the truth was that using marijuana daily made it impossible to get any motivation going, much less summon the intense focus and creative energy necessary to write a book.

To reclaim my ambition, I attempted to moderate my use. I tried limiting myself to smoking on weekends or only with friends. Frustratingly, nothing seemed to quell my need to keep the THC flowing in my daily life.

I came to realize that what made quitting marijuana so hard was the delusion that it made my life more fun, along with the belief that it wasn't really hurting me. However, the truth was that every day I spent smoking weed was a day that I would never get back—and one that I could have spent writing this book and making the kind of difference I wanted to make in the world.

## Compared to Alcohol, Marijuana Seemed Harmless

When I thought about the difference between how alcohol and marijuana had impacted my life, it was like night and day. With drinking, it was obvious. Picking up a drink was like dropping a nuclear bomb on my life. Within a few weeks of drinking, the mushroom cloud was fully formed and getting ready to drop the pieces of my life all around me: my romantic relationship, my work, my health, my weight, my finances, my self-esteem, my reputation, and my dignity.

But the self-destructive aspect of being a regular marijuana user was so subtle that, in many ways, it was hardly noticeable at all. This is what made this drug so insidious. After the initial honeymoon with marijuana, instead of it being a fun party where everything looks, sounds, feels, and tastes better, you're left with a bong, a bag of weed, and Netflix. You may have a friend you get high with or friends you party with. Sometimes the conversations are philosophical, funny, and interesting, but at the end of the day, nothing changes in your life.

You may delude yourself into thinking you come up with more creative ideas while high, but what you don't realize is your brain has been hijacked, leaving you with nothing but dreams and fantasies—all without an ounce of ambition to ever get any of them off the ground.

## Coming Out of the Haze of Denial

Once I got hip to what marijuana was doing to me, I couldn't stay in denial any longer. Over time I found that being a daily marijuana smoker was like having a slow-moving cancer that was gradually pushing my hopes and dreams further and further out of reach. The odd thing about it is since the weed keeps you comfortably numb, you don't feel the pain or discomfort of watching your future slip away. So, you don't have the motivation or ambition to do anything about it.

Once you find more friends to get high with, your lifestyle and goals become more about getting together to party versus going after your hopes and dreams. By then, having a lifestyle focused on partying with friends versus one with life-enhancing goals seems normal because everyone you hang out with is doing the same thing.

One thing I had going for me was I knew what I was missing. My life had been all about pursuing my hopes and dreams for the previous thirty years. So, I knew what it felt like. It was exciting, and it felt awesome to see myself and my clients growing and evolving. It required that I face my fears, and by doing so, I got to feel proud of myself. I also loved how it felt to know I was inspiring others to go after their hopes and dreams too.

Being a daily marijuana smoker was just the opposite. It made me feel bad about myself because I knew I was wasting my life. I knew I wanted a life where I was pursuing and achieving life-enhancing goals and making the difference I wanted to make in the world. Yet, I was letting my life slip away in a foggy haze of frivolity.

This was when I knew I needed to get honest with myself and face the fact that as long as I continued to smoke weed, I would need to kiss this book and my dreams goodbye. Thank God I was able to pull myself out of the fantasy of believing my life could be better with it and got the support I needed to quit for good.

If I hadn't, you wouldn't even be reading these words because this book would never have seen the light of day.

## Reinvention

Once I'd recovered from the breakup and quit smoking marijuana, I was ready to start a new chapter in my life. Although I knew I was committed to finishing this book, I also needed income due to a long-term consulting gig ending. That meant my primary focus needed to be on activities that would generate income.

I was fifty-six years old and wanted to be sure that my next career move would be the kind of work I truly loved and one I could make a decent living with. Given my age and the window of time closing in on my career opportunities, I knew I needed to hit the target for the next chapter of my work life. I no longer had the luxury of time to play around with one or two-year jobs or consulting gigs.

The only thing I knew for sure about my calling was that I wanted to help people transform their lives by being true to themselves and living their purpose. I kept exploring different personal growth programs and teachers to get clear about my purpose and eventually came up with the idea of launching my own live-stream transformational talk show.

The reason I chose becoming a transformational talk show host for my next career move was because when I thought about it, there's nothing I love more than being in the conversation of transformation. Whether having a one-on-one conversation with a friend or a client or connecting with a guest as a talk show host, I love the connection that happens when people get vulnerable and share from their hearts.

Although I knew I would eventually need to monetize the show through advertising or by promoting my coaching practice, my first priority was to make sure the show delivered on motivating and inspiring my audience to live their best lives.

I then got busy learning everything I could about launching a live stream show on Facebook Live and YouTube. I hired a live-streaming expert to help me set up my live-stream home studio, including choosing the right camera, mic, lighting, and green screen. I also had him teach me how to use special live-stream video software. After a good six months of receiving coaching on how to produce a live-stream talk show and doing plenty of testing, I was ready to launch my show.

I named it *Mary Giuliani LIVE* and set the launch date for January 2017. I scheduled it to air every Wednesday night. I booked my first handful of guests, sent out the launch announcement in my email newsletter, and posted it to my website and social media feeds.

**mary giuliani LIVE**
Transformational Talk Show

Connect    Reflect    Transform

Wednesdays 7pm PST
MaryGiuliani.net/WatchLive

The day finally came when the show was to launch. I was extremely nervous since this was a live show and new territory for me. Although the first show had some technical issues due to my guest logging into the live stream with spotty internet, when all was said and done, it went very well.

I felt a huge sense of relief once the first show was over. The following day I felt a blissful feeling of healthy pride wash over me. It was a fantastic feeling of empowerment that I hadn't felt in a really long time. I remember saying to myself, "Wow, if I can walk through this level of stress and vulnerability, I can walk through anything!"

For over a year, I live-streamed my show, interviewing dozens of authors, coaches, psychotherapists, and thought leaders who all shared inspiring stories of how they or people they'd worked with had overcome adversity and trauma and were able to heal and transform their lives.

Launching my talk show was one of the scariest things I've ever done. Since it was a live show, it stretched my willingness to risk being vulnerable. Anyone who tuned in for the live stream could see not only all the wonderful moments but all the technical glitches as well. It was a major stretch, and although I was really uncomfortable doing it initially, I noticed my fear began to diminish the more I got into the rhythm and routine of doing it each week.

I was really proud of myself for walking through my fears and taking all the steps to launch the show. Although I had every intention of it being a long-term venture and was fully on board with growing my audience and finding the best guests to interview, I had no idea that within a year of launching it, I would read a book about childhood trauma that would take me on a journey that would change everything—including continuing the show.

# PART II

---

# MY DISCOVERY

# CHAPTER 11

---

# DISCOVERING IT WAS TRAUMA CHANGED EVERYTHING

Trauma is perhaps the most avoided, ignored, belittled, denied, misunderstood, and untreated cause of human suffering.

—Peter Levine, Ph.D.

## 2017: AGE 57

One day in the fall of 2017, while listening to Holly Whitaker—one of my favorite recovery podcasters—on her *Home* podcast, I heard her mention that she'd compiled a list of her favorite books from 2017 and posted it to her website. When I reviewed her list, a book about childhood trauma, *The Body Keeps the Score: Brain, Mind, and Body in the Healing of Trauma,* stood out.

Although I didn't think the book would apply directly to me since I didn't think I had trauma, I had recently noticed more books about trauma showing up on other podcaster's favorite book lists that I followed. And since trauma was one of the mental health topics I had never studied, being the total psychology geek that I am, I was curious to learn more about how it developed and how it impacted people's lives.

By the end of Holly's over-the-top rave review, she rated it as the best book she'd ever read about trauma. At some point during her review, she boldly states, "Just read it!" Since I loved some of the other books I'd read on her list, I decided to purchase the audio version through Audible.

As I listened to the first few chapters, veils began lifting that I didn't even know I had about how childhood trauma was linked to some of the most difficult struggles I'd been suffering with for decades!

Before reading *The Body Keeps The Score,* I thought childhood trauma could only happen when a child was sexually or physically abused. Yet, here I was, reading page after page by leading trauma expert Bessel van der Kolk, M.D., who stated that I didn't have to be sexually or physically abused to experience trauma. According to Van der Kolk, being raised by an alcoholic, depressed mother who went on drunken tirades against her husband on a regular basis provided more than enough toxic stress for me to become traumatized. Realizing this for the first time was totally mind-blowing.

After experiencing so many epiphanies after reading *The Body Keeps the Score*, I felt compelled to read everything I could get my hands on about childhood trauma and how to heal. I also began researching many subtopics of trauma, including the link between trauma and various trauma symptoms, such as addiction, obesity, anxiety, depression, and relationship difficulties.

I was also drawn to studying trauma's impact on attachment styles, resilience, and post-traumatic growth. This research played a key role in helping me better understand how trauma had impacted me and what types of trauma-based therapies and practices would best serve my healing.

Over a five-year period, I listened to or read dozens of books and blogs, visited countless websites, and attended several conferences, conventions, and movie screenings related to childhood trauma. I went through family photos and spoke to family members to gain a deeper understanding of what had happened to me and what had happened to my parents growing up.

In many ways, I felt like a forensic psychologist searching for and sifting through mountains of clues and evidence from all the books and media I found to make sense of what had happened to me. In the following pages, I share what I experienced as I uncovered layer after layer of how childhood trauma had impacted me throughout my life. I discuss the context of what led to my trauma, how it influenced my identity and worldview, how I coped, and who I became.

Most importantly, I share what I did to heal.

## Why Childhood Trauma Is So Misunderstood & Unacknowledged in Our Culture

As I continued learning everything I could about childhood trauma, I still couldn't shake wondering why I hadn't discovered sooner that trauma could be behind so many of my struggles.

Given that I've had my nose to the ground for decades in the latest science and research in the recovery field and healing the wounds from being raised in a dysfunctional family, the fact that it still took three decades for me to link my struggles to childhood trauma seemed really odd. In my mind, if anyone had discovered a direct link between addiction, severe obesity, and childhood trauma, it would have been me.

I also found it strange that I hadn't heard anything from my friends and colleagues in the recovery and personal development fields about the links between childhood trauma, addiction, obesity, and relationship difficulties. It seemed conspicuous in its absence. It kept gnawing at me. I needed to know why.

As I began racking my brain for reasons, I recalled some discussions with friends and colleagues shortly after discovering I had trauma. I'd shared how excited I was to finally find that untreated childhood trauma was behind so many of my struggles. What was strange about these conversations was how rarely my friends and colleagues shared with me that they, too, had experienced similar types of adversity or trauma growing up.

After reading in *The Body Keeps The Score* that CDC studies show that 25% of adults in the U.S. grew up with alcoholic or drug-addicted parents or relatives, 17% grew up with a parent with depression, anxiety, or other mental health issues, and 20% of girls are sexually molested before turning eighteen, I assumed a lot more of my friends would share that they'd experienced similar types of childhood adversity. But strangely enough, hardly any of them did.

As I pondered what could be behind this lack of disclosure, I thought maybe it had to do with what the word *trauma* means or triggers for people. When I thought about it, the word *trauma* can be defined in radically different ways for different people, making it highly prone to misinterpretation.

After doing quite a bit of research into why hardly anyone I knew or followed discussed their own childhood trauma or the impact that childhood adversity and trauma have on a person throughout their life, I came up with some answers.

# 12 Reasons People Don't Recognize Their Own or Others' Childhood Trauma

## 1. Survivors Are Unaware Being Raised By Parents Who Chronically Fight, Are Addicted, or Suffer From Depression or Anxiety Can Cause Them To Develop C-PTSD

Many people are unaware that physical or sexual abuse or other horrific incidents are not the only way for a child to experience trauma. A child can also develop trauma by being raised in a home with parents who are addicted, anxious, depressed, emotionally abusive or emotionally neglectful, or who chronically fight.

Childhood trauma develops over long periods of time in the context of close family relationships where a child is supposed to feel safe, connected, and cared for, but instead, they feel afraid, alone, and disconnected. This is why childhood trauma is also known as relational trauma. The clinical term for childhood trauma is complex PTSD or C-PTSD. It's considered a more severe form of PTSD since it occurs over many years during critical periods of a child's brain and emotional development.

Common phrases I've heard psychotherapists use when describing different types of trauma are big T trauma and *little t trauma*. Sexual and physical abuse, rape, assault, combat, serious car accidents, or natural disasters are considered *big T trauma*. Relational types of trauma, such as children who experience emotional abuse and neglect or who witness parents emotionally abuse each other, are considered *little t trauma*. The problem with differentiating trauma as big or little is how it implies "little t trauma" is not as impactful as "big T trauma," even though the ACE-adverse childhood experiences study has proved otherwise. I've written about the ACE study in much more detail in future chapters.

Although a child may not have been hit or sexually abused, living in a family where there is chronic tension, fighting, addiction, or where a child feels emotionally invalidated, abandoned, and on their own is something that happens every day for years or even decades. This is the essence of relational trauma, and it is well documented that it can be just as traumatizing as physical or sexual abuse.

Believing that I had to have been physically or sexually abused to suffer from childhood trauma was the reason I never thought to seek out trauma-based therapies to heal. Had I known, I could have saved myself from years of needless pain and suffering. One of my goals with this book is to dispel this myth.

## 2. When Parents Feel Unjustly Blamed For Traumatizing Their Child, They Go Into Denial or Minimize What Happened for Self-Protection

I believe one of the main reasons childhood trauma is so minimized and unacknowledged in our culture is due to how sensitive and painful any topic about harming children is, especially when it involves how they were parented. Anytime a parent feels they are being unjustly accused of harming or traumatizing their child, it triggers the guilt most parents already feel about how they've raised their children.

Parents who feel blamed or judged often respond defensively by minimizing or denying how their parenting could have hurt their child. My intention in bringing the facts about childhood trauma to light through this book is not to blame or shame parents. Parents can only parent to the degree that they were parented. And a child's grandparents could only parent their parents to the degree that they were parented as well!

Therefore, there is literally no one person to blame. If there is anyone or anything to blame, it's human nature. Humans have certain irreducible needs, and when they are met, they thrive, and when they are not met, they often develop C-PTSD.

Even though there is no one person to blame for a child developing trauma, we still need to know how to address this topic to help survivors heal and to stop the cycle of passing traumatizing parenting practices down through the generations.

I appreciated the balanced perspective taken on this issue from the excerpt in the following article *The Cost of Blaming Parents.*

In general, we can't forgive our parents until we have some clarity that we didn't deserve their mistreatment. It is equally important to realize that in the world of the family, traumas often beget traumas: Most parents who mistreat their children were likely also mistreated. In order to break this sad cycle, a goal might be to see one's parents not only as neglectful or hostile but as ill-equipped to create the kind of family environment that fosters confidence and secure attachments.

Source: Joshua Coleman, J Carolyn Cowan, & Phil Cowan, Greater Good Magazine, 12-23-14

This excerpt helped me see the value in recognizing a parent's abuse and neglect for what it is and that you didn't deserve it or cause it. This is the first key to gaining a coherent narrative of what happened to you. Recognizing your parent's unresolved trauma made them ill-equipped to parent you and that it resulted in you developing trauma is the second step in piecing together your new narrative. This doesn't mean we shouldn't feel our anger or pain about what happened since we must. Regardless of who's to blame for our trauma, we need to feel the pain and process it to resolve it. And we can't forgive our parents until we resolve our pain about what happened.

To reiterate, healing trauma is not about blaming parents. Parents do the best they can. I am bringing this information to light for two reasons. One is because I want to help survivors stop blaming themselves for what happened and how they coped. And two, the only way we can break the chain of trauma from being passed down from generation to generation is to educate parents on how common parenting practices can inadvertently traumatize children and to teach them specific parenting skills to help their children thrive.

### 3. The Lack of Awareness Parents, Therapists & Doctors Have About C-PTSD Is Similar To Our Ignorance of Infectious Disease in the 1860s

The issue of parents being offended or ashamed about being blamed for traumatizing their children reminds me of the period before we understood germ theory and how disease could be spread back in the 1860s. Back then, doctors were highly offended for being blamed for causing patients' deaths due to infection due to them neglecting to wash their hands between seeing patients.

Even though French chemist Louis Pasteur discovered that diseases could be transferred from person to person via germ theory in 1861, it took several decades for the medical community to accept that diseases could be spread through a lack of handwashing by doctors.

Even in the late 1860s, almost ten years after germ theory was discovered, when doctors implied to their colleagues that their lack of hand washing was responsible for transmitting the infectious diseases that killed their patients, the doctors (who were ignorant or in denial about germ theory) were extremely offended.

Since germ theory was new and doctors weren't trained about it in medical school, many were skeptical. It wasn't until the 1870s that doctors realized that going straight from an autopsy to the maternity ward without washing their hands was risking their patient's health. Even though germ theory was discovered in 1861, many hospitals refused to require hand washing practices for many years.

What do the doctors from the 1860s and today's parents, therapists, and doctors have in common? The vast majority are unaware of the latest science on what causes harm (the spread of infection for the former and the cause of C-PTSD for the latter), resulting in them being offended when blamed for causing harm to those in their care. And if you are unaware of what causes harm to someone in your care, you can't be blamed for the harm caused. And tragically, (today's parents, therapists, and doctors who aren't aware of what causes C-PTSD) won't be able to protect those in their care from being traumatized or provide referrals for trauma-informed treatment to help survivors heal.

If we hadn't confronted doctors about how their lack of handwashing was spreading disease and causing their patients to become sick and die due to not wanting to offend them, millions of lives would have been lost. Thank God we did since it is now common sense that hand washing prevents the spread of disease.

Since it is well-documented by the landmark Adverse Childhood Experiences Study that physical and sexual abuse are not the only ways children develop C-PTSD, we must educate parents, therapists, and doctors on what causes childhood trauma, what symptoms to look for, and what types of therapies and practices are necessary to prevent and heal it.

And just like handwashing is a common sense practice to prevent the spread of disease, by staying committed to educating parents, therapists, and doctors about C-PTSD—over time, trauma-informed parenting will be a common-sense practice to prevent C-PTSD, and trauma-informed therapies will be common sense approaches to help those heal from trauma.

### 4. Being Unaware That Childhood Trauma Is Not Only the Event But Is More About How Trauma Gets Reactivated and Relived Throughout Survivor's Lives

Before I embarked on this journey, I thought the actual horrific event and the disturbing memories of it were what traumatized a person. I was surprised to learn that childhood trauma is more about what continues to happen inside the survivor due to how the trauma has changed their brain and nervous system.

For this reason, a person doesn't so much remember their trauma; they relive it through the sensations in their bodies and the thoughts in their minds when they get triggered. In my case, when I feel tension between my partner and me, I don't consciously remember the chronic tension I was forced to witness between my parents. Instead, the tension I'm experiencing in my relationship reactivates my previous trauma to where I begin reliving the sensations of the past trauma in my body and the fear-based thoughts my nervous system generates.

Often a chronic state of endangerment persists for survivors. It's as if the survivor's internal threat alarm is stuck in the "On" position. Unless a survivor is aware they have C-PTSD and knows what to look for, they'll be unaware that their intense reactions and feelings may have nothing to do with the present but are instead their nervous system, body, and mind reliving a past traumatic experience.

This is why what continues to happen inside the brain, body, and mind throughout a survivor's life due to the effects of trauma are typically much more severe than the traumatic event or period itself.

### 5. Minimizing Childhood Trauma as Something Everyone Has Experienced

After sharing how I'd recently discovered that childhood trauma had been the root cause of so many of my lifelong struggles, I noticed that several people responded with the same assumptive question, "Well, hasn't everyone experienced some form of childhood trauma?"

When I asked them to clarify how they define childhood trauma, many said it meant a child who experienced a tragedy or something deeply upsetting while growing up. I would respond by sharing: *What I'm referring to as childhood trauma is when a child grows up in a home filled with ongoing abuse, neglect, or dysfunction that permanently resets their nervous system and significantly impacts their emotional and physical health—and unless there's an intervention will affect them for the rest of their lives. So, based on this definition, I wouldn't say that everyone has experienced childhood trauma, but I would agree that everyone has experienced something disturbing or deeply upsetting in their childhood.*

I also let them know that my explanation isn't to discount or overlook any type of pain or deep distress someone experienced as a child. It's to help better differentiate what is and what isn't childhood trauma.

### 6. Denial Due To Fearing Being Shamed For Dishonoring Your Parents

Once people are faced with how a parent can inadvertently cause their child to develop C-PTSD by how they raised them, there is often a knee-jerk reaction to minimize the impact parenting has on a child. Some people get extremely agitated and defensive when faced with the fact that their parents may have traumatized them.

The reason I believe this topic is so triggering is because so many people believe that acknowledging they have trauma means they're dishonoring their parents.  And if they blame their parents for their trauma, they are breaking the cultural and religious rules that dictate children honor their parents no matter what.

My purpose in writing this book is not to blame parents. It's about how to stop blaming ourselves for what happened to us or how we coped so we can move forward in our healing process. As we face and heal the past, we're freed up to be fully present, which enables us to move on to creating rich and rewarding lives.

## 7.  Denial Due To Believing Trauma Means You're Weak

Many people deny they were traumatized because they view being impacted by trauma as being weak. Our culture likes heroes. We don't like victims or losers. We like people who are strong and can overcome anything life throws at them.

Since trauma always involves being powerless and being powerless is equated with weakness, acknowledging trauma often triggers shame. Taking on the shame of being seen as weak can generate a knee-jerk reaction to automatically defend, deny, or minimize that childhood trauma could be driving their presenting problems, such as addiction, obesity, anxiety, depression, or difficulty with close relationships.

Victim-shaming statements, such as "When are you going to take responsibility for your life and stop blaming your parents or your childhood for your problems?" are extremely common in our culture. Sadly, attitudes like this play a huge role in stopping people from even considering that their struggle with relationships, obesity, or addiction may be due to what they experienced growing up. Instead of believing that trauma may be the root cause of their issues, they vehemently deny it because they fear looking weak or being victim shamed.

The problem with this view is if we don't acknowledge that we've been hurt, we can't heal. And if we don't heal our trauma, we inadvertently allow every area of our lives to be colored by it.

## 8.  Minimizing Childhood Trauma As Something People Should Get Over on Their Own

Sadly, our culture touts the lie that if you're a strong, competent person, you'll have the strength to overcome adversity—including childhood trauma—by simply staying strong, stoic, and moving on. I often hear people say, "Everyone has had some type of trauma, but it's important to move on with your life and not allow yourself to stay stuck in the past," or "Since I can't change what happened, there's no use in revisiting it."

I completely agree with this philosophy if there truly are no lingering unhealed trauma symptoms and the person's life is working. But if they struggle with classic trauma symptoms such as relationship difficulties, addiction, and obesity, there are obviously unhealed issues they haven't moved on from.

Given that most people don't understand the impact childhood trauma has on a survivor, they don't realize that it's impossible to simply get over or move on from the brain, body, mind, and nervous system impacts of trauma by the sheer power of their will. It would be like expecting a person with a traumatic brain injury to "just get over it" by being strong without providing evidence-based medical treatment to give them the best chance at a full recovery.

## 9.  Believing You Can't Have Childhood Trauma Unless Your Siblings Have Trauma

Just because a sibling doesn't experience symptoms of childhood trauma doesn't mean your trauma symptoms should be denied or minimized. It's common for some siblings in the same family to seemingly not be impacted by childhood trauma while others are. Below are the most common reasons why this happens.

Some children inherit genes that predispose them to be highly sensitive. The term used for someone born with these inherited sensitivities is HSP or a highly sensitive person. Being an HSP can be a great strength and asset if a child grows up with emotionally attuned parents who teach their HSP child how to use their heightened sensitivity. But if the parents aren't attuned to their child's emotions, the child will probably be affected even more deeply by the absence of emotional attention. This type of childhood adversity is known as emotional neglect.

Parents' stress levels from the child's birth through their early years can also impact whether or not a child develops trauma. Protective factors can also buffer one child from developing trauma from high levels of adversity. These include positive childhood experiences and supportive relationships with teachers, coaches, neighbors, or close friends who believe in the child and whom they can confide in.

It's also common for one sibling to display obvious trauma symptoms, such as a serious addiction, obesity, or the inability to form close relationships, while their siblings don't. Yet frequently, the siblings without overt trauma symptoms suffer in less obvious ways. Many stay in toxic or unfulfilling relationships and jobs or suffer from low levels of depression or anxiety. They may also suffer from more acceptable addictions, such as work, food, shopping, screen time, gambling, toxic intensity, porn, or "busyholism."

The most important thing to remember is that just because your sibling isn't suffering from symptoms of childhood trauma—or doesn't appear to be—it doesn't mean you aren't.

## 10. Believing Childhood Trauma Only Happens to Poor or Marginalized People

Trauma is part and parcel of the human condition. It's very common, and it's not personal. It doesn't matter what neighborhood you grew up in, how much money you have, what race you are, your spiritual or religious beliefs, or what country you live in.

This isn't to discount the fact that poor and marginalized children experience more stress and trauma than children who aren't. The point here is when you put any child in an environment with enough chronic toxic stress, coupled with a lack of resources to help weather this stress, they will experience trauma no matter who they are.

Humans, just like plants, are organisms. All organisms have specific needs to survive and thrive. When a plant doesn't get its essential needs met with enough sunlight, water, and healthy soil, its growth is stunted, it gets sick, and it typically dies sooner. The same goes for the human organism. When a child's needs are met, the predictable outcome is for them to thrive. And when a child's needs aren't met over long periods of time, the predictable outcome is for them to develop childhood trauma.

## 11. The DSM Delegitimizes Childhood Trauma By Failing To Include It As A Formal Diagnosis in The DSM-5

The Diagnostic and Statistical Manual of Mental Disorders—The DSM, published by the American Psychological Association, is what all therapists use to diagnose and treat mental health disorders. It is also where therapists must get their diagnosis codes to be paid by insurance companies. Although Dr. Bessel van der Kolk led a team proposing including the term Developmental Trauma Disorder as a childhood trauma diagnosis in the DSM-5, it was denied.

Since the DSM-5 does not yet recognize complex PTSD or any other formal diagnosis for childhood trauma, therapists are forced to diagnose their patients with symptom-based conditions such as anxiety, depression, substance use disorders, obesity, etc., instead of what they are really suffering with, complex PTSD.

Although complex PTSD is included in the ICD-11-International Classification of Diseases, published by the World Health Organization, since many insurance companies do not accept ICD-11 codes to pay mental health providers, it leaves them with no other alternative when billing insurance than to use a DSM-5 symptom-based diagnosis code to get reimbursement.

## 12. Psychotherapists Fail to Recognize or Inform Their Patients They Have Complex PTSD

After seeing over a dozen therapists and several psychiatrists over the past thirty years (with whom all knew my history) and not one of them recognized or informed me I was suffering from complex PTSD or any other term used for childhood trauma and needed trauma-based therapies to fully heal, it's clear how uninformed the mental health community is about childhood trauma.

Regardless of whether C-PTSD is recognized in the DSM-5, given that the ACE Study and other peer-reviewed studies have proven that childhood trauma exists, is common, and can be treated, I believe the mental health community has an ethical and moral obligation to inform their patients if they believe they are suffering from it and refer them out for specialized trauma treatment.

If just one of my past therapists over the past three decades had mentioned they suspected I was suffering from childhood trauma, I would have immediately gotten into treatment and could have saved myself decades of needless pain and suffering.

### How Shame & Ignorance Keep C-PTSD Alive

When I took the time to review what the *12 Reasons Why People Don't Recognize Their Own or Other's Childhood Trauma* had in common, I noticed two themes. The first is shame, and the second is ignorance.

The price we pay for being ignorant or the shame and denial we have about childhood trauma is second only to the trauma itself. Since we can't heal or change what we can't face or accept, facing the fact that childhood trauma exists is the first step toward healing it.

My hope is that putting a face, name, and a story to illustrate what C-PTSD is and that it's possible to prevent and heal will help other survivors know they're not alone and inspire them to pursue their own healing and recovery journey.

### Hurt People Hurt People & Healed People Heal People

When people are unaware or unwilling to address and heal their trauma, it plays havoc with their ability to create a life they love. Unhealed trauma often keeps survivors stuck in a chronic state of survival. Tragically, trauma's damage doesn't stop with them. Like a virus, unresolved trauma remains alive, operating underneath the surface, searching for a way to express itself. Sadly, trauma also hurts the survivor's family members and those they come in contact with. This is where the saying *hurt people hurt people* comes from.

By the same token, healed people heal people. People who heal their trauma automatically stop the cycle of passing it down to their children or those around them and often are motivated to help others heal. This is the path I've taken. My hope for this book is to inspire survivors to heal their trauma, recover from addiction or other common trauma symptoms, break the chain of trauma from being passed down through their generations, and motivate them to help other survivors heal.

## Defining Childhood Trauma

### Common Terms Used for Childhood Trauma by the Mental Health Community

Below are the terms trauma experts use for childhood trauma and the criteria that must be met to receive a childhood trauma diagnosis.

**Complex Post-Traumatic Stress Disorder (C-PTSD)** is the most frequently used diagnostic term I've seen used for childhood trauma. The term was coined in 1992 by psychiatrist and trauma expert Dr. Judith Herman in her book *Trauma & Recovery.* However, it wasn't until 2018 that C-PTSD was officially recognized when it was included in *The World Health Organization's -WHO's ICD-11,* a medical diagnostic manual recognized by the medical community.

**Developmental Trauma Disorder (DTD)** is used by many clinicians and psychiatrists when referring to childhood trauma. This term was developed by a team led by trauma expert and psychiatrist Bessel van der Kolk to be included in *The Diagnostic and Statistical Manual of Mental Disorders-5* (DSM-5) as a childhood trauma diagnosis but was denied. Although DTD wasn't included in the DSM-5, many trauma experts and practitioners use it in current literature when referring to the sequelae of childhood trauma.

**Disorders of Extreme Stress Not Otherwise Specified (DESNOS)** was included in the DSM 4–Field Trial but not in the DSM 5. Before DESNOS was excluded from the DSM, many clinicians used it when diagnosing their patients suffering from childhood trauma since the criteria was similar to C-PTSD.

**Post Traumatic Stress Disorder (PTSD)** is occasionally used for childhood trauma survivors who meet its criteria. However, most patients who suffer from C-PTSD don't meet the criteria for PTSD. This is what prompted Dr. Bessel van der Kolk to lead a team proposing the new term Developmental Trauma Disorder be included in the DSM to recognize childhood trauma as its own separate diagnosis. Unfortunately, it was denied.

## The Criteria for Diagnosing C-PTSD By The ICD-11

### The three PTSD symptom criteria of:
1. Re-experiencing
2. Avoidance
3. Hypervigilance

### And three disturbances of self-organization (DSO):
1. Emotional dysregulation
2. Interpersonal difficulties
3. Negative self-concept

## Definition of C-PTSD By Trauma Expert Pete Walker, MA, LMFT

C-PTSD is a more severe form of Post-Traumatic Stress Disorder-PTSD. It is delineated from this better-known trauma syndrome PTSD by five of its most common and troublesome features:

- Emotional flashbacks
- Toxic shame
- Self-abandonment
- A vicious inner critic
- Social anxiety

### Most Common Terms I See Used for Childhood Trauma & Trauma Survivors

I hear clinicians and colleagues often refer to childhood trauma as complex trauma, C-PTSD, complex post-traumatic stress disorder, childhood trauma, trauma, developmental trauma, childhood PTSD, and PTSD.

Throughout this book, I predominantly refer to childhood trauma as complex PTSD, complex trauma, and C-PTSD. However, I also use the terms trauma, childhood PTSD, and childhood trauma.

I, along with many of my colleagues, use the terms survivor and trauma survivor when referring to people who have experienced significant adversity in childhood or who have been diagnosed with C-PTSD or PTSD.

### The Most Common Misdiagnosis' For C-PTSD

Tragically, more often than not, survivors are misdiagnosed with C-PTSD symptom-related mental and behavioral health disorders. This was certainly true for me. Up until my mid-fifties, instead of being diagnosed with C-PTSD, I was diagnosed with six different disorders. These include generalized anxiety disorder, dysthymia, attention deficit hyperactivity disorder- ADHD, binge eating disorder, morbid obesity (has since been renamed to class III, or severe obesity) and alcohol and substance use disorders. The truth is, all of these disorders were merely symptoms of my real diagnosis: C-PTSD.

Trauma expert and psychotherapist Pete Walker discusses the tragedy of this common phenomenon in his book *Complex PTSD From Surviving To Thriving*:

> Renowned traumatologist, John Briere, is said to have quipped that if Complex PTSD were ever given its due – that is, if the role of dysfunctional parenting in adult psychological disorders was ever fully recognized, the DSM (The Diagnostic and Statistical Manual of Mental Disorders used by all mental health professionals) would shrink to the size of a thin pamphlet. It currently resembles a large dictionary.

> In my experience, many clients with Complex PTSD have been misdiagnosed with various anxiety and depressive disorders, as well as bipolar, narcissistic, codependent, and borderline disorders. Further confusion arises in the case of ADHD (Attention Deficit Hyperactive Disorder), as well as obsessive/compulsive disorder, which is sometimes more accurately described as an excessive, fixated flight response to trauma. This is also true of ADD (Attention Deficit Disorder) and some dissociative disorders, which are similarly excessive, fixated freeze responses to trauma.

> This is not to say that those so diagnosed do not have issues that are similar and correlative with said disorders, but that these labels are incomplete and unnecessarily shaming descriptions of what the client is afflicted with. Calling complex PTSD "panic disorder" is like calling food allergies chronically itchy eyes; over-focusing treatment on the symptoms of panic in the former case and eye health in the latter does little to get at root causes.

> Feelings of panic or itchiness in the eyes can be masked with medication, but all the other associated problems that cause these symptoms will remain untreated.

> Moreover, most of the diagnoses mentioned above imply deep innate characterological defects rather than the learned maladaptations to stress that children of trauma are forced to make– adaptations, once again, that were learned and can, therefore, usually be extinguished and replaced with more functional adaptations to stress.

> In this vein, I believe that many substance and process addictions also begin as misguided maladaptations to parental abuse and abandonment – early adaptations that are attempts to soothe and distract from the mental and emotional pain of complex PTSD

## Discovering How Common Childhood Adversity and Trauma Is

It was astounding when I first learned, according to the CDC-Centers For Disease Control:

- 20% of adults reported being sexually molested as children
- 25% grew up with an alcoholic relative
- 33% of couples have engaged in physical violence
- 25% were beaten to the point of it leaving a mark on their body by a parent

This doesn't even cover emotional abuse, neglect, or other types of adversity children frequently experience. I cover these topics in-depth in an upcoming chapter about the landmark ACE-adverse childhood experiences study.

## Adult Symptoms of Childhood Trauma

Since childhood trauma symptoms fall on a spectrum from subtle to overt, I have included the following questionnaire to help you assess if you are experiencing or have experienced some or many of the more common symptoms for adults with C-PTSD.

The author of this questionnaire is Anna Runkle. Anna is known as *The Crappy Childhood Fairy*. She is a survivor who has done a substantial amount of work to recover from C-PTSD. She has coached thousands of survivors to recognize and heal their adult symptoms of Childhood PTSD through her coaching programs, educational videos, and website.

## Do You Have Childhood PTSD?

The below 13 questions can help you determine if you've experienced some of the more common symptoms of dysregulation associated with early trauma.

1. Do you have trouble regulating intense emotions, having outbursts of sadness or anger when it doesn't seem appropriate?
2. Have you struggled with depression, anxiety, or other mental health problems?
3. Does a crippling feeling of fear sometimes hold you back from expressing yourself, taking action, or being your real self?
4. Do your relationships have an unusually high amount of arguing, or is there violence?
5. Does the fear of abandonment or of being alone cause you to stay in negative relationships?
6. Do you get clumsy at random times, tripping over things or dropping things?
7. Do you have trouble staying present or feel physically numb when you try to talk about your feelings?
8. Have you found yourself saying yes to sex, even when you knew it was dangerous, hurtful to yourself or others, or likely to lead to an STD or unwanted pregnancy?
9. Do you smoke cigarettes, vape, or use food, alcohol, or drugs in an addictive way?
10. Do you feel that no matter how much a partner or friend tries to be there for you, you feel alone, unloved or unheard?
11. After a big emotional upset, do you sometimes feel nothing?
12. Do you find people so triggering that you avoid social situations?
13. Do you have unexplained health problems that seem to have no clear cause?

If you answered yes to one or more of these questions, you might be suffering from C-PTSD. The good news is that C-PTSD is treatable, and you can heal. Reading the remainder of this book will help you learn more about the nature of C-PTSD and provide the information you need to choose a healing path that resonates for you.

## The Symptoms of Childhood Trauma Occur on a Spectrum from Mild to Severe

One of the more interesting aspects I've learned about childhood trauma is that the severity of its symptoms occurs on a spectrum. This is due to every person who was abused or neglected as a child having different parents, experiences, and temperaments. In addition, several protective factors can buffer the severity of a child's trauma, making one child with severe trauma have fewer symptoms than one with similar trauma without protective factors.

The source of my trauma—being raised in an extremely dysfunctional, alcoholic home—and my overt trauma symptoms, such as addictions, anxiety, depression, shame, severe obesity, and difficulty in school, are easy to spot. However, some people experience more subtle forms of childhood trauma symptoms.

Children who were emotionally neglected (when parents don't notice a child's emotions or treat them as unimportant, invalid, excessive, or less important than other issues) may grow up to struggle with anxiety, mild depression, a sense of emptiness, unexplained medical issues, or a lack of fulfilling relationships.

These symptoms can be difficult to trace to emotional neglect because this type of neglect is about what didn't happen but what needed to for the child to develop in an emotionally healthy way.

There are also genetic and epigenetic factors that can prime one sibling to be drawn to using drugs, alcohol, or food to cope with the toxic stress of a dysfunctional home and another to use less overt coping mechanisms such as excessive work, over-caretaking, or over-spending.

## It's Not Your Fault

The first thing to remember when you learn you're struggling with C-PTSD is:

It's Not Your Fault

Although it can take a while to accept this fact, the truth is that you didn't ask to be traumatized as a child. C-PTSD shaped your nervous system, brain, and mind to adapt to living in an emotionally barren or scary home as a lonely or terrified child. Even though you no longer need this adaptation as an adult, your body, brain, and mind never got the memo, so it's still running the old survival program from your childhood.

Having C-PTSD is like being stuck with a thermostat that runs either too hot or too cold. Some survivors' nervous systems tend to run anxious (too hot), and some run overly spaced out (too cold.) Some survivors alternate between being too anxious or too lethargic or spacey. The good news is that you can reset your nervous system to be more regulated by accessing trauma-based treatments and practices.

## The Difference Between the Brain & the Mind

Since the topic of childhood trauma requires frequent references to the brain and the mind, I've included a brief, basic medically-based description of their differences to avoid confusion between them.

The brain is an organ that's the center of the nervous system. It coordinates motor activity and sensations in the body and generates thoughts and feelings. The brain can be measured, whereas the mind cannot be measured through physical attributes. The mind consists of a person's thought process, beliefs, self-concept, and worldview.

An analogy I have found helpful to easily distinguish between the brain and mind is to look at the brain as the computer and the mind as the data the computer generates.

# My Initial Aha Moments When Learning About Childhood Trauma

## Why Making Sense of Why I Struggled Was So Healing

Before I learned I had trauma, I never completely understood why I struggled in the ways that I did. One of the most powerful benefits of reading *The Body Keeps The Score* was that it taught me about the nature of trauma and how it had changed the structure and function of my brain, and how those changes impacted my nervous system, body, mind, behavior, and relationships.

It helped me finally answer the question that had been swirling around in my mind for decades: *What's wrong with me?* Being able to make sense of what happened to me and how it accounted for why I struggled in the ways that I did was in and of itself, extremely calming and healing.

Human beings are meaning-making machines. When we're unable to make sense of why we struggle in the ways we do, we'll come up with our own assumptions for its cause and often assume it's because we're crazy or defective. When we realize the reasons we've struggled are not because of some inherent defectiveness but because of what happened to us, we're able to stop judging ourselves, which opens the door to self-compassion, the first step toward healing trauma.

## Learning Being Exposed To Chronic Toxic Stress Causes Complex PTSD

I never thought a certain type of stress could cause a child to develop trauma until I learned about complex PTSD. Tolerable or "good" stress can challenge a child to stretch and grow without overwhelming them. An example of good stress could be a student performing in a class play. Although their body's fight or flight stress response system may briefly kick in and pump them with the stress hormone cortisol, with enough supportive adults present to help buffer the stress, eventually, their body returns to normal, and the experience will help them become more resilient.

Unlike good stress, the toxic stress of being raised in a home with addiction, violence, abuse, or neglect is so overwhelming and lasts for such long periods of time that a child's body doesn't return to normal but instead develops complex PTSD.

## How Childhood Trauma Changes The Brain & Nervous System

One of the reasons I loved listening to *The Body Keeps the Score* is that it's based on undeniable, hard-core science. In it, Dr. Bessel van der Kolk cites dozens of studies, including brain scans and other neuroscience-based technologies. These peer-reviewed studies prove that kids' brains, bodies, and minds are changed when exposed to chronic toxic stress that results in childhood trauma.

## Brain Scans Don't Lie

The below image is of a PET scan comparing two children's brains. The image on the left is of a normal child's brain, and the one on the right is of a severely neglected child's brain. When you compare the two white circles on each scan, you'll notice the dark areas in the circles on the traumatized child's brain on the right. You'll also notice that the area at the top of the traumatized child's brain contains a fraction of the color red compared to the healthy child's brain.

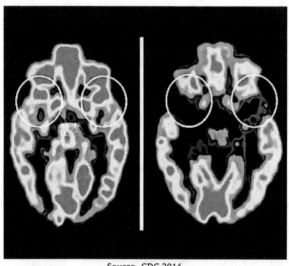

Source: CDC 2016

The dark areas in the traumatized child's brain are due to there being little to no brain activity in them. These areas either developed improperly or not at all due to this child being raised in an environment with severe ongoing neglect. The areas at the top of the traumatized child's brain that have a fraction of the color red compared to the healthy child's brain are also due to a lack of brain activity. This brain area (the prefrontal cortex) is responsible for emotional regulation, impulse control, judgment, planning, and focus.

This absence of activity in the image on the right is the physical manifestation of a child with a traumatized brain. The lack of brain development in certain areas causes children and adults with trauma to operate much differently than those with normal brain function.

This brain scan is irrefutable proof that childhood trauma not only impacts a person emotionally but also impacts a child's brain function. Tragically, unless there is an intervention, these brain changes will negatively impact this child throughout the rest of their life.

When I first laid eyes on this image and understood what I was seeing, I was stunned. It was one thing to read the many peer-reviewed studies on the impact of childhood trauma on kids' brains. Yet, it was a whole other reality to be looking at an image of a brain in living color, contrasting the difference between a normal brain and a traumatized brain.

This image proved to me beyond a shadow of a doubt that if this child's brain had been changed because of severe neglect, then my brain, too, would have been changed because of the severe neglect and abuse I lived through as a child.

In some ways, I was relieved that I finally could see with my own eyes a huge piece of the puzzle of why I struggled for so long. In other ways, I felt a deep sadness for how seriously I'd been hurt and for how long I'd struggled as a result.

## How A Traumatized Brain Adapts to Cope with the Environment

Another aha moment was learning why traumatized children's survival brains (the part that handles the fight, flight, and freeze area) overdevelop and why their prefrontal cortex (the part that regulates impulses, emotions, and attention) under-develop.

The survival brain overdevelops to handle living in an environment filled with chronic, toxic stress. In contrast, the prefrontal cortex—the part of the brain responsible for emotional regulation, impulse control, and focus must under-develop to dedicate more resources to overdeveloping the survival brain. As a result of these brain changes, traumatized children tend to have problems with anxiety, attention, emotional regulation, and impulsivity.

## How Brain Changes Impact Trauma Survivors

A traumatized brain hijacks the nervous system, causing survivors to live in reactive and defensive states. Living in these states causes a lot of suffering.  Below are examples of how brain changes impact survivors.

### Chronic Anxiety and Tension

The overdeveloped fight, flight, and freeze areas in survivors' brains cause chronic anxiety and tension.  A child dealing with chronic stress and anxiety will naturally seek ways to calm themselves down.  Without a calm, attuned caregiver to help them calm down, a child will seek whatever means are available or modeled. This is where food can become a soothing, calming solution for a child's emotional distress.  As teens and adults, survivors often graduate to using alcohol, drugs, or other high-risk coping behaviors to calm down their anxiety-ridden brains.

### Emotional Reactivity

Since survivors overdevelop the fight, flight, and freeze parts of their brains to cope with the stress of their environment, they become hypersensitive to external stimuli. As a result, they are easily upset by situations that don't cause children with normal brains to become upset. When a non-traumatized child gets angry, sad, or upset, they can self-soothe or find a caregiver to help them calm down in a relatively short period of time.

However, due to the changes in the structure and function of a traumatized child's brain, they tend to be more sensitive to becoming emotionally triggered. This is why they can overreact to a seemingly mild incident and have wider emotional swings that take much longer to calm down.

### Pleasure Center Deficits

Brain scan studies have shown that pleasure centers in the brains of traumatized children under develop. This contributes to survivors often struggling with depression and fatigue, resulting in craving larger quantities of food to experience a sense of satiety, energy, and well-being, resulting in obesity.  As teens and adults, survivors often graduate to using alcohol and stimulants to satisfy these deficits. As tolerance builds, they find that they need larger quantities to feel satisfied, leading to substance use disorders.

### Impulse Control Deficits

Behavioral problems in school, work, or relationships often reflect a survivor's impulse control deficits due to their underdeveloped pre-frontal cortex (the part of the brain in charge of impulse control.) These deficits can also account for a survivor's struggle to resist cravings for food, drugs, alcohol, or other high-risk or self-defeating behaviors.

### Attention Deficits

Learning and behavioral problems in school often reflect survivors' attention deficits due to their underdeveloped pre-frontal cortex (the part of the brain in charge of attention.) Attention deficits can also account for a survivor's careless mistakes, being easily distracted, losing things, and having difficulty staying organized and sitting still.

## Don't Panic- The Brain Is Plastic & Can Heal

Although it may seem overwhelming and depressing when you first learn how much havoc childhood trauma reeks on a child's brain, body, and mind, there is no need to panic since trauma is treatable, and the brain can heal!  Just as adverse childhood experiences can change the structure and function of a child's brain, positive experiences in childhood and adulthood can also change the neuropathways in the brain and result in positive health and social outcomes.

The reason the brain can recover from trauma is due to a phenomenon known as neuroplasticity. When survivors access trauma healing practices and therapies designed to heal the brain, they can build new neuropathways to help them achieve better emotional and nervous system regulation. And since addiction and mood disorders are in part a function of a chronically dysregulated brain and nervous system, providing therapies and practices to help survivors heal their brains can make a huge difference in their lives.

Unlike an illness, C-PTSD develops as a result of what happened to a child. This is why some therapists refer to it as a neurological injury. Just like when a person sustains an injury to an arm or leg, a period of rehabilitation is typically necessary for it to fully heal. In this way, the brain also needs a period of rehabilitation to heal. This is where brain, body, and nervous system trauma therapies and practices are helpful in healing the neurological aspects of C-PTSD.

## Childhood Trauma Lives in the Emotional Brain

Before I learned what childhood trauma actually was, I thought that it impacted survivors solely on a psychological level and that talk therapy and possibly medication would be the best solution for healing.

After reading the excerpt below by trauma expert and psychiatrist, Dr. Bessel van der Kolk from *The Body Keeps the Score,* I had an entirely different understanding of how childhood trauma works and what's necessary for healing.

> The engines of posttraumatic reactions are located in the emotional brain. In contrast with the rational brain, which expresses itself in thoughts, the emotional brain manifests itself in physical reactions: gut-wrenching sensations, heart pounding, breathing becoming fast and shallow, feelings of heartbreak, speaking with an uptight and reedy voice, and the characteristic body movements that signify collapse, rigidity, rage or defensiveness.
>
> The rational executive brain is good at helping us understand where feelings come from. However, the rational brain cannot abolish emotions, sensations, or thoughts (such as living with a low level sense of threat or feeling that you are fundamentally a terrible person, even though you rationally know that you are not to blame for having been raped). Understanding *why* you feel a certain way does not change *how* you feel. The more frazzled we are, the more our rational brain takes a back seat to our emotional brain.
>
> The fundamental issue in resolving traumatic stress is to restore the proper balance between the rational and the emotional brain so that you can feel in charge of how you respond and how you conduct your life.
>
> If we want to change posttraumatic reactions, we have to access the emotional brain and do "limbic system therapy": repairing faulty alarm systems and restoring the emotional brain to its ordinary job of being a quiet background presence that takes care of the housekeeping of the body, ensuring that you eat, sleep, connect with intimate partners, protect your children and defend against danger.
>
> Limbic system therapy is not about understanding or figuring things out because that's not where the trauma sits.
>
> Trauma sits in your automatic reactions and your dispositions, and how you interpret the world.
>
> In order to rewire these automatic perceptions, you need to have deep experiences that, for your survival brain, contradicts how you are now disposed to think.

Van der Kolk goes on to share how limbic system therapy helped a woman who felt physically powerless due to being traumatized as a child. After having the experience of kicking somebody's butt through a martial arts class, her body's disposition was completely transformed. By having the visceral experience of being powerful and protecting herself through martial arts training, she rewired her limbic system to contradict how it had been disposed to think. As a result, it helped to heal her trauma.

It's important to note that, in my experience, a limbic-system approach to healing trauma doesn't have to involve something as physical or aggressive as martial arts. This is just one example of how having an emotional and visceral experience that contradicts how you feel about who you are can help heal the limbic system area of the brain and thereby heal trauma.

I have experienced significant relational trauma healing by using a limbic-system therapy approach in how I interact in my relationships. I share several examples of using this approach in Parts II and III.

## The Body Keeps The Score, But The Mind Hides The Score

I was struck by how succinctly Ezra Klien captured the essence of complex PTSD in his New York Times article *This Conversation Will Change How You Think About Trauma*. In the below excerpt from the article, Klein shares what he experienced after interviewing Dr. Bessel van der Kolk about his book *The Body Keeps the Score* on his podcast, *The Ezra Klien Show*.

> The core argument of the book is that traumatic experiences — everything from sexual assault and incest to emotional and physical abuse — become embedded in the older, more primal parts of our brain that don't have access to conscious awareness. And that means two things simultaneously. First, that trauma lodges in the body. We carry a physical imprint of our psychic wounds. ***The body keeps the score. But — and I found this more revelatory — the mind hides the score.*** It obscures the memories, or convinces us our victimization was our fault, or covers the event in shame so we don't discuss it.

There are several ways the brain and mind can hide the memories of childhood abuse or neglect from survivors. The brains of children younger than three have not developed the capacity to record explicit memory, so they won't have a memory of their trauma. Even for older children who can record explicit memory, when trauma is severe, it can flood the brain with cortisol, which can shut down the area responsible for recording explicit memory, making it impossible for them to remember the trauma.

Another reason a child or an adult survivor may not remember being traumatized is due to the memory of the abuse or neglect being so disturbing, shameful, and overwhelming that it is blocked or repressed for self-protection. In fact, Dr. Bessel van der Kolk speaks to this point in his book *The Body Keeps The Score*, where he states, *Total memory loss is most common in childhood sexual abuse, with incidence ranging from 19 percent to 38 percent*. Although repressing memories is common among survivors, it's not uncommon for repressed memories to surface later in a survivor's life.

Although explicit memories of trauma may have never been recorded due to a child being too young or were recorded but repressed, humans also possess another type of memory known as implicit memory. Implicit memory specializes in recording bodily sensations (sights, smells, sounds, touch, and emotions) and begins as early as in utero. These sensations and emotions can be triggered when a survivor is in a situation similar to when they were traumatized. Implicit memory is the essence of the body keeping the score.

What all of this points to is how powerful the body and mind are in protecting us from experiences that are too overwhelming to bear. The good news is we don't need to have an explicit trauma memory to be able to heal.

## Trauma Changes How You View Yourself, the World, & Other People

Another aspect of C-PTSD I was surprised to learn about is that one of the most significant impacts of trauma is typically not what happened or the memory of it but how the survivor experiences themselves as a result of what happened. Trauma changes survivors' views of themselves, their worldviews, and how they expect people to treat them.

If you experienced being seen and attuned with when you were upset as a child, and your primary caregiver tried to soothe you and also shared in your joy when you were happy, your brain got wired to experience the world as a safe place where you expected to get your needs met. But if you were not seen, heard, and cherished by your caregiver, your brain became wired to experience the world as unsafe, where you expected to be on your own.

As long as you feel safe, known, and loved by your parents, your brain wires so that you can cope with most challenges. However, if this fails to happen often enough and you lack the resources or support to cope, you'll likely experience trauma.

## Why Human Connection Is Essential

Although humans can be resilient in many ways, we're also vulnerable to being traumatized when we're not seen, known, or valued enough. This is why having a present, attuned primary caregiver and a strong family support system and community is the most powerful protective factor in preventing trauma. Studies show that having just one attuned, present, caring adult during a traumatic period or experience can determine whether a child develops trauma or not.

Being cast out or ostracized from your family or community can be a fate worse than death for a child. This is because we're wired for connection. We have lived in tribes for hundreds of thousands of years as a species. We'd die without being accepted and protected by our tribe. We're social beings who need to be seen, known, and valued by our tribe to feel safe and thrive.

## Childhood Trauma Is Relational Trauma

Since childhood trauma happens in the context of close relationships, where we're supposed to feel safe and loved, it's also known as relational trauma. It often seriously impacts survivors' ability to love and accept themselves and also their ability to feel safe and worthy of being loved by others.

Although relationships are the most powerful catalyst for healing trauma, many survivors avoid people because they are so triggering and feel so unsafe.

According to Van der Kolk, a trauma survivor needs a visceral experience of feeling safe, loved, and valued by a safe person to heal their trauma. Insight or a cognitive understanding is helpful but not enough to heal relational trauma.

Learning that childhood trauma is, at heart, relational trauma was another light bulb moment for me. When I looked back at my relationships with romantic partners, friends, and family members through a relational trauma lens, a whole new perspective opened up for me as to why I had so much difficulty with them. I go into much more detail about how childhood trauma impacted my relationships and what I have done to heal in upcoming chapters.

## How Trauma Shuts Down Emotions & Body Sensations

> Trauma is much more than a story about something that happened long ago. The emotions and physical sensations that were imprinted during the trauma are experienced not as memories but as disruptive physical reactions in the present.
>
> —Bessel van der Kolk, M.D.

Before reading *Trauma and Addiction: Ending the Cycle of Pain Through Emotional Literacy* by trauma psychotherapist Tian Dayton, Ph.D., I had no idea that trauma could render a survivor "emotionally illiterate." Up until then, I didn't even know what emotional illiteracy was. According to Dayton, "emotional illiteracy is the inability to put feelings into words so that those feelings can be understood with some sort of psychological context."

It was fascinating to learn that emotions have cognitive and bodily sensation components. According to Dayton, due to how trauma impacts the nervous system, it's very common for survivors to lack the capacity to fully feel their physical sensations. And since we must be able to feel physical sensations to feel emotion, our ability to identify or understand our feelings can be significantly compromised. The clinical term for emotional illiteracy is *alexithymia*.

When I learned that trauma could shut down a survivor's ability to feel bodily sensations, it began to make sense why engaging in high-risk activities has been so appealing to me. I thought, *Oh my God, no wonder the thrill of driving at high speeds or barreling down a ski slope was so much fun for me. It was the only way I could get back into my body and feel a sense of aliveness.*

## What Are Body Emotions?

For survivors who suffer from alexithymia, instead of consciously feeling a scary or painful emotion, the body goes into a self-protection mode and blocks the painful emotion by sending it into the body. This is known as somatization. When we somaticize an emotion, it gets expressed as changes in the body's stress-response system. These changes can include various physical symptoms, such as nausea, dry mouth, stomach issues, diarrhea, or headaches. Somaticizing painful emotions are not only common but, according to Van der Kolk, ubiquitous among survivors. This is why body and brain-based trauma therapies are necessary to fully heal trauma.

Until body emotions are healed, they stay alive and continue to cause survivors to relive the same sensations from the previous trauma in their bodies. This occurs when a survivor misinterprets a similar situation or person that reminds them of the previous trauma, and their fight, flight, or freeze response gets triggered. This is an example of how it's not the previous traumatic event that's troubling the survivor. It's in how the event lives on in present time in body sensations when something reminds the survivor of the past event.

## Discovering Talk Therapy Alone Can't Completely Heal Trauma

After binge-listening to several chapters of *The Body Keeps the Score,* I reached a point where I heard Van der Kolk state: "No amount of talk therapy can completely heal trauma."

*Wait a minute,* I thought, hoping I'd heard him wrong. *Did he just say what I think he said?* I nervously reached for my phone to hit the thirty-second rewind button on my Audible app. While carefully listening to the replay, I heard, "No amount of talk therapy can completely heal trauma."

*Oh my God, he really did just say what I thought he said. Ugh!* I sighed. Hearing this news sent me into an emotional tailspin. After all, talk therapy was the only type of therapy I'd pursued over the past thirty years. Since nobody ever told me I'd been traumatized as a child, I never knew that I also needed special trauma-based therapies to fully heal. I was shocked and angry to think that every therapist and psychiatrist I'd seen (all who were aware of the adversity I experienced in childhood) had missed that I was suffering from complex trauma.

After realizing that if I'd gotten the right types of trauma treatment to begin with, I could have avoided years of suffering, I was filled with a deep sense of grief for all the ways I'd struggled and the many times I'd failed to heal my issues.

I'm certainly not saying that all the work I've done to heal in therapy or through 12-Step groups has been in vain. I've overcome mountains of adversity and found long-term recovery with alcohol, drugs, food, and weight. As a result, my life is infinitely better than it used to be.

But had I known I was dealing with trauma, I could have also incorporated trauma-based brain and body therapies that would have sped up my healing saved me loads of pain and suffering and made my journey more joyful and fulfilling.

I also would have had the true explanation for why I struggled for so long and could have let go of the deep shame I had for feeling so weak and like such a failure for all the years I struggled with substances, food, weight, and my body.

## My Past Healing Journey Took Me Far—But Not Far Enough to Heal My Trauma

Once I learned all the ways childhood trauma had impacted my brain, body, and mind and understood what was necessary to heal, I came to a stark realization. No matter how much talk therapy, antidepressants, self-acceptance, Twelve-Step work, or time sober, without utilizing body and brain trauma-based therapies, I would still have a dysregulated brain, body, and mind that none of these things could touch.

CHAPTER 12

# THE INVISIBLE TRAUMAS: EMOTIONAL NEGLECT & EMOTIONAL ABUSE

Emotional neglect, alone, causes children to abandon themselves and to give up on the formation of a self. They do so to preserve an illusion of connection with the parent and to protect themselves from the danger of losing that tenuous connection.

—Pete Walker, MA.

## The Invisibility of Emotional Trauma Keeps It Underground

Since I assumed that childhood trauma had to include physical, sexual, or other overt types of abuse, I never thought that what I'd been through could have traumatized me. But, once I read *The Body Keeps the Score*, it became clear I was wrong.

What I found most tragic after learning that emotional neglect and abuse could traumatize a child is that most people have no idea they were neglected or abused in these ways. This is why emotional trauma unless it's overt, remains invisible. And, since you can't heal what you can't see, many survivors have never understood why they feel so empty and lonely, why they struggle to form fulfilling relationships, or why they suffer from many of the other common symptoms of being emotionally neglected or abused.

Although a person may not be aware that they were emotionally abused or neglected as a child, since trauma has changed their brain and nervous system and has become embedded in their body, they must find a way to cope with these changes.

Many don't feel safe with people and cope by isolating at home or keeping painful feelings at bay by overworking, over-caretaking, or overusing drugs, alcohol, or food.

I can certainly relate to many of these feelings and coping behaviors.

## What Is Childhood Emotional Neglect and Abuse?

**Childhood emotional neglect** happens when a parent fails to respond enough to a child's emotional needs. This leaves a child feeling alone, unseen, unheard, and that their emotions don't matter. Over time they can come to feel that they don't matter.

**Childhood emotional abuse** happens when a child is repeatedly made to feel worthless, unloved, and alone or witnesses a parent emotionally or physically abusing their spouse or another family member.

## We Must Know What We Know and Feel What We Feel

In *The Body Keeps the Score,* Van der Kolk shares the wise words of one of his teachers, Dr. Elvin Semrad:

> Semrad taught us that most human suffering is related to love and loss and that the job of therapists is to help people "acknowledge, experience, and bear" the reality of life with all its pleasures and heartbreak.
>
> The greatest sources of suffering are the lies we tell ourselves." He'd say, urging us to be honest with ourselves about every facet of our experience.
>
> He often said that people can never get better without knowing what they know and feeling what they feel.

After contemplating the above excerpt, it struck me how the essence of childhood trauma is all about love and loss. It's about the loss of connection to ourselves and others due to emotional and sometimes physical abandonment from a primary caregiver or a parent. And it's also about the inability to know what we know and feel what we feel about that loss. For self-protection, trauma causes the body to shut down, making us unable to fully feel a painful or overwhelming experience.

# Childhood Emotional Neglect

While studying childhood trauma, I came across the term *childhood emotional neglect* (CEN) mentioned in an article by CEN psychotherapist Jonice Webb, Ph.D. I was intrigued to understand what CEN was. The following excerpt from Webb's website helped me gain a better understanding of the nature of CEN:

> Childhood Emotional Neglect is literally what it sounds like. It is the neglect of your emotions. Emotionally neglectful parents may be loving and providing for all of your needs. But these parents simply do not notice, respond, or validate your feelings enough.
>
> If you grow up with your emotions ignored, you end up with your own feelings walled off and relatively inaccessible to you. This leads to a multitude of predictable struggles in adulthood, like a feeling of being different, alone, and unsatisfied with your life.

I had no idea how emotionally and physiologically damaging it could be for a child to be raised by parents who don't respond enough to their emotional needs. I also hadn't realized until finding Webb's work that, given the invisible nature of CEN, how easy it is to miss that you may have been emotionally neglected as a child.

This is because CEN is about what didn't happen but should have regarding how your parents responded to your emotions. When I thought about it, I wondered how I would have known what I was missing from my parents on an emotional level when I was a child. Our parents are likely the only parents we've ever known. The way our parents did or didn't respond to our emotions is what we were used to. We likely didn't have any other parents to compare them to.

Emotional abuse is obvious: a parent, teacher, coach, or classmate who frequently shames, belittles, is sarcastic, or yells at a child is clearly emotionally abusive. It's a tangible action taken toward a child. But emotional neglect is about the absence of something that needed to happen but didn't.

Emotional neglect is about your parents not seeing, knowing, or validating your emotional reality. When our emotional reality is seen and known, our parents' words, facial expressions, empathy, compassion, and actions mirror our own back to us. This is called attunement. An attuned caregiver makes us feel cared about, safe, loved, comforted, understood, and protected, which calms us down.

This is what's supposed to happen in a normal, healthy household. This is also how a child achieves emotional regulation. When this happens consistently, it helps the child's brain wire enabling them to eventually regulate their own emotions when dealing with stressful feelings.

But when a child doesn't have an attuned, present parent to see their reality and mirror it back to them, they are left to identify and regulate their own emotions. Unfortunately, children aren't yet equipped to handle this task. Instead of being calmed down by a caregiver, they're left in a chronic state of hyperarousal or hypoarousal.

A hyperaroused brain causes anxiety and agitation and is a very painful place to be. A hypoaroused brain makes us shut down and become tired, spacy, and disengaged. Both hyperarousal and hypoarousal are very uncomfortable states that drive us to do whatever we can to regulate to a more bearable state.

Once I learned more about CEN, I realized why it's so overlooked. First, it's due to it being a passive or hidden form of childhood neglect. It's also due to the individualistic (pull yourself up by your bootstraps) culture we live in. In many families and in the overall culture, there's an individualistic narrative that states that to be considered strong and capable, you shouldn't need anyone's support. Therefore, those needing empathy, care, or guidance are often seen as weak or needy. This perception can cause parents to consciously or unconsciously avoid providing the necessary emotional attunement for their children's brains, bodies, and minds to develop properly.

## Emotional Neglect Is Emotional Abandonment

The below excerpt from *Complex PTSD: From Surviving to Thriving* by trauma therapist and fellow survivor Pete Walker helped me understand on a deeper level how emotional neglect had impacted me.

### Emotional Neglect: The Core Wound in Complex PTSD

Minimization about the damage caused by extensive emotional neglect is at the core of the C-PTSD denial onion. Our journey of recovery takes a quantum leap when we feel and understand how devastating it was to be emotionally abandoned. An absence of parental loving interest and engagement, especially in the first few years, creates an overwhelming emptiness.

Many survivors never discover and work through the wounds that correlate with this level. This happens because they over assign their suffering to overt abuse and never get to the core issue of their emotional abandonment. As stated above, this is especially likely to occur with survivors who dismissively try to compare their trauma with those who were abused more noticeably and more dramatically.

Emotional neglect makes children feel worthless, unlovable, and excruciatingly empty. It leaves them with a hunger that gnaws deeply at the center of their being. They starve for human warmth and comfort.

### Emotional Hunger and Addiction

The emotional hunger that comes from parental abandonment often morphs over time into an insatiable appetite for substances or addictive processes. When the survivor has no understanding of the effects of trauma or no memory of being traumatized, addictions are often understandable misplaced attempts to regulate painful emotional flashbacks.

Reading this excerpt was extremely validating. It helped explain why I could never find satisfaction or be satiated with food. Food worked as a quick fix in a pinch, but it could never satisfy the connection I longed for that a present, attuned parent could.

This brings to mind what ACE Study co-founder Dr. Vincent Felitti famously said: *You can never get enough of what almost works.* What I really needed was a present parent who could show up, see me, and mirror back to me what I was feeling. But since neither one of my parents could fit that bill, I did the best I could to get my needs met by using food.

## How The Still Face Experiment Captures The Impact of Childhood Emotional Neglect

To gain a deeper understanding of what young children experience when they're emotionally neglected by their parents, I highly recommend viewing developmental psychologist Dr. Ed Tronic's *Still Face Experiment* on YouTube. The experiment starts by showing a mother and her one-year-old baby being playful and having fun while facing each other. Then the mother turns away for a moment. When she faces the baby again, she intentionally displays a still face without any emotion. Within seconds the baby notices that the mother has emotionally disconnected from him and attempts to get her to reengage. When his attempts fail, he's clearly upset and begins to cry. Shortly after that, the mother is instructed to return to normal emotional attunement with her baby. Within a few moments, she is able to repair the rupture between them. Once again, the mom and baby are fine and having fun playing together.

Watching this video was truly astounding. I had no idea how critical it is for babies to feel that their parent is connected and attuned to them. Watching the distress in such a young baby after only a few seconds of his mother disengaging from him was gut-wrenching.

What's even more disturbing is that the emotional neglect that occurred in this experiment lasted for less than a minute. But what if a child is emotionally neglected for hundreds of minutes a day, day in and day out, for years or even decades? This made me realize the massive toll that CEN can take on a survivor.

True emotional neglect is not an occasional occurrence. A parent who never received adequate emotional attunement from their primary caregiver can't give what they never got and (without intervention) will inadvertently emotionally neglect their own children and spouse.

The need for emotional attunement doesn't end in childhood. Since humans are fundamentally social beings, we require emotional attunement throughout our lives. Being deprived of this fundamental human need can have devastating consequences. That's the bad news. The good news is we can heal from emotional neglect and go on to create lives we love. I'm a living example of this.

It's important to mention that this is not about blaming parents. It's about acknowledging that emotional connection is a fundamental human need from the cradle to the grave. And until we acknowledge this need exists, we won't be able to prevent or heal CEN.

## Ways I Didn't Realize I'd Been Emotionally Neglected

When I look back at my life between the ages of eight and eighteen—when my mother's drunken tirades toward my dad were at their height—it's obvious that she was emotionally abusing my dad. What wasn't obvious was how she was also emotionally neglecting my sister and me.

Before I learned about CEN, I hadn't realized how emotionally neglectful it was of her never to attempt to see or know the reality of what my sister and I were going through due to witnessing her emotionally and sometimes physically abusing our dad.

My sadness, anger, rage, and fear were never acknowledged during or after her drunken rages. Even the next day, when she sobered up, she never asked my sister and me how we were doing or apologized for keeping us up. I don't know if she was too hungover, had too much shame, or wasn't aware that we needed emotional support for what she put us through.

Our dad also emotionally neglected us by not protecting us from having to witness our mother's abusive, toxic behavior and by not checking in with us about how we were doing.

The only time the issues between my parents were brought up was when my mother confided in me about how depressed she was over my dad's on-again, off-again affair and his refusal to talk things over with her. So instead of her being there for me, I was expected to be there for her.

This is an example of how a child is traumatized not only by witnessing chronic emotional and physical abuse between parents but also by the lack of parents providing attuned, compassionate support during or after these painful experiences.

## Learning to Shut Down My Tears

I remember feeling so sad, angry, and frustrated after trying everything I could to stop having to hear my drunk mother yelling and banging on the locked bedroom door while my dad was trying to sleep.

I cried myself to sleep for many years until finally, when I was about thirteen, I said, "Obviously, crying isn't helping me feel any better, so maybe if I stop crying, I won't feel so bad." From that point on, I consciously stopped myself from crying. It was one more way I attempted to protect myself from such overwhelming emotional pain.

Normally when a child is in this much pain, they go to their mother for soothing and support. Since my mother was the source of my pain, I didn't have that option.

After learning about CEN, I realized that what I had experienced by being left to cry myself to sleep is the essence of emotional neglect: a child in deep emotional pain with no one to mirror, attune with, or soothe their pain.

## The Remembered Experience of "Nobody There"

When I read the below quote from Robert Stolorow and George Atwood in *Understanding and Treating Chronic Shame*, I finally understood on a deep level that having to face my pain alone, with nobody there to soothe me for so many years, was the crux of my trauma.

> What persists as pathology isn't the memory of childhood trauma. It's the remembered experience of nobody there.
>
> Pain is not pathology. It is the absence of adequate responsiveness and attunement to the child's painful emotional reactions that render them unendurable and thus a source of traumatic states and psychopathology

I used to think most of my trauma came from remembering my mother's drunken tirades. But this passage revealed that the deeper pain was remembering being completely alone while facing the pain of having to listen to or watch them. No one was there to soothe, protect, or care for me. All I had was my overwhelmed young self, who survived the best way she knew how to get through another night of my mother's insanity.

## How Emotional Abandonment Leads to Acute Dysregulation & Toxic Shame

> The isolating experience that turns painful events into long-term pathology is also the experience that creates acute dysregulation and intense shame.

Reading the above excerpt by Patricia DeYoung from *Understanding and Treating Chronic Shame* was instrumental in my understanding that the cause of shame is not limited to being explicitly shamed by a person. It taught me that shame is also a natural outcome for a child when a mother or primary caregiver fails to give their child adequate responsiveness and attunement while in painful emotional states.

When a lack of responsiveness and attunement happens often enough, the pain and dysregulation can be so intense and feel so bad that the child can only surmise that they must be bad. This is the genesis of toxic shame.

Until I understood this, I thought my shame came from my mother, the Catholic Church, the homophobic culture, and the bullies at school since they had explicitly shamed me.

But once I understood how an emotionally neglected child couldn't help but experience shame simply by being emotionally abandoned, a whole new understanding opened up about why I struggled with so much shame for so long.

Thankfully, I also noticed I had a whole new level of compassion and understanding for the sad, frightened little girl who was left to face her pain alone for so long.

## Neglecting to Guide a Child Is Also a Form of Emotional Neglect

While studying CEN, I was surprised to learn that neglecting to guide a child is also a form of emotional neglect. Looking back, I can't say I ever felt that my parents truly guided me in setting goals and going after what I wanted in life. It's not that they constantly put me down. They failed me in this area by simply neglecting to guide me.

Although my dad made a good living through his businesses and tending bar in high-end dinner houses, I don't recall my parents focusing on achieving long-term personal or professional goals. I can only surmise that this is why they didn't think to instill goal-setting or long-term planning in me. Unfortunately, this set me up for significant challenges with willpower, self-discipline, and being motivated to plan for my future.

It wasn't until I was twenty-seven, sober, and found coaches and mentors through my personal growth journey that I started getting guidance on setting and achieving goals.

As I reached those goals, my self-confidence grew and gave me the courage to set even bigger goals. What my parents failed to provide, I found in the groups I joined, the coaches and mentors I worked with, the books I read, and the people I hung out with.

While writing this chapter, it occurred to me that my parents' lack of guidance in setting and achieving goals is likely what drew me to seek guidance and support from the many self-help books I read and the personal growth programs I enrolled in. In a real sense, the authors of the books I read and the coaches and therapists I worked with functioned as wise, guiding parents I needed to help me make my way in life.

## Adults Who Were Emotionally Neglected As Children Tend to Blame Themselves

People who were emotionally neglected as children (but had no other abuse or neglect) typically have no childhood memories to explain their difficulties. So, they often blame themselves for their emotional, relationship, and self-discipline struggles.

One of the saddest aspects of CEN is that it's invisible and unmemorable. The things that should have happened (emotional attunement and validation) are overshadowed by more visible, tangible topics, like physical, sexual, and emotional abuse.

Because their emotional needs weren't validated as children, they may not know how to deal with their own or other people's emotions as adults.

## Common Signs of Childhood Emotional Neglect In Adulthood

- Depression
- Anxiety
- Loneliness
- Emptiness or lack of meaning
- Lack of fulfilling relationships
- Feeling deeply personally flawed
- Guilt and shame
- Lack of willpower and self-discipline
- Alcohol, drug, food, or behavioral addictions (work, sex, shopping, gambling, porn, screen time, codependency)

### Parents Can Attune With Us Only As Well As They Were Attuned With

Adults who experience CEN without intervention will likely emotionally neglect their children and romantic partners. This is because their parents didn't teach them the importance of their own emotions. As a result, they won't have the capacity to recognize and nurture emotions in their children and close relationships.

Although unhealed CEN is at the root of many troubled relationships, the good news is it's treatable, and you can heal. There are proven practices and therapies you can use to heal and go on to experience a rich and rewarding life and have deeply fulfilling relationships.

### Healing Childhood Emotional Neglect Must Occur Within Relationships

Understanding childhood emotional neglect and what is necessary to heal won't help you recover unless you implement what you've learned by stretching outside your comfort zone in your relationships.

Practicing emotional awareness and being open to discussing difficult or joyful feelings in a healthy way in close relationships will allow you to create corrective experiences. The key, in the beginning, is to pick safe people to practice with, like a trauma-informed therapist, coach, or a safe spouse or friend. I discuss different approaches for healing CEN in upcoming chapters.

# Childhood Emotional Abuse

Childhood emotional abuse is one of the most common forms of child abuse. Unfortunately, there's still quite a bit of misinformation and many assumptions about the long-term effects of emotional abuse that minimize or deny its impact. However, many studies have shown that emotional abuse's long-term impact can be just as harmful as physical or sexual abuse. Also, emotional abuse is known to be particularly damaging to a child's self-esteem and emotional well-being.

### Child Witness Abuse

If a child frequently sees or hears emotional or physical abuse between parents or spouses, the child is also being emotionally abused. Many people are not aware of this. Sadly, this lack of awareness can make adult survivors not even realize they were abused as children

# Types of Childhood Emotional Abuse

(I've **bolded** the ones I experienced)

- **Repeatedly seeing or hearing rage, contempt, shaming, humiliation, hostility, or criticism between parents** or significant others

- **Seeing or hearing physical violence between parents** or between a spouse or sibling

- **Repeatedly experiencing teasing, bullying, yelling, humiliation, blame, criticism, shaming, and hostility from parents,** siblings, **schoolmates, random strangers,** friends, teachers, or coaches

- A parent shaming or threatening violence in response to a child's emotions ("Crying is for sissies" or "Stop crying or I'll give you something to cry about.")

- **Being rejected regularly** by parents, siblings, friends, or **classmates**

- **A parent manipulating a child to do things through fear** or **threats of** violence or **shame**

- A parent making a child feel less valued or loved than other family members or peers

- **A parent having unrealistic expectations for a child** (constantly rushing the child, **expecting the child to be a surrogate parent, friend, spouse, confidant, or therapist)**

- A parent not allowing a child to explore their interests, make friends, express their authentic self or ask for their needs to be met
- **A parent shaming or mistreating a child because of things they can't change** (due to disability, gender, **body shape or size, sexuality,** athletic ability, hair type)

Since emotional abuse and neglect played such a significant role in my developing C-PTSD, taking the time to understand it and learn how it had impacted me was extremely healing.

It was really validating to review the above list and recognize my younger self in them. Just knowing that there was a reason I struggled helped me have compassion for myself for what I endured and how I managed to cope.

### Understanding Emotional Neglect & Abuse Gives Us The Power To Heal & Transform Our Relationships

Once I understood how emotional neglect and abuse had impacted my brain, body, and mind—and especially my ability to form healthy, fulfilling relationships—I was able to do something about it. As a result of this awareness and taking action to heal, I am in the most fulfilling relationship I have ever been in, have several close friends, and truly love my life.

Had I not learned that I was suffering from C-PTSD, there is little doubt that I would have struggled in close relationships for the rest of my life.

This is why understanding how emotional neglect and abuse may have impacted you and what you can do to heal is vital in giving yourself the best chance to experience fulfilling relationships.

# The Impact of Emotional Abuse

### 1. Witnessing Emotional & Physical Abuse Between Parents

Trauma expert and psychotherapist Terrance Real discusses the concept of childhood witness abuse in his book, *US: Getting Past You & Me To Build a More Loving Relationship*. In the below excerpt, he shares a transcript of a couple's therapy session where he's defining childhood witness abuse to the wife and mother of a five-year-old child. This is in response to her husband raising concern about his daughter being hurt by his wife screaming at him on a regular basis.

> Therapist-Children have no boundaries...they're wide open systems. When she (the mother's five-year-old daughter) hears you scream at William (her husband), it goes into her as if you were screaming at her. I would do the same trauma work with her as a kid who had been sworn at.

This transcript made me realize that when I'd witnessed my mom rage at my dad for almost a decade, the same rage going into him was also going into me. Given how this type of emotional abuse was central to my trauma, reading Terrance Real's definition and discussion about it was extremely validating. Tragically, this type of abuse is widely unrecognized, and what we don't recognize, we can't heal.

### Study On Harm Done To Children Who Witness Emotional vs. Physical Abuse Between Spouses

The below study by Naughton, O'Donnell, and Muldoon reveals that children who witness psychological abuse fare worse emotionally than those who witness physical violence between parents.

> Childhood exposure to parental psychological abuse—name-calling, intimidation, isolation, manipulation, and control between parents—appears to be more damaging to children's future mental health than witnessing physical violence between parents, according to a new study conducted at the University of Limerick (UL), Ireland.

According to study coordinator Naughton, "When children were exposed to physical violence in the home as well as psychological domestic abuse, they were more likely to be happier with the social support they were able to access.

Psychological domestic abuse, when it occurs alone, seems to be the most damaging, perhaps because people are unable to recognize and speak out about it."

Source: Effects of Children Witnessing Parental Psychological Abuse - Psych Central. https://psychcentral.com/news/2017/05/16/witnessing-parental-psychological-abuse-may-do-more-harm-than-physical-abuse

It made sense when I thought about how kids who witnessed parents physically abusing each other received more support and fared better from a mental health standpoint than kids who witnessed emotional abuse alone. Since physical domestic violence is taken so seriously in our culture, this support provided the necessary buffering to help offset the level of trauma these kids experienced.

Tragically kids who witnessed emotional abuse alone between their parents didn't have that protective factor to offset their pain. This article helped me understand how seeing and hearing my mother get drunk and rage at my dad for so many years was so traumatizing for me. Since ninety-five percent of her abuse was psychological, no one took it seriously. This is what makes this type of child abuse invisible.

This research reveals that emotional abuse between parents or spouses is an act of domestic violence, just as physical abuse is, and needs to be taken as seriously. It also demonstrates how imperative it is for children who witness emotional and/or physical violence between parents to receive the support necessary to process their feelings to prevent them from developing trauma.

Feeling trapped in having to witness my Mother's insane, hostile behavior toward my Dad day in and day out for so many years is what made it so horrible. My hope is that sharing this part of my story will raise awareness of how damaging it is for children to be exposed to this type of emotional violence, and without intervention, it can cause grave damage to them for their entire lives.

## Realizing My Father Was a Silent Victim of Domestic Violence

It wasn't until I was almost done writing this book that I realized that my dad was a silent victim of domestic violence. I had never thought of him this way because I had unknowingly bought into the cultural narrative that a woman can't abuse a man. Until this point, I didn't look at my mom's behavior as domestic violence because most of it was verbal abuse, and when she did get physical, it involved her pushing or slapping him or throwing small objects at him. Yet if my dad had exhibited the same behavior toward my mom, there is no doubt it would be considered spousal abuse.

Upon further research, I was surprised that men tend to stay with their abusive spouses for the same reasons women stay with abusive husbands. Below are the most common reasons both men and women stay in abusive relationships.

- Guilt
- Lack of self-esteem
- Economic insecurity

Another reason men stay in abusive relationships with women is because our culture teaches them that "real men" should be immune to a woman's emotional or physical abuse. This accounts for why most men never report their abuser or reach out for support. Instead, they suffer in silence.

Realizing my dad was a direct recipient of my mom's emotional and physical abuse helped me have more compassion for him, given the amount of trauma he had to have experienced at the hands of my mom. This isn't to excuse his affair or how he emotionally abused and neglected my mom (although not nearly as much as she did him). It's simply to shine a light on the fact that we (my dad, my sister, and I) were all deeply traumatized by my mom's insane behavior. I believe that my dad's story is a wake-up call for the many men who suffer in silence at the hands of their abusive spouses.

## 2. Shaming, Blaming, & Parentifying

After I learned that childhood trauma was relational trauma, it helped me understand why I had so much anxiety about relationships. It was directly related to my mom's covert style of emotional abuse. The primary tactics she used on me were manipulation through shame and guilt. She also abused me by parentifying me.

Instead of being a mom and taking care of me, I was expected to take care of her. I'd be accused of being a selfish, bad daughter if I didn't continually listen to her woes. When I got the courage to set a boundary with her or say that her drinking bothered me, she wouldn't acknowledge my feelings and needs. Instead, she would attempt to manipulate me with guilt and shame by saying things like, "You've hurt me more than anyone has ever hurt me before." Or "I didn't raise you to be selfish."

The main message I got from her was that I was responsible for her and other people's feelings and well-being and that taking care of others first was what good girls did. If I behaved otherwise, I was simply a selfish, bad person.

By understanding that childhood trauma is relational trauma, I know today that my hottest relationship triggers are when I sense someone may attempt to blame, shame, or drain me since that's what I experienced with my mom.

Healing these issues has involved me learning to set expectations and boundaries in my relationships. If people don't respect my boundaries or don't align with my expectations, I'm completely OK with letting them go. I know today that I'm not a bad or selfish person if I take care of my needs in my relationships. Taking care of my needs actually makes me a healthy person who knows who she is, what she wants, and what works and doesn't work for her in relationships.

As a result of my relational healing, today, my life is filled with people I feel safe with, who know how to take care of their needs, and who respect the needs of others. And for this, I'm truly grateful.

## 3. Bullying & Living In A Fat-Phobic Culture

Being bullied at school for being an overweight kid was another form of emotional abuse I endured from second grade till about ninth grade. Since I automatically assumed being overweight was my fault, I had enormous shame over it.

Obviously, a six-year-old little girl isn't responsible for managing her own weight, but I didn't know any better. All I knew was that I felt disgusting and unwanted. One of the most difficult things about enduring this abuse was that my parents never attempted to protect me. Had they contacted the school to complain or demand that the abuse stop, it may have prevented further abuse and trauma. But since they never did, it left me feeling like the abuse would never end because the bullies never faced any consequences.

Being bullied at school and walking through life as an overweight child and then as a severely obese woman meant always being on the alert for the next implicit or explicit insult to be hurled at me due to my unacceptable body. The fact that the bullying over my weight took place for so long during my most formative years, along with living in a fat-phobic culture as a severely obese woman, made me realize how much toxic stress my poor nervous system had to endure for so long.

## 4. Homophobia

I never considered that living in a homophobic culture could contribute to someone developing symptoms of complex trauma until I reviewed several research studies proving otherwise.

The year was 1972 when I realized, as a fourteen-year-old teenager, that I was attracted to girls instead of boys. The moment I understood what my attraction to girls meant, a flash of terror with a flood of homophobic messaging, a ubiquitous part of the seventies and the Catholic church's culture, flooded every aspect of my being.

After doing my homework on the psychiatric history of homosexuality, it made even more sense why I was so terrified of accepting I was a lesbian. From 1952 to 1972, the Diagnostic Manual of Mental Disorders-DSM classified homosexuality as a "sexual deviation" within the larger "sociopathic personality disturbance" category of personality disorders.

And get this... the sexual deviation diagnosis listed several subtypes. Homosexuality just happened to be one of them. The entire group included homosexuality, transvestism, pedophilia, fetishism, and sexual sadism. Yep, we were put in the same club as the pedophiles!

After twenty-one years, homosexuality was finally declassified as pathology and removed from the DSM in 1973. But as the LGBTQ+ community knows all too well, it's one thing to take homosexuality out of the DSM, but it's a whole other thing to take homophobia out of the culture.

In the 70s, telling fag or dyke jokes was perfectly acceptable, and effeminate men were the butt of many jokes on TV and in movies. Gays and lesbians had no rights whatsoever, and it was even illegal to engage in gay sex in many states. If you dared to come out, you could lose your job, family, friends, and in some areas, even your life. Conversion therapy was alive and well, and the Catholic Church and my Catholic high school kept reminding me that I would burn in hell forever for being my authentic lesbian self.

I didn't tell a soul about my attraction to women until I was nineteen. Even then, I told just one close friend. I didn't come out to my family until I was twenty-three, and only because I was moving in with my girlfriend and didn't want to lie that we were just roommates. Feeling the need to hide a fundamental part of yourself due to the constant threat of being shamed, ostracized, or even physically attacked simply for having a different sexual orientation or identity has consequences.

## Survey On LGBTQ+ Discrimination

**Percent of Lesbian, Gay & Bisexuals Saying They'd....**
**Because of Their Sexual Orientation or Gender Identity**

- Been subject to slurs or jokes 58%
- Been rejected by friend or family member 39%
- Been threatened or physically attacked 30%
- Been made to feel unwelcome at a place of worship 29%
- Received poor service in a restaurant, hotel, or place of business 23%
- Been treated unfairly by an employer 21%

Source: Pew Research Center, LGBTQ+discrimination 2013 © MaryGiuliani.net

While reviewing the various types of discrimination listed in the LGBTQ+ survey done in 2013 by Pew Research Center, I realized as a lesbian, I'd experienced all but one of these forms of discrimination throughout my life.

## Homophobia's Role In Negative Mental & Behavioral Health Outcomes

The level of trauma that blatant, structural homophobia has inflicted on the gay, lesbian, bi, trans and queer community has consequences. These consequences were revealed in a National Epidemiologic Survey on Alcohol and Related Conditions. The study compared the difference in the prevalence of substance and psychiatric disorders between sexual minorities and sexual majorities.

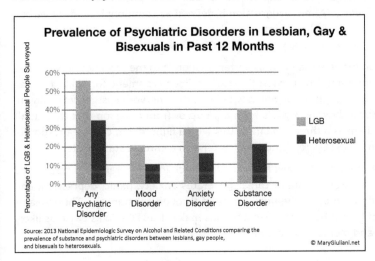

Prevalence of Psychiatric Disorders in Lesbian, Gay & Bisexuals in Past 12 Months

Source: 2013 National Epidemiologic Survey on Alcohol and Related Conditions comparing the prevalence of substance and psychiatric disorders between lesbians, gay people, and bisexuals to heterosexuals. © MaryGiuliani.net

This study revealed that twice as many lesbian, gay, and bisexual individuals suffer from substance use disorders as their straight counterparts. In addition, about 50% more lesbian, gay, and bisexual individuals suffer from mood and psychiatric disorders than their straight counterparts. These numbers reflect the toll that homophobia takes on the lesbian, gay, and bi community.

Another study done in 2016 by UCLA School of Law Williams Institute found that 17% of LGB-

lesbian, gay, and bisexual adults had attempted suicide during their lifetime, compared to 2.4% of the general U.S. population. This means my risk of attempting suicide is over 800% higher than it is for my straight counterparts. Until I discovered this research, I had no idea that simply living as a lesbian in a homophobic culture put me at a much higher risk of suffering from mental health issues, alcohol, and drug addiction, and even attempting suicide.

## Homophobic Microaggressions

Even after doing a significant amount of work on healing my internalized homophobia, I was surprised to find it rearing its ugly head on a recent Alaska Cruise my partner Maria & I were on. While booking our tickets, we were asked if we were celebrating a special occasion. Since it was our anniversary, we checked off the box to inform them about it.

Although the cruise line went above and beyond in celebrating us by decorating our room with special towel-shaped Swans with rose petals and a Happy Anniversary sign, when it came time to acknowledge our anniversary publicly in the main dining room, the energy shifted for me. We were seated at a table with two straight couples that we'd exchanged small talk and stories of how our cruise was going but to who we hadn't come out.

When a group of servers gathered around our table with a special cake and announced they were there to celebrate an anniversary, the two straight couples automatically looked at each other, assuming they could be the only ones that qualified as couples to be celebrated. Finally, when the cake was placed in front of Maria and me, and the servers started singing happy anniversary to us, they understood it was for us. Interestingly, the wives of both couples immediately congratulated us, but their husbands remained silent.

I'd noticed I'd been uncomfortable for the entire dinner since I knew we would be outed when the special anniversary dessert was delivered to our table. When I thought more about it, I had good reason to feel unsafe. I'd learned both couples were from extremely conservative states known to vote against LGBTQ+ civil rights. Although I didn't know their political views, I felt threatened enough to be on guard for whatever might come up once we were outed. Interestingly, Maria didn't share the same anxiety. She gets more triggered when we hold hands in public since she fears it may make straight folks uncomfortable.

Although I was initially bugged about how uncomfortable I was about possibly being judged about my sexual orientation, I did my best to stay mindful and curious about it instead of beating myself up over it. I was actually surprised that I still had so much fear of others judging me over my sexual preference. It taught me that the scourge of homophobia was still alive in me, as it is in so many of us.

I would learn that the stress LGBTQ+ folks experience is due to a phenomenon known as microaggressions. According to Wikipedia, "A microaggression is defined as commonplace, daily verbal, behavioral or environmental slights, intentional or unintentional, that communicate hostile, derogatory, or negative attitudes toward stigmatized or culturally marginalized groups.

There's a neurological explanation for why the nervous system responds to the threat of homophobic microaggressions. Humans are programmed to constantly scan their environment for signals to tell them if they do or don't belong. When they get the signal they belong, their nervous system calms down, and they feel safe and regulated. But if they get signals from a group or from a person that they don't belong, their nervous system views them as a threat and mobilizes with a fight, flight, or freeze response. Exposure to chronic homophobia puts LGBTQ+ folk's nervous systems in a chronic state of alert.

Over time the nervous system becomes sensitized and can stay stuck in a hyperaroused state or be highly reactive to threats. Being in a chronic state of threat generates anxiety, panic, depression, and other painful emotional states, which then drive the need for relief through substances. This explains why exposure to a chronic stream of homophobic microaggressions makes LGBTQ+ folks twice as likely to suffer from substance addictions and mental health issues.

Maria and I could have declined to have our anniversary celebrated in such a public way. However, one thing I know is true is that the more conservative people get to know LGBTQ+ folks, the more they see our humanity, and the less they'll feel justified in voting for legislation to limit or take away our rights. I've also learned when I'm willing to walk through my fears, they typically lessen and free me up to live a more authentic, fulfilling life.

# CHAPTER 13

---

# CODEPENDENCY: AN ATTEMPT TO STAY SAFE IN A CRAZY FAMILY

Allowing others to suffer the consequences of their own actions without enabling them is the best motivation for them to undertake the difficult task of change.

—Darlene Lancer, JD, LMFT

Although I'd done quite a bit of work on healing my codependency issues in the nineties, I had no idea codependency was an actual nervous system-based trauma response until I learned I had trauma.

While I'd frequently read about the fight, flight, and freeze trauma responses in childhood trauma books, I noticed in Pete Walker's book *Complex PTSD: From Surviving to Thriving* that he states there is a fourth "F," which is the fawn trauma response. In this context, fawn refers to codependency. I've also heard other authors in the trauma field refer to codependency as the "please, appease, fix or submit" trauma response.

Codependency, or the fawn trauma response, develops in a child due to having a primary caregiver who practices an active substance or behavioral addiction; is codependent; or suffers from depression, anxiety, or another mental illness. It can also develop when a child grows up in a home with emotional or physical abuse, emotional or physical domestic violence, or any other type of significant dysfunction.

Becoming codependent is a child's best attempt to cope with someone else's abuse, neglect, dysfunction, illness, or addiction. The nature of codependency requires a child to lose themselves by taking care of a dysfunctional other to protect the attachment bond with the primary caregiver.

Codependency develops over time. The child puts more energy into coping with a dysfunctional caregiver or a stressful environment than into growing and going through the necessary developmental stages that forge healthy emotional development. Sadly, without recovery, a person in the grip of codependency will be severely limited in their ability to find and maintain healthy relationships.

Below is an excerpt from Walker's book *Complex PTSD: From Surviving to Thriving* that defines the fawn response to trauma.

> A fourth type of triggered response can be seen in many codependents. (Codependency is defined here as the inability to express rights, needs, and boundaries in relationships; it is a disorder of assertiveness that causes the individual to attract and accept exploitation, abuse, and/or neglect.) I have named it the fawn response...the fourth 'f' in the fight/flight/ freeze/fawn repertoire of instinctive responses to trauma.

Fawn, according to Webster, means: "to act servilely; cringe and flatter," and I believe it is this response that is at the core of many codependents' behavior. The trauma-based codependent learns to fawn very early in life in a process that might look something like this: as a toddler, she learns quickly that protesting abuse leads to even more frightening parental retaliation, and so she relinquishes the fight response, deleting "no" from her vocabulary and never developing the language skills of healthy assertiveness. (Sadly, many abusive parents reserve their most harsh punishments for "talking back" and hence ruthlessly extinguish the fight response in the child.)

The abused toddler often also learns early on that her natural flight response exacerbates the danger she initially tries to flee," I'll teach you to run away from me!" and later that the ultimate flight response, running away from home, is hopelessly impractical and, of course, even more danger laden.

Many toddlers, at some point, transmute the flight urge into running around in circles of hyperactivity, and this adaptation "works" on some level to help them escape from uncontainable fear. This, then, is often the progenitor for the later OCD-like adaptations of workaholism, busyholism, spendaholism, sex, and love compulsivity, and other process addictions.

A final scenario describes the incipient codependent toddler who largely bypasses the fight, flight and freeze responses and instead learns to fawn her way into the relative safety of becoming helpful. She may be one of the gifted children of Alice Miller's Drama Of The Gifted Child, who discovers that a modicum of safety (safety, the ultimate aim of all four of the 4F responses) can be purchased by becoming useful to the parent. Servitude, ingratiation, and forfeiture of any needs that might inconvenience the parent become the most important survival strategies available.

Boundaries of every kind are surrendered to mollify the parent, as the parent repudiates the Winnicottian duty of being of use to the child; the child is parentified and instead becomes as multidimensionally useful to the parent as she can: housekeeper, confidante, lover, sounding board, surrogate parent of other siblings, etc. I wonder how many of us therapists were prepared for our careers in this way.

All this loss of self begins before the child has many words, and certainly no insight. For the nascent codependent, all hints of danger soon immediately trigger servile behaviors and abdication of rights and needs.

I found Walker's description of the fawn response spot-on. It reminded me of how I became useful to my mom by her parentifying me. I became her confidant, coach, and sounding board. I didn't do this consciously. It was what she expected and needed from me, and in a desperate attempt to stop the insanity and feel safe, I complied.

It was really enlightening to realize that the fawn or the codependency trauma response is a response to a threat, just like the fight, flight and freeze trauma responses are. The threat the child faces as a codependent is emotional or physical abandonment.

Codependency, or the fawn response, is an attempt to please or appease our primary caregiver in childhood or our partner as an adult so they will love us and won't emotionally or physically abandon us.

When I learned that codependency is an actual trauma response versus solely a psychological issue, it helped me understand how the entire nervous system, body, and emotions are activated when a person gets triggered. At the more extreme end of the spectrum, codependency can be just as destructive or lethal as substance addiction. But instead of being addicted to drugs or alcohol, the codependent is addicted to people-pleasing or fixing other people's lives to get approval and avoid being abandoned.

## My Codependency Recovery Journey

A considerable part of my recovery from codependency was joining Codependents Anonymous-CoDA after I got sober in the late eighties. It was instrumental in helping me understand the nature of my self-destructive patterns in my relationships.

CoDA helped me put myself first in a healthy way without feeling guilty; set healthy boundaries with my mom, other family members, and friends; and ask for my needs to be met.

Over time my life satisfaction and relationships improved dramatically. Also, once I learned that my codependency was also related to trauma, I had more compassion for myself.

In a nutshell, CoDA helped me reclaim my lost self.

One thing I know for sure is unless we're willing to heal codependent relationship dynamics or leave abusive or toxic relationships, we'll stay stalled in healing our trauma. This is because codependent relationships keep us stuck, feeling unsafe and unfulfilled, just like we felt as children. This is retraumatizing and keeps our trauma symptoms alive.

The healing process requires us to set up a whole new support system of emotionally healthy allies who are just as committed to their emotional health as we are.

## How Unhealed Codependency Sabotaged My Adult Relationships

As a little girl, I became codependent, or fawned, to feel safe and maintain my sanity with my very depressed, alcoholic mother. However, it became a serious problem in my adult relationships. When I was in the thick of my codependency, I read books with a total focus on how they could help save whomever I was focused on fixing at the time.

I would then try to figure out how to get the other person to read the book, or I would ask them if I could read certain chapters to them, hoping they would change!

Here I was, replaying the same scenes from my codependent relationship with my mother with my friends and lovers. Once I got into recovery through Co-Dependents Anonymous (CoDA), I realized that I had no power over whether another person chose to change, and I was able to stop this behavior.

I also learned that it was rather arrogant to think I had the magic solution for other people instead of trusting them to manage their own lives. In CoDA, I learned I needed to focus on my own healing and let other people find their own way.

When I got to this level in my recovery, I discovered that to do this, I had to feel the grief of letting go of my fantasy that the person I was being codependent with would ever change. This also meant that to look out for my best interests, I might even need to let them go.

## Telling the Hard Truth in Relationships Is Required for Healing Codependency

It's one thing to learn or read about healing your relationships, but it's an entirely different thing to initiate difficult conversations, set boundaries, or ask others to meet your needs. Telling the hard truth in my relationships was some of the most uncomfortable and challenging things I've ever faced. Yet, once I began doing so, my relationships and my life completely transformed.

Getting to a place where I was willing to upset or disappoint people—or even let people go to be true to myself wasn't easy. But once I began taking baby steps, it became easier. I had to get to the point where I recognized that my needs were just as important as other people's, and I wasn't bad or selfish for putting my needs first.

Since my mom and the Church shamed and blamed me throughout my childhood for being selfish whenever I attempted to put my needs first, making my needs a top priority was a tall order. I started with many baby steps, and with time and repetition, it got easier. Today it's practically a non-issue.

I now know that if I fail to tell the hard truth in my relationships, I'll stay spinning around in unfulfilling, soul-sucking relational drama. The only thing this accomplishes is to make healing my trauma impossible, which keeps my C-PTSD symptoms alive.

Although telling the hard truth was scary at first, over time, it became easier. In the long run, doing so has made my relationships much deeper and more satisfying which has significantly improved the quality of my life.

## Build Your Support System Before You Start Telling the Hard Truth

Before you start healing your codependency, building your support system of healthy, conscious friends and allies is critical. You need to know you have people who will support you and have your back when you start telling the hard truth in your relationships.

This way, if people need to leave or if you need to let go of people who aren't willing to respect you and your boundaries, you know you have a solid support system that's there for you. Without a support system like this, it's too easy to cave into unhealthy relationships.

## Why Healing Codependency Is Worth Every Ounce of Energy You Put Into It

Before healing my codependency, my ability to form and maintain healthy relationships was so influenced by the dysfunctional patterns I learned growing up that there was no way I could attract or maintain healthy relationships.

Healing my codependency has been a critical piece of my trauma-healing journey because it has given me the precious gift of being able to connect in safe, healthy, secure relationships. Since close, safe connection with other humans is essential to our health, healing, and living our best lives, being able to do so is literally keeping me healthy, alive, and thriving. This is why it's so worth doing the work to heal codependency. I cover how to do so in Part III, The Trauma Healing Journey.

# CHAPTER 14

# CHILDHOOD TRAUMA IS RELATIONAL TRAUMA

*Our longing is not only to feel safe but to feel safe in the arms of another.*

—Stephen Porges, M.D.

### Relationship Difficulties & Trauma

When I learned that childhood trauma is also known as relational trauma, another piece of my life puzzle fell into place. I finally understood why finding and maintaining close friendships and fulfilling romantic relationships seemed to be so challenging for me. Until then, I had no idea that I had been navigating my relationships with a nervous system and psyche full of emotional landmines, constantly on the alert and ready to go off at the slightest hint of danger.

Close relationships are stressful for survivors because our brains were wired to expect stress since this was what we experienced growing up with our family members. Understanding the dynamics of relational trauma helped explain how it had sabotaged my past romantic relationships with fellow survivors.

When former partners, who were also survivors, and I attempted to connect in a romantic relationship, our unhealed relational trauma issues would inevitably get triggered. Instead of understanding that 90% of our conflicts were due to triggers from unresolved childhood trauma issues and not the presenting problem, we blamed the problem on ourselves or each other. But we never got to the root cause of why we kept fighting about the same issues. After repeatedly running up against the same problems, we became convinced that our conflicts were insurmountable and that the only solution was to give up on the relationship.

What I didn't understand until I learned I had C-PTSD is that when we're triggered, our unhealed trauma replays past bodily sensations and thoughts, making it impossible to be in the present. When you're unaware you have C-PTSD, you won't realize you've been triggered into a state from your past. It's as if there's a gaslighting effect going on since you really believe what you're feeling is solely related to the conflict in the relationship you're in, even though it's not.

Thankfully today, I'm fully aware when a relational trauma trigger hits. Instead of blaming myself or my partner, I can slow down and be more mindful of my feelings and where the trigger is coming from. I'm also aware that it's in the relationship's best interest for me to wait until my nervous system has calmed down before talking to my spouse about a conflict.

## Discovering I'd Adopted a "People Aren't Safe" Worldview

Learning that childhood trauma is relational trauma also helped explain why I struggled so much with social anxiety. For over a decade of my childhood, I witnessed an out-of-control alcoholic mom who regularly shamed my dad and frequently shamed me. I also experienced walking through life as an overweight child and later as a severely obese lesbian in a fatphobic and homophobic culture.

What did all of these experiences have in common? People who were hurting, judging, or condemning me. This taught me that people weren't safe since they were the source of my deepest pain. This insight helped me understand why for the first ten years of my recovery in AA, the only people I hung out with were lesbians who were also in recovery with alcohol, drugs, and food. They were the only people I felt safe with since they were just like me. How could they judge me? They were me!

I had no idea I'd adopted a worldview that people weren't safe until I discovered this aspect of childhood trauma. With this new awareness, I saw that my "people aren't safe" worldview had significantly impacted my ability to connect with new people. I've made a lot of progress in this area, yet it's often still challenging to feel safe being open about my history of trauma, obesity, and addiction with people I don't know well.

Since I wasn't aware of having a "people aren't safe" worldview until a few years ago, I couldn't understand why I had hardly any close friends. It baffled me because I really like people and love having fun with friends. Once I feel safe, I love connecting with people.

Today I'm aware that when I don't feel safe with someone, a stress response gets triggered in my body, making me anxious and uncomfortable. As a result, I feel the impulse to distance myself or leave for self-protection. Understanding how I'd adopted this worldview and how it has impacted my social interactions and relationships has been extremely helpful.

Now that I have this awareness, I'm much more mindful when I start assuming that people aren't safe. When it comes up, I challenge my assumption and ask if it's true or if it's just an old default stress-response program running.

Now when I attend social functions, I set goals designed to foster corrective relational experiences to help rewire my brain and rewrite my narrative to "most people are safe enough." As a result, I've experienced significant progress in feeling safe and connected with people I would never have felt safe with before.

## How I Avoided Conflict By Gradually Leaving Relationships

Before I'd done some major healing work on my relational trauma, I had a pattern of gradually leaving friendships when there was some type of conflict rather than risking addressing what was bothering me. Learning about the nature of relational trauma has helped me understand what was behind this pattern.

I realized that the reason relationship conflicts were such an issue for me was because they sent me into an emotional flashback of the unresolved trauma I witnessed in my parent's conflict-ridden relationship. As a little girl, I learned that conflicts could quickly turn volatile, and since they never got resolved anyway, it was better to avoid them.

Since conflict is bound to come up at some point in any long-term relationship, I realized that if I didn't learn to face and resolve my relational trauma triggers, I would eventually find myself alone.

Looking back, I now see that when I was faced with a conflict with a close friend, my brain, body, and mind experienced a post-traumatic stress reaction that was so emotionally and physically overwhelming that, in many ways, I felt that I had no other choice than to avoid it by gradually pulling away. Sadly, over time the relationship withered and died.

Part of me didn't want these friendships to end, yet the idea of bringing up the conflict or continuing to tolerate what was bothering me was too stressful and overwhelming. So, I froze and avoided dealing with it. Looking back, I can see how it felt safer to allow the relationship to die slowly than to face the terror of the conflict.

Now that I understand relational trauma, I've learned to slow down and be compassionate with myself when I get triggered in my relationships. I now have the tools and awareness to wait until I feel more regulated to raise my concerns.

Becoming aware that the impulse to avoid conflict is due to past trauma getting triggered, and knowing how to handle it, has been incredibly liberating and extremely helpful for me in maintaining the health of my relationships.

## Understanding Emotional Flashbacks

While reading *Complex PTSD: From Surviving to Thriving,* I learned that emotional flashbacks were a common C-PTSD symptom. At first, I found it hard to wrap my mind around what an emotional flashback was. I even questioned whether I'd ever experienced one. When I thought about it, I hadn't recalled having any dramatic or over-the-top emotional experiences related to what happened during my childhood.

Yet as I learned more about emotional flashbacks, I realized they don't need to be over the top and dramatic. Before learning about C-PTSD, I'd associated the word *flashback* with movie scenes in which a combat veteran with PTSD hears a car backfire and has an intense emotional reaction or dives for cover.

In contrast, a C-PTSD emotional flashback can be a noticeable shift in your mood from being calm to becoming anxious, agitated, overwhelmed, sad, ashamed, or panicked. It can range from subtle to more pronounced and last for various lengths of time.

## Examples of My Emotional Flashbacks

Since I had a hard time understanding what emotional flashbacks were when I first learned about them, I thought it would be helpful to share some examples of what my emotional flashbacks feel like and what contexts typically trigger them. The good news is that since I've been working on healing my trauma for many years, most of these flashbacks are mild, and some are completely gone.

However, occasionally I can still be caught off guard and thrown into a significant emotional flashback. I've found that just reminding myself that I'm experiencing an emotional flashback helps me calm down quickly and allows me to practice mindfulness as I look for ways to get regulated. Now that I understand the nature of emotional flashbacks, I can use them as an opportunity for healing. I go over how I've incorporated this healing process into my life in Part III.

Below are the most common relationship-based emotional flashbacks I've experienced and their typical triggers.

**Social anxiety:** Social anxiety has been challenging, especially when it involves small talk at parties. I frequently feel the impulse to leave social events soon after I've arrived. I also tend to be drawn to overindulging with food or caffeine at parties to cope with my anxiety. I now know this is an emotional flashback to my "people aren't safe" worldview. I've had some significant breakthroughs in my ability to feel safe with people, and, as a result, my social anxiety has significantly decreased.

**New relationships:** I tend to get triggered when a new person enters my life, and there appears to be the possibility of a close friendship. My discomfort can range from mild to extreme until I assess how safe I feel about their emotional health. If I get the sense that they're not emotionally healthy, I know I need to be careful about whether or not to allow them in my life. This trigger goes back to being shamed, blamed, and drained by my mother.

A big part of my healing is recognizing that now that I'm an adult, I can protect myself by setting expectations and healthy boundaries in my relationships. If someone isn't healthy for me or isn't willing to respect my boundaries, I know I don't have to include them in my life.

I'm also aware that I may inadvertently assume that someone is unsafe without any evidence to support my concerns due to my trauma history. For this reason, I do my best to stay mindful of this possibility while deciding whether or not to allow a new person into my life.

**Conflict:** Relational conflict, in general, is triggering for me, given the chronic conflict I witnessed between my parents. But I get especially triggered when people attempt to manipulate me with shame or guilt, are overly needy, judgmental, or get angry with me. I can also become triggered by witnessing people having emotionally or physically abusive arguments, a parent shaming a child, couples fighting in front of children, or excessively angry people.

These scenarios include in person, in movies, or on TV shows. This flashback goes back to witnessing my mom raging at my dad, being shamed by my mom, the church, and school bullies, and tolerating my mom's chronic negativity and neediness.

**Watching Politically Oriented Cable News Shows:** When I first learned what emotional flashbacks were and became more embodied, I noticed how my stomach and shoulders would tense up, and I'd feel a sense of unease when I tuned in to politically oriented cable news shows. As I continued to watch, the tension would often morph into anxiety.

I told myself I needed to watch these shows to stay abreast of current events. Yet, as I learned more about trauma, I could tell the programming was designed to trigger fight-flight responses in my nervous system to keep it jacked up in a chronic state of hypervigilance.

Knowing that hypervigilance compels humans to obsessively search for threats helped me understand what compelled me to continually tune in to the show each night. Being fed a constant source of threats coupled with the promise that the congress, president, or a political protector might swoop in to save me provided my nervous system with a modicum of relief to keep me watching. That was until the show delivered the next breaking news threat. Once I got hip to how I was allowing my nervous system to be hijacked by my favorite news anchor, I was eventually able to quit.

Once I quit watching, I noticed it was much easier to regulate my nervous system. Gradually a new level of peace and expansiveness emerged. Giving myself the gift of a more regulated nervous system not only makes me feel better in my day-to-day life but it's also been a significant catalyst in my having the presence of mind to write this book. This is an example of what can occur simply by removing toxic stress from your environment.

**Abandonment:** The most intense emotional flashback I experience is when I fear being abandoned in my close romantic relationship. I find that it's extremely tough for me to calm down after a conflict or fight with my partner until we resolve our differences. Even using the numbing strategy of food and caffeine can't quell my distress when it comes to my most important attachment relationship being threatened.

Now that I understand the nature of emotional flashbacks and complex trauma, I see that my fear of abandonment is my hottest trigger. This is connected to the overwhelming pain of the chronic emotional abandonment I experienced as a child.

Since I now understand that this is a flashback, I do my best to use it as an opportunity for my healing. Instead of staying in a reactive state, I try to calm myself down by bringing in my wise inner parent to provide comforting, compassionate, reassuring support to my scared, hurting inner child.

Also, given that I've shared with my partner, Maria, the nature of my C-PTSD and what is most helpful when I'm triggered, she's very understanding and compassionate, which is extremely regulating for me.

## Loneliness & C-PTSD

The United States Surgeon General Dr. Vivek Murthy discusses the tragic epidemic of loneliness in the U.S. in his book *Together*. According to loneliness studies, he cites:

- 22% of American adults state they often or always feel lonely or socially isolated
- 33% of Americans over the age of forty-five state they are lonely
- 20% of respondents said they never or rarely feel close to people

I had no idea how prevalent loneliness was in the overall population until I learned about these studies.

What I do know is that C-PTSD and loneliness go hand in hand. This is because the nature of trauma is about disconnection. In fact, Stephen Porges, author of *The Polyvagal Theory,* has stated that "Trauma is a chronic disruption of connectedness."

Once I understood the impact C-PTSD had on me, I could see why relationships had been so difficult for me. Before healing my relational trauma, my nervous system and worldview prevented me from being able to connect with people due to how unsafe I felt and how dysregulated I got when I tried.

When I reviewed the following *UCLA Loneliness Scale* and applied it to the time before I had healed my relational trauma, I would have rated myself "some of the time" or "often" on all three questions related to feeling lonely, isolated, or left out. These answers point to how painfully lonely I was when living with unhealed relational trauma.

## UCLA Loneliness Scale (Short Version)

Answer the following questions as either: hardly ever, some of the time, or often.

1. How often do you feel you lack companionship?
2. How often do you feel left out?
3. How often do you feel isolated from others?

Tragically, loneliness is part and parcel of those living with unhealed relational trauma. The good news is relational trauma is treatable, and you can heal. Once I learned I'd been suffering from C-PTSD and implemented several trauma-healing practices and therapies, my answers to the above loneliness survey completely turned around to "hardly ever" for all three questions.

If you struggle with loneliness, know that you're not alone, it's not your fault, there's nothing wrong with you, and you can feel safe to connect with others by healing C-PTSD.

## Survivors Have Difficulty Leaving Unhealthy or Unfulfilling Relationships

Another common aspect of relational trauma is that many survivors find it difficult to leave unhealthy, abusive, or unfulfilling romantic, platonic, or work relationships.

When I got into recovery with codependency, I did a lot of work on healing my ability to choose healthy relationships and, when necessary, leave unhealthy ones.

Interestingly, if parents stay together despite having an unfulfilling, toxic, or abusive relationship, their children learn that this is how relationships are supposed to work. As a result, they're automatically drawn or attracted to partners and friends with similar dysfunctional relational styles. This is due to humans feeling drawn to people who feel similar to those they experienced growing up.

Healing the root cause of why we're drawn to choose or tolerate unhealthy or unfulfilling relationships requires us to resolve our codependency and relational trauma. The good news is healing relational trauma is possible, and I've shared all the steps I've taken to do so throughout the remainder of this book.

## Engaging in Healthy Relationships Is the Best Way to Stay Regulated

Countless studies show that the best way for human beings to regulate their emotions and nervous system is to engage in healthy, close relationships. This is known as co-regulation. Unfortunately, intimate relationships often trigger stress responses in survivors, making them want to avoid close relationships.

This is why many survivors choose relationships with dogs, cats, or other pets versus people because animals are the safer alternative. It's well documented that dogs and cats can be very therapeutic because of the deep soothing connection they provide for their owners. Although I love my cats dearly and am all for connecting with pets, the deepest level of trauma-healing and connection has come through moving through the ups and downs of my relationship with my partner Maria and my close friends.

Although the journey of healing relational trauma hasn't been easy and has required me to stretch outside my comfort zone, the fruits of my labor continue to pay dividends every day in the wonderful connections I have with my friends and partner.

I share this because it's important to know that you can experience profound healing in your capacity to be in intimate relationships through healing relational trauma. In Part III and the appendix, I share all the tools and teachers that have helped me heal.

## The Importance of Learning How to Repair Relationship Ruptures

How our parents worked out their relationship conflicts often predicts how we'll work out ours. If our parents were dysfunctional or avoided dealing with conflict and we don't learn healthy conflict-resolution skills—we'll use similar dysfunctional patterns when repairing relational conflicts. This is why it's critical to learn how to repair ruptures during or after a conflict.

I don't recall my parents ever resolving or repairing any of their relationship conflicts. Due to their unhealed trauma, lack of self-awareness, and conflict-resolution skills, their resentment, hurt, and anger toward one another grew for twenty years until it finally blew up and resulted in their divorce.

My relational recovery began in AA and CoDA in the late eighties and continued with the support of various therapists, coaches, support groups, and the many books I read. Working on healing my ability to have healthy relationships was helpful, but it could take me only so far without healing my trauma. Back then, I wasn't aware of how childhood trauma triggers hijacked my nervous system when I attempted to connect in relationships.

Now I'm much more mindful of how I feel, and I intentionally track how my stress-response system is doing during my interactions in my close relationships. As a result, I now know when I'm triggered and have the tools to calm myself down before discussing a conflict with my partner.

## Relationship Repair Leads to Self-Regulation and Secure Attachment

When a relationship conflict is successfully repaired, it's known as having *a corrective experience*. Successfully repairing a relationship conflict proves we can find healthy resolutions in close relationships. Over time and with enough corrective experiences, our narrative shifts from relationships being unsafe to them being nurturing, flowing, fun, and worth engaging in.

Successfully repairing relationship conflicts changes your brain and stress-response system, resulting in improved self-regulation. Eventually, old triggers rarely fire, and our relationships become more harmonious and grow stronger. Over time, our brain rewires, and we're on our way to building secure attachments.

In *Befriending Your Nervous System: Looking Through the Lens of Polyvagal Theory*, Deb Dana speaks about how healthy relationships need to include connection, rupture, and repair to stay healthy and resilient.

> We don't need relationships that are always in balance, though. In fact, it's in relationships in which we feel connected, feel a rupture, and find our way back to repair that we build resilience. The cycle of reciprocity, rupture, and repair is the nature of healthy relationships. It's when a rupture happens without repair that our longing for connection brings suffering.

One of the most helpful things that Maria and I have found to repair conflicts in our relationship is agreeing to use a repair process. The repair process we use can be found in psychotherapist Terry Real's audio program, *Fierce Intimacy: Standing Up to One Another with Love.*

Knowing you have a repair process in place that worked to handle prior conflicts is extremely regulating since it gives you the confidence that the relationship will survive your current conflict. Regardless of the repair process you choose the main key to maintaining the health of your relationship is to find one you both agree to use and stay committed to using it. Otherwise, you risk subjecting your relationship to the winds of whatever you trigger in each other.

Finding and learning to use a repair process is a minuscule price to pay for what is the most precious gift in life—the ability to love and be loved in an intimate relationship.

## Why Attuned, Face-to-Face Contact Is Key to Healthy Relationships

Stephen Porges, author of *The Polyvagal Theory: Neurophysiological Foundations of Emotions, Attachment, Communication, and Self-Regulation,* is a leading expert who studies the impact that childhood trauma has on relationships. In the *Polyvagal Theory,* Porges states how critical it is for children and adults to have face-to-face interactions to regulate their nervous systems and emotions.

What I love about the Polyvagal Theory is that it focuses on building connections between humans through learning how to foster trust and safety. I was struck when Porges shared in the below excerpt how crucial it is for human beings to be connected to one another:

> The biological imperative for humans is to be connected. As a species, we survive because we require mutual help and cooperation. Many people go into therapy not because they don't want relationships but because when they do try relationships, their bodies react in a state of threat and defense.
>
> Trauma sets up children to experience a chronic disruption of connectedness, shifting the ANS- autonomic nervous system into the flight, fight, freeze response which distorts social awareness.
>
> The most important thing in life is how we connect and relate with one another. Trauma disrupts this capacity to connect. It doesn't allow survivors to co-regulate with one another.
>
> Calm face-to-face interactions regulate states. This is called co-regulation. This face-to-face behavior includes facial expressions, gestures, prosodic vocalization, listening, and reciprocity.

In the below excerpt from *The Polyvagal Theory,* Porges shares the evolution of the autonomic nervous system and that to connect with fellow humans, we must learn how to shift into our Social Engagement System.

## The Social Engagement System: The Portal To Safety & Connection

### The 3 Stages of How The Autonomic Nervous System (ANS) Evolved

**1. Immobilization (freeze):** The freeze response is the oldest pathway. It involves an immobilization response to cues of extreme danger. We become frozen, numb, and shut down.

**2. Mobilization (fight or flight):** The fight-or-flight response helps us mobilize in the face of a danger cue. We spring into action with an adrenaline rush to escape danger or fight off a threat.

**3. Social engagement:** The social engagement response is the newest addition to the hierarchy of responses. It responds to feelings of safety and connection. It makes us feel anchored, safe, calm, connected, and engaged.

The first two stages, *Immobilization-freeze, and mobilization-flight and fight,* function as survival states to respond to threats. Stage three, *social engagement,* the most recent stage, evolved for humans to feel safe enough to forge close relationships.

## Autonomic Nervous System States

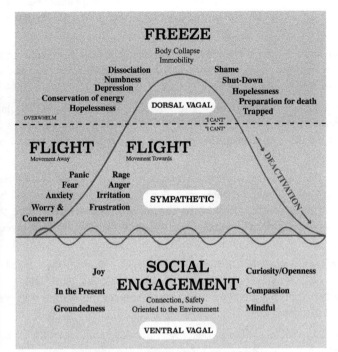

**FREEZE**

Body Collapse
Immobility

Dissociation     Shame
Numbness     Shut-Down
Depression     Hopelessness
Conservation of energy     Preparation for death
Hopelessness     Trapped

DORSAL VAGAL

OVERWHELM

"I CANT"
"I CANT"

**FLIGHT**    **FLIGHT**
Movement Away     Movement Towards

Panic    Rage
Fear    Anger
Anxiety    Irritation
Worry &    Frustration
Concern

SYMPATHETIC

DEACTIVATION

Joy    **SOCIAL**    Curiosity/Openness

In the Present    **ENGAGEMENT**    Compassion

Groundedness    Connection, Safety    Mindful
Oriented to the Environment

VENTRAL VAGAL

AROUSAL INCREASES

Source: Adapted by Ruby Jo Walker from Cheryl Sanders,
Steve Hoskinson, Steven Porges & Peter Levine

### How To Identify Your Nervous System's Current State

By reviewing the infographic of Autonomic Nervous System States, you can identify your current state by matching what feelings, thoughts, or impulses you are experiencing to what state they are listed under. For example: If you are curious, open, or in the present moment, you are in a social engagement state. If you are frustrated or angry, you are in a fight state. If you are worried or anxious, you are in a flight state. If you are depressed or shut down, you are in a freeze state.

## How Using Facial Expressions, Reciprocal Gestures & Vocal Intonation Help To Shift Others Into Their Social Engagement System

According to Porges, our facial expressivity, reciprocal gestures, and vocal intonation are critical in making others feel safe enough to shift into their social engagement system. Unfortunately, texting, messaging, email, and social media posts can't deliver these essential safety cues. Humans need real-time, in-person, interactive facial expressions, a safe tone of voice, and reciprocal gestures to make these cues land. This is why face-to-face contact is essential in establishing healthy, connected relationships. If it's impossible to meet in person, doing FaceTime or Zoom calls is the next best thing.

## Learning How to Shift into the Social Engagement System

I loved learning how to work with my social engagement system (SES) since I knew it would help me achieve one of my main goals: having fun connecting with people.

One of the practices I've implemented in working with my SES is to get curious about my nervous system state by checking in with myself during social events.

I do so by asking myself, *How am I doing? Am I enjoying myself? How comfortable or uncomfortable do I feel? Do I feel the impulse to leave, scroll through my phone, or overindulge in food?* I'll also ask myself, *Is there any tension in my body? If so, where? What kinds of thoughts am I having? What are the sensations in my body trying to tell me?*

My goal with these inquiries is to gain a felt sense of what's going on in my body and mind to assess the state of my nervous system. If I'm not in my SES, my goal is to take steps to shift into it. I love the saying, "When you name it, you tame it," since it's true. Just noticing and naming all of your sensations, impulses, and thoughts helps calm down the nervous system and moves us in the direction of our SES.

I intentionally look for people I feel safe talking to and avoid or excuse myself to move away from those I don't feel safe with. Also, whenever I feel uncomfortable, I know it's safe to speak to Maria about it. I've found that discussing with her in advance how the day or evening will go when we have plans to socialize is very regulating for me.

When Maria and I first got together, social events were challenging for us. In an attempt to manage my social anxiety, I always wanted to know how long we would stay. Maria wanted to be more spontaneous and not have to commit to any time frames.

When I explained to her my struggle with social anxiety and how this was my way of regulating myself, she had more empathy and compassion for my social challenges. Now we always negotiate a time frame that works for both of us before we arrive at large gatherings. This alone calms me down and helps me pace myself.

Another regulating strategy I use for social events is to set an intention of what I'd like to experience before arriving. I often ask Maria in advance about the background or history of people who will be at her family events. This helps me set an intention to get to know one or two people who will be there by giving me a way to strike up a fun conversation with them. It also calms me down since it gives me something to focus on.

Also, giving myself permission to take a walk around the block or take refuge in my car when I feel overwhelmed is helpful. I find I do best at smaller gatherings versus large ones. And I give myself permission to decline invitations to events that include people who aren't safe for me, even if others may be disappointed by my absence or take offense.

Now that I'm so intentional about using social events to heal my relational trauma, I look forward to going since I actually have fun at them.

## Our Brain State Drives Our Thoughts, Beliefs, Behaviors, & Worldview

I had a major aha moment when I learned from Porges that when we are in a threat state *(fight, flight, or freeze)*, we lose the ability to be objective because our physiological state automatically overrides our thoughts and emotions.

According to Porges, the reason for this is when we shift from a calm state to a more mobilized, protective state, our perspective of the world changes to support our mobilization. Therefore, when we're in a fight-or-flight state, we can't help but perceive people and the world as dangerous. This is an example of how our physiological state overrides our thoughts and emotions.

The problem for those of us with unhealed C-PTSD is due to brain and nervous system dysregulation issues; we may perceive a person or an environment as unsafe even though there is no evidence to support our perception. However, once you are aware of this possibility, you can be more discerning in determining whether the threat you're feeling is accurate or that it's just a program that your brain is running due to your unhealed C-PTSD. I've found that just having this level of awareness calms me down to where I can shift into my SES.

## Relationships Are the Perfect Training For Regulating Our Nervous Systems

Porges states that we need to intentionally develop relationships to regulate the ANS and heal trauma. This is because relationships make us go through different forms of neural exercises, such as play and social interactions.

All of these activities make us healthier mentally, socially, and physiologically. This is why talk therapy can sometimes have a profound healing effect. It involves two bodies (the therapist and the client) feeling safe with one another after sending cues of safety to each other. And once our bodies feel safe, we automatically allow the other person to co-regulate with us.

## Tracking Your Nervous System's State in Real Time

The beauty of learning about the Polyvagal Theory and the social engagement system is that it taught me to identify the nervous system state I'm in and then consciously shift into a new state if I choose. As a result, I've gotten pretty good at tracking and shifting my state in real time.

When at a social function, I know when I'm in a flight state when I have the impulse to leave, escape to the bathroom, numb with food or caffeine, or scroll on my phone. When I'm in a freeze state, I tend to dissociate while I'm with someone who's monopolizing the conversation. When I'm in a fight state, I'm agitated or angry and find myself complaining or having the impulse to be passive-aggressive. When I'm in a social engagement state, I feel safe, calm, and connected, and I'm really enjoying talking, laughing, and being playful with the people I'm with.

The greatest gift of learning about the Polyvagal Theory is that when I want to connect with people, I now have the tools to do so because I know what steps to take to get into a social engagement state. I also know how to help others feel safe to do so as well. As a result, I have much more fun at social events because I associate them with safety and connection instead of stress and discomfort.

## Even If We've Given Up On Relationships, Our Nervous System Never Gives Up

The excerpt below from Deb Dana's book *Befriending Your Nervous System* reminded me that engaging in safe, close relationships isn't just a "nice to have" but an essential need we all must get met for our survival.

> While you may have a story of giving up looking for people to connect with, we know your nervous system doesn't give up looking, waiting, and wanting. Until the day we die, our nervous system is longing for a safe, reliable ongoing connection with another nervous system. We are looking to regulate and be in a reciprocal relationship with someone else.

This excerpt speaks to the fact that we need each other to survive and thrive, whether we believe we do or not. Therefore, finding a way to get this need met must be a critical part of our trauma healing journey. According to Porges, our health, well-being, and literal life depend on it.

I certainly can attest that being able to connect in close relationships is the most precious gift I've received from healing my trauma. The beauty of this is it can be learned. I cover all the ways I've been able to do so in the remainder of this book.

# CHAPTER 15

---

# THE ORIGINAL WOUND: EARLY ATTACHMENT TRAUMA

There is no more effective neurobiological intervention than a safe relationship.

—Bruce Perry, MD, PhD

Before I learned about childhood trauma and attachment theory, I wouldn't have thought if a mother frequently ignored her baby's cries or shamed them for expressing their emotions, the baby could be harmed in any significant way since I thought the baby would be too young to remember it. But I discovered I was wrong once I learned the crucial role that early attachment plays in impacting a baby's long-term development.

## Early Attachment Trauma

It was really eye-opening to learn how crucial the quality of the attachment between a baby and their primary caregiver (especially in their first few months) is in how it impacts their long-term emotional, relational, and physical health.

When a baby doesn't receive adequate attunement from their primary caregiver, they experience what is known as early attachment disruption. A baby experiences attunement when their emotional reality is seen and mirrored back to them by their primary caregiver's words, facial expressions, empathy, touch, and actions. An attuned caregiver makes a baby feel cared about, safe, loved, understood, and protected, which helps them relax and feel content. This is what's supposed to happen with a healthy bond between a primary caregiver and her baby.

Going through the early attachment process is how a child's brain gets wired to regulate emotions so they can face stressful feelings on their own as an adult. If a baby doesn't have an attuned, present, emotionally healthy parent to see their reality and mirror it back to them, they're left to regulate their own emotions. Unfortunately, a baby isn't yet equipped to handle this task.

When this happens, the baby is left in a chronic state of hyperarousal (agitated, crying), hypoarousal (being shut down), or a combination of the two. Since a baby's brain is going through critical complex developmental stages, it can set the stage for them to stay stuck in these states resulting in them developing C-PTSD.

What does a lack of attunement look like between a primary caregiver and her baby?

- A baby signals for the mother to pick them up or connect, and she stares off into space or is preoccupied with her phone or other duties.
- A mother is frequently overwhelmed or struggles to deal with anger, anxiety, addictions, depression, or trauma and can't tune into her baby because she's too focused on her own distress.
- A baby cries, and the mother either ignores them, is inconsistently present, gets upset, yells at, spanks, or pushes them away.

In summary, an early attachment disruption occurs when there's a consistent pattern of a baby's reality not being seen, known, or responded to enough in an empathetic way by the primary caregiver.

## The Architect of the Child's Reward, Stress-Response & Relational Systems

While studying various authors on attachment trauma, I had another major aha moment when I learned that the primary caregiver is the architect of the child's reward, stress response, and relational system. In a real sense, the primary caregiver provides a template of their nervous system for the baby to replicate as their own.

Since a baby automatically fine-tunes its nervous system to align with and map to the primary caregiver's, if the caregiver's nervous system is frequently shut down, depressed, or anxious, the baby's nervous system will be as well. For better or worse, these early relational experiences become the major determinants for the baby's set point for their stress-response system for life (unless there's an intervention).

This is why the mother's emotional and nervous system health is crucial for the child's ability to manage stress and form healthy relationships throughout their lives. When the mother cannot provide adequate attunement, the child is set up for various stress-response, developmental, and relational challenges.

## Attachment Disruption & Chronic Dysregulation

In her book, *Neurofeedback in the Treatment of Developmental Trauma: Calming the Fear-Driven Brain,* trauma psychotherapist and neurofeedback clinician Sebern Fisher shares an observation she and her colleagues had while working with severely traumatized children.

> It did not take us long to detect a correlation between the level of attachment disruption in early childhood and treatment outcomes. The more motherless the child was or perceived himself or herself to be, the worse the prognosis.

> We had been focusing on early childhood trauma as an indicator of early damage done. But it was never as predictive of treatment failure as the internalization of the absence of a mother, of no one taking care of the helpless infant. This feeling can lead to a profound attachment disruption long past the stage of infancy.

> According to Dr. Alan Shore's seminal work: *Affect Regulation and the Origin of Self in 1994,* the single greatest cost of a mother's inability to regulate herself, we learned, is to the development of her child's right hemisphere, the part of the brain that governs regulation of emotion. Poor right hemisphere development means that the child, like her mother, would be unable to regulate the intensity or the expression of her feelings.

Reading the above excerpts by Sebern Fisher and Dr. Alan Shore are two more examples illustrating how the state of a mother's emotional health directly transfers to her baby. Since my mother was clearly unable to regulate her emotions, this explains how my brain also got wired to struggle with emotional regulation

## Making Sense Of My First Attempts At Self Soothing

My mother told me she had trouble nursing me when I was a baby, so she opted for bottle feeding instead. She also mentioned that she couldn't get me to give up my bottle until I was two and a half years old, which is apparently quite late for a baby. When I thought about why I would have such an intense need to hold onto my bottle for so long and why I reportedly went into so much distress when my mom attempted to take it away from me, it became obvious that it was due to it being a critical source of soothing for me.

Interestingly, once my bottle was taken away, I began sucking my thumb. Then, shortly before I entered first grade, my mom told me my classmates would tease me if they saw me sucking my thumb. Since I feared being teased more than being soothed by my thumb-sucking, I was able to quit. The problem was that I no longer had a way to soothe myself. That's when I discovered all the ways that food could fit the bill to comfort and soothe me.

Now that I can look at my early attempts at self-soothing through a trauma-informed lens, I can see that using my bottle, food, and sucking my thumb were all attempts to self-soothe due to not receiving the soothing and emotional regulation I needed from my mother.

What I found especially interesting about attachment disruption is that it doesn't matter how much a parent loves or cares for their child. If a parent cannot attune to and mirror their baby's emotional state back to them, the baby will experience distress, and if it happens on an ongoing basis, it can lead to childhood trauma.

In my case, I have no doubt that my mother deeply loved and cared for me. The problem was she never received adequate emotional attunement from her mother; therefore, she couldn't provide it for me. She was too anxious, depressed, and dysregulated to do so. Sadly, love is not enough to meet a baby's needs. Love is definitely one aspect of what a baby needs to thrive. But they also need a parent who can attune to and mirror their child's emotional state back to them.

## Don't Panic: Attachment Trauma Can Be Healed

When I first learned that my mother was the architect of my reward, stress-response, and relational systems, my first reaction was, "Oh my God, I'm so screwed!" I felt so ripped off for drawing such a horrible hand, given how loaded it was with generational trauma that had trickled down to me through my mom.

Although this news may seem gloomy if you're struggling with attachment trauma, the good news is it can be healed. One of the most powerful ways to heal is having corrective experiences in close relationships. These include relationships with therapists, coaches, safe friends, or romantic partners. Interestingly, several psychoanalytical theories state that one of the primary purposes of the relationship between a patient and a psychotherapist is for the patient to achieve a corrective experience of healthy attunement.

## This Isn't About Blaming Our Parents

It's important to recognize that this work isn't about blaming our parents. It's about understanding that all humans have essential needs, and when these needs aren't met, there are predictable outcomes. One of the outcomes for a baby who doesn't receive adequate attunement is they'll develop C-PTSD.

It's also important to mention that most parents don't intentionally neglect their children's attachment needs. The primary reason a child experiences attachment trauma is because their primary caregiver never received adequate attunement from their own caregiver. Since a parent can only give what they received from their primary caregiver, it makes sense that attachment trauma would automatically transfer down through the generations. One of the goals of healing trauma is to break this chain.

It's very common for survivors to instinctively protect their parents when presented with the idea that they may have been hurt or traumatized due to not receiving adequate attunement from them when they were children. Hopefully, by realizing their parents could only attune with them to the degree they were attuned with, it will become easier to accept that their attachment needs may not have been met.

We can't begin to heal until we can accept that how our primary caregiver attuned with us may have fallen short of what we needed and that we were hurt because of it.

By understanding what happened to us, we can also stop blaming ourselves for how we've struggled and coped. We can then gain access to the healing support we need so we can go on to live happy, healthy, productive lives.

## Attachment Styles and Relationships

Although I was aware of attachment theory, it wasn't until I learned about childhood trauma that I discovered that a primary caregiver's attachment style directly influences which attachment style their child develops. If the primary caregiver's attachment style is insecure vs. secure, their child will likely develop a similar style. This is important because a person's attachment style sets the foundation for how they'll be able to attach in close relationships for the remainder of their life.

## Attachment Theory

Attachment theory is based on the work of John Bowlby, a twentieth-century British psychologist, psychiatrist, and psychoanalyst. It suggests that children come into the world biologically pre-programmed to form attachments with others because it helps them survive.

Bowlby states that the infant produces innate social releaser behaviors, such as crying and smiling, stimulating innate caregiver responses. He suggests that a child initially forms only one primary attachment, and that the attachment figure acts as a secure base for exploring the world. The attachment relationship serves as a prototype for all future social relationships, so disrupting it can have severe consequences.

According to attachment theory, the primary caregiver's level of responsiveness and attunement will determine which of four attachment styles a child will develop in the first year of life. Once a person's attachment style is set, it becomes the prototype for all future relationships.

Bowlby identified four adult attachment styles: secure, insecure-anxious, insecure-avoidant, and insecure-disorganized. Approximately 50% of the population have a secure attachment style, 20% have an insecure-anxious attachment style, 25% have an insecure-avoidant attachment style, and 5% have an insecure-disorganized attachment style. Below are descriptions of each adult attachment style.

## Attachment Styles

**Secure:** This type of attachment is born from a healthy, sufficient, attuned primary caregiver. Intimate relationships feel comfortable for securely attached people. They also feel fine being alone and independent. They enter a romantic relationship trusting their partner to be emotionally available for them in hardship and distress. They see themselves as worthy of care and affection. They see others as accessible and reliable and expect people to have good intentions for them. Their relationships tend to be intimate and trusting.

**Insecure-anxious:** This style develops when the primary caregiver is inconsistent with attunement 70% or more of the time. These people tend to worry that their partner doesn't love them or won't stay with them. Sometimes their need to cling or be reassured can inadvertently drive a partner away. They often see themselves as unworthy of love and care. They tend to idealize their partner. They're prone to an obsessive preoccupation with their partner and tend to be emotionally dependent on them.

Since they know what it's like to experience and lose closeness, they can become preoccupied with keeping people close and avoiding rejection. They focus on the outside world and whether people like them. They often wonder if they did something wrong and feel like everyone keeps letting them down. They fear abandonment, and any hint of it can trigger them to worry about being abandoned. When stressed, they prefer to be with their partner.

**Insecure-avoidant:** This style develops when a caregiver isn't physically or emotionally present for the child or has a flat, unemotional affect 70% or more of the time. They may also reject or be nonresponsive to negative emotions or emotional neediness.

This style can also develop when a child is given attention only when completing a task or achieving a goal. People with this attachment style are uncomfortable being emotionally close and find it hard to trust a partner and share feelings. They get nervous when a partner wants more emotional intimacy. They tend to suppress their emotions. They expect a partner to be emotionally untrustworthy.

With this style, the caregiver often refers to her infant as a "good baby" because they never cry. Given that babies have to adapt to the caregiver's deficits, not crying may signify that the baby has given up hope of having their needs responded to and has learned to stop signaling a parent. The baby knows from experience that they're on their own and doesn't expect any response to their needs. These people may also take pride in being independent. When stressed, they prefer to be alone versus with their partner.

**Insecure-disorganized:** This attachment style develops when there's severe, unprocessed trauma, abuse, significant loss, or a frightening caregiver. When a child feels stress or distress, they usually turn to the primary caregiver for comfort. However, if the primary caregiver is also a threat, the child's nervous system gets overwhelmed and can't develop a coherent strategy for staying safe.

As adults, this style manifests as a negative self-image and a view of the world as untrustworthy or chaotic. People with this style can display erratic behavior and view relationships unclearly, leading to outbursts and unpredictability. They tend to be anxious and depressed, making job advancement difficult and intimate relationships challenging.

## How Early Attunement Sets Up a Person's Attachment Style in Adult Relationships

It was interesting to learn that a mother or primary caregiver only has to attune to her child's emotional and physical needs 30% of the time for it to be considered good-enough parenting. However, when a parent fails to meet this threshold, it sets the child up to develop an insecure attachment.

Tragically, mothers with addiction, depression, or anxiety tend to be so distracted by their own emotional pain or are so emotionally numb that they simply can't tune into their child's needs. Also, if a mother is extremely busy caring for many children or has many other responsibilities, she may not have enough time to adequately attune with her child.

A child with an attuned caregiver learns they can get stressed and turn to the mother to calm down. With enough repetition, the child builds a resilient nervous system response. Over time, the child internalizes that they can get stressed and soothe themself. This is how a child develops the ability to regulate their own nervous system and emotional states as they grow up.

Sadly, if a child doesn't experience an attuned, present mother at least 30% of the time while growing up, turning to people for help as an adult tends to be stressful because experience has taught them that people can't be trusted to be there for them.

Children who experienced severe abuse or neglect may not even think to turn to others for help because turning to their mother as a child was futile or even dangerous. Their caregivers were either completely nonresponsive or became upset or abusive when the child had needs.

Given infants are 100% dependent on their caregiver for survival, experiencing a lack of attunement is highly stressful. Since this type of stress in early infancy is toxic for a child's nervous system, brain, and psyche, it often causes them to develop C-PTSD.

When the level of distress is ongoing and reaches critical levels, it can cause mood disorders, such as depression, anxiety, or other psychiatric issues. It can also set the stage for later childhood problems with attention issues and obesity.

As adults, survivors with chronically dysregulated nervous systems often seek relief through drugs, alcohol, food, or other addictive behaviors.

## Identifying Your Attachment Style

Although there are four distinct attachment styles, each person's style can fall on a spectrum. People often display traits of different attachment styles based on their stress levels. For this reason, it's completely normal to find that you're a mix of two styles or lean more toward one style or another based on the relationship you're in or the circumstances in your life.

Although Bowlby states that a baby's initial attachment style is set for all of their future relationships, studies show that people with insecure attachment styles can take steps to transition into a secure attachment style. They can do so by having a healthy relationship with a securely attached partner, receiving attachment-oriented therapy, or having other corrective relational experiences. Transitioning from an insecure to a secure attachment style is known as "earning secure attachment."

## How Learning Attachment Theory Improved My Romantic Relationship

After studying attachment styles, I easily identified my initial style as insecure-anxious. But thanks to the work I've done on myself over the years and the healing I've experienced in several long-term relationships, I would rate myself somewhere between having an anxious and a secure attachment style.

## How The Lack of Awareness of Attachment Styles Can Sabotage Relationships

Before understanding attachment styles, I recall one of my former partners and me running in circles by how triggered we got when we asked for what we needed to feel safe in our relationship. I was often triggered if my partner was distant or wanted to take space from me.

I assumed her needing space meant she was either unhappy in the relationship or didn't love me as much as I loved her. It felt threatening because I thought it could mean the beginning of the end of the relationship.

My partner (who had an avoidant attachment style) got triggered by me being triggered about her being distant or needing space. Her trigger told her that to be with me, she would need to lose herself, be smothered by me, or have to deal with the stress of my being upset with her for taking space.

When we attempted to resolve our issues, it eventually came down to my feeling blamed and judged for being too needy or smothering or my partner feeling blamed or judged for having a fear of intimacy.

At the beginning of the relationship, one of us would accept the blame and agree to work on our neediness or fear of intimacy in individual therapy or by reading a self-help book. Sometimes we'd both accept blame and work on our neediness or intimacy issues simultaneously by discussing them with each other or in couple's therapy. Yet, it was just a matter of time before the same issue would pop up again and land us in the same fight.

After rehashing the same issue repeatedly, year after year, with no lasting resolution, we would eventually throw our hands up, thinking that we just weren't compatible, and end the relationship while secretly blaming each other for not dealing with their unhealed issues.

## What Couples Must Learn to Provide Safety for Each Other

Once I understood that attachment styles are based on what a person did or didn't get from their primary caregiver, aren't a pathology, are involuntary, and are embedded in the nervous system, I understood that each person has specific needs that must be met for them to feel safe. Once both partners' relational safety needs are met, the stage is set for a secure attachment to form.

## Requirements For Both Members of A Couple To Feel Safe In The Relationship

1. Each must have a basic understanding of attachment theory.
2. Each must have identified their own attachment style and know what they need to request of their partner to feel safe.
3. Each must know their partner's attachment style, understand that it's an automatic nervous system response, and refrain from judging or pathologizing it.
4. Each must know and be okay with responding to their partner's requests to feel safe.

Typically, when anxious types get triggered, they need reassurance that they're loved and won't be abandoned. When avoidant types get triggered, they need reassurance that it's okay to take space, that they won't be smothered, and that their partner won't be angry or leave them. When a disorganized type gets triggered, they need one or both of the above reassurances to feel safe.

## How My Partner & I Navigate Each Other's Attachment Style

When I get triggered, the learning curve for me is to not personalize it when Maria (who has an avoidant attachment style) becomes distant or needs to take space. Her learning curve with me is to understand that if I (who has an anxious attachment style) feel any hint of distance from her, it's okay for me to ask if everything is okay with us. If there isn't an issue, Maria is okay with reassuring me that she loves me and isn't going to leave me. If she is distant because she has an issue with me or the relationship, we've agreed we'll either discuss it then or will set a time and day to discuss it.

## Learning How To Become Securely Attached

The excellent news about insecure attachment styles is our brains are plastic. So, with some work, we can rewire them to become securely attached.

The best way for an anxious type to earn secure attachment is to stretch outside their comfort zone by going within to self-regulate versus looking to their partner to make them feel better. Also, since anxious types can have difficulty absorbing their partner's love and attunement, it can be helpful to look at how much of the love they can take in and receive.

The best way for avoidant types to stretch outside their comfort zone is to reach out to their partner or other safe people to regulate their emotions versus going within as much.

The best way for disorganized types to earn secure attachment is to utilize a combination of the same processes that avoidant and anxious types use to earn secure attachment.

Additionally, anxious, avoidant, and disorganized attachment types can earn secure attachment by being in a romantic relationship with a securely attached partner.

## Benefits of Earning a Secure Attachment Style

**It supports emotional regulation:** Secure attachment gives you the flexibility to co-regulate with people you have close relationships with and regulate your own nervous system and mood. Also, when you get thrown off and become dysregulated, you can return to a state of regulation much more quickly and have the insight to understand and learn from what happened.

**It makes it easier to resolve conflicts:** When you understand the nature of attachment, you can approach conflicts with compassion and understanding, which creates the safe space necessary for conflict resolution.

**You're more likely to have long-term, fulfilling relationships:** Since the nature of secure attachment is for both partners to get their needs met, developing a secure attachment style gives you the best chance of enjoying a long-term, fulfilling, intimate relationship. This, in turn, gives you the best chance of living a satisfying, meaningful life.

## More Resources for Developing Securely Attached Relationships

Below is a collection of my favorite books on creating securely attached relationships.

- *Wired for Love, Wired for Dating, and We Do* by Dr. Stan Tatkin
- *Healing Your Attachment Wounds: How To Create Deep & Lasting Relationships* by Dr. Diane Poole Heller
- *Us: Getting Past You and Me to Build a More Loving Relationship, & Fierce Intimacy* by Terrance Real
- *Conscious Lesbian Dating & Love: A Roadmap to Finding the Right Partner and Creating the Relationship of your Dreams* by Ruth L. Schwartz, Ph.D., and Michelle Murrain, Ph.D.

Also, see the appendix for a complete list of recommended books and resources on forming and maintaining healthy relationships.

# CHAPTER 16

# RELIGIOUS EMOTIONAL ABUSE AND NEGLECT: BEING RAISED CATHOLIC

My religion is very simple—my religion is kindness.

—Dalai Lama

Catholicism goes way back on both sides of my family. My mother came from an especially devout Irish Catholic family. In fact, one of the reasons her father wouldn't approve of her marrying the boyfriend she'd become pregnant with before she married my dad was because he wasn't Catholic.

My official membership in the Church began when my parents had me baptized soon after birth. My Catholic education began when I was enrolled in catechism at age five. Catechism provides Catholic religion classes for children who are in public school.

I went to catechism every Saturday morning at our church parish for three years. In fourth grade, I transferred to a Catholic grade school, where religion classes were part of the curriculum, so I no longer needed to go to catechism. In addition to religion class, the entire student body was required to attend Mass every Wednesday morning. Even though we went to Mass on Wednesdays, we still had to go on Sundays because Sunday was considered a holy day of obligation.

In the ninth grade, I continued my Catholic education by spending four years in a Catholic high school. From the age of five through seventeen, I spent a total of twelve years immersed in the teachings of the Catholic religion.

### Realizing I Was Still Under the Spell of Original Sin in My Fifties

In 2015 I began doing a lot of work on letting go of some long-held guilt and shame. Part of my healing process involved learning how to forgive myself. Even though I thought I'd let go of believing that a priest was the only way I could be forgiven back in my teens, I hadn't gotten clear on how self-forgiveness could work for me on my own.

While struggling with self-forgiveness, I realized I hadn't consciously placed the authority of forgiveness back into my own hands. Instead, I'd left it unresolved, but I wasn't consciously aware of it until I started digging into my self-forgiveness work.

While working on forgiving myself, my mind would automatically respond with thoughts such as, *Who am I to forgive myself?* And *I can't just forgive myself!*

After thinking about what was causing me to feel so uncomfortable giving myself the authority for self-forgiveness, I realized it had to do with the lack of trust I had in myself to make sound moral decisions.

Then it dawned on me: *Oh my God! This is really old original-sin programming!* It was then I recalled being taught in Catholic school that I was born morally corrupt due to original sin, and unless I had God to guide me, I would automatically be tempted to do bad or immoral things.

It finally made sense why I was so uncomfortable forgiving myself. After all, who in their right mind would trust a morally corrupt person to forgive themself? If I took myself as someone who actually was morally corrupt and gave myself the power to forgive my own sins, who knows what I would do with it? Heck, I might become a full-blown hedonist and go hog wild, destroying my life and the lives of anyone in my path!

Once I uncovered this crazy, illogical belief and realized it was a lie, I knew right then that I had to change it. As I contemplated how to do so, I knew that all I needed to do was ask myself one simple question: *Can I trust myself to make sound moral choices and thereby give myself the authority for self-forgiveness?* It took less than a second to say, *YES, of course I can!* Up until that moment, I'd never thought to ask myself this question.

Even after thirty years of personal and spiritual growth work, I had no idea that this toxic belief installed in me by the Catholic Church was still lurking in the background of my consciousness. What's really mind-blowing is that it wasn't until I actually asked myself if I could be trusted to make sound moral choices that I got my answer as a resounding YES. This is the power of self-inquiry.

# Religious Emotional Abuse

### What Is Religious Emotional Abuse?

When clergy uses religious dogma to teach children that they're born morally corrupt due to original sin and cite a vengeful God who will punish them in cruel ways if they don't believe and follow the standards of their moral code, those clergies are perpetuating religious emotional abuse.

Religious emotional abuse often requires children and adults to give up many of their normal, healthy human needs and ways of being. Being raised Catholic and attending Catholic school meant being taught that many of the healthiest forms of my self-expression—including my sexuality, pleasure, relaxation, and healthy self-interest—were selfish, sinful, and evil.

The Catholic Church isn't the only religion known for emotionally manipulating and abusing its members. My partner Maria shared with me that one of the core tenets of the evangelical church she was brought up in taught her that the Rapture (the moment Jesus returns to earth for his people) is coming and can happen at any time. And when the Rapture happens, the "Righteous Christians" (aka, the ones without sin) would suddenly disappear since they had ascended to heaven with Jesus, while the "sinners" would be left behind to suffer.

Maria shared with me how terrifying it was for her as a child to be shown dramatic, rapture-themed movies showing people suddenly losing everyone they loved due to being the only one left behind since they were sinners. Apparently, Maria wasn't alone in her terror as a child. After reading the article *For Some Christians, "rapture anxiety" can take a lifetime to heal\**, I discovered how common this type of anxiety is for many Christians, and for some, it can even lead to complex PTSD.

Source, CNN.com AJ Willingham

## The Core Teachings of the Catholic Church

As I reflected on what I'd been taught during my twelve years in Catholic school, I began to see that being told I was morally corrupt due to being born with original sin was just one of the ways the Church had emotionally abused me.

Below I have listed how the core teachings of the Catholic Church seeped into the very core of my being and shaped how I saw myself and the world.

**Original Sin:** The explanation for original sin originated with the biblical story of Adam and Eve. Since Adam was to be the model for all humanity, when he sinned, he stained the entire human race, causing every person born after that to be born with original sin. According to the Catholic Church, being born with original sin is to be born morally corrupt.

As such, we couldn't be trusted to come up with our own moral code. This is why we needed to follow God's Ten Commandments as our moral guide. Being born morally corrupt is also why we couldn't be trusted to forgive our own sins and needed a higher moral authority to forgive us, such as a priest.

**The Devil:** Throughout my years in Catholic grade school, there was a big focus on the cunning power of Satan. We were taught that unless we steadfastly avoided sin and stayed on God's good side, we could easily be seduced and taken over by Satan. If we weren't careful, in a weak moment, we could give in to being tempted by his cunning, powerful force. If it happened often enough, we might not ever make it back to God and would suffer for eternity in the fires of hell with Satan himself.

The nuns who taught my religion classes had me so terrified of the devil that, as a little girl, I feared Satan could be lurking around any corner, looking for ways to tempt me away from God. On top of that, since I was taught I was an inherently bad, morally corrupt person, I wasn't too confident I would be able to resist falling under his spell. This left me feeling even more vulnerable and afraid of such a powerful, demonic force overtaking me.

At just eight years old, I remember feeling terrible anxiety about having to sit through a series of special classes on the cunning and powerful force of Satan. By the third class, I began worrying that Satan would take possession of my body and mind while I was lying alone in bed at night. By the end of the series, my fear of the devil became a full-blown obsession. Being unable to stop obsessing about being hurt or terrorized by the devil was terrorizing in and of itself.

**Confession: Humiliation in the Name of God:** One of the most humiliating aspects of being Catholic was having to go to confession to be forgiven for my sins. Given that most of the behaviors considered "sins" by the church that children and teenagers commit are natural and normal stages of human development, I often had to confess the same sins every week.

That added even more shame to the mountain of it I already had because I felt that I was truly bad to the core for continually committing the same sins. I remember thinking I should just leave out these sins. But the nuns who taught religion reminded us that the whole confession would be invalid unless we bared all of our sins to the priest.

If there were any unforgiven sins on our souls when we died, we'd burn in hell forever. Therefore, to avoid the risk of burning in the fires of hell, I couldn't leave anything out of my confession. Needless to say, bearing it all in confession each week was totally humiliating and was one more thing that added to the profound shame I felt just for being a normal kid.

## How the Church Took Ownership of My Soul

The entire system set up by the Catholic Church made sure that the only way I could find any joy or peace in this life or any hope of making it into Heaven after I died was to:

- Believe I was morally corrupt and needed a priest to cleanse me of my sins to save me from burning in hell when I died
- Believe in the power of the devil to tempt me to sin and that I needed God to protect and save me from Satan's lure

- Believe that I had to attend church every Sunday, and if I failed to do so, I would be committing a sin punishable by burning in hell forever unless I went to confession before I died
- Have an unwavering belief in the Church's teachings, the Bible, and God, and accept that if I stopped believing, I would be committing the sin of blasphemy, which is punishable by burning in hell for eternity

I hated having to go to religion class and Mass twice a week. I also hated having to go to confession even more. But I went because I was taught that if I didn't go, I was a bad, selfish, ungrateful sinner and risked—you guessed it—burning in hell for eternity.

## The Long Shadow of Religious Guilt & Shame

When I had my first lesbian dream at fourteen and realized I was attracted to girls instead of boys, I was terrified. After all, the Church and the Bible said that homosexuality was a mortal sin and that I would burn in hell forever for being my authentic lesbian self. This left me feeling deeply ashamed of my sexuality and terrified to tell anyone about what I was going through due to my fear of being shamed or ostracized.

Although I'd thought I'd let go of my allegiance to the Church and its ideology in my late teens, I still wondered well into my late twenties if it was really okay with God that I was a lesbian.

One time, when I was twenty-nine and getting ready to make love with my girlfriend for the first time, I felt compelled to ask her to remove the crucifix that hung on the wall above her bed and put away the large photo of her mother that she kept on her dresser. I wanted to be present with her rather than preoccupied with the sexual shame of my Catholic upbringing.

## What Makes the Catholic Church's Teachings Abusive

**Moral Shaming:** Anytime a religion shames an innocent child as inherently bad or immoral for being born with "original sin," and they need a priest or God to cleanse them of their sins or risk burning in hell for eternity, they're perpetuating religious emotional abuse.

**Sexual Shaming:** Many survivors have no idea of the profound impact that sexual and homophobic shaming by their church has on their ability to freely express their sexuality. These deep-seated, toxic beliefs cause survivors to continuously feel inhibited in their ability to fully embrace their sexuality or enjoy sexual pleasure, whether they're gay, lesbian, straight, bi, queer, or trans.

For some, the extreme guilt and shame over their sexuality or gender is so overwhelming that they avoid sexual relationships altogether or marry or stay with someone they're not in love with to please God or their families. Hiding or denying our true sexuality or gender is toxic emotionally, physically, and spiritually. The emotional pain of denying our true self causes many people to seek relief through substances, food, or other self-destructive behaviors.

**Self-Abandonment:** Since the Church teaches the virtues of charity, self-sacrifice, and putting others' needs first, when parishioners fail to toe the line, they fear being judged by God and fellow parishioners as bad or selfish. Self-abandonment, suffering, and ultimately martyrdom is often considered the noblest and most highly valued virtues and are promoted as a surefire way to get into Heaven. Self-abandonment is directly linked to negative relational, mental, physical, and behavioral health outcomes.

**Self-Alienation:** The Catholic church's ideology causes self-alienation by shaming parishioners simply for having normal human needs. Anytime our reality—in this case, normal self-interests or natural human emotional, physical, and sexual needs—are denied, not seen as valid, or viewed as selfish, evil, or immoral, we become alienated from ourselves. By doing so, we abandon ourselves. Anytime we abandon or become alienated from ourselves due to religious ideology, we're experiencing religious, emotional abuse.

It's well documented that when people deny their essential needs and get stuck in angry, depressed, anxious, or frustrated emotions, their risk of developing mental, physical, or behavioral health disorders increases dramatically.

**Coercion—Either Believe or Burn in Hell for Eternity:** Coercion means persuading someone to do something by using force or threats. Anytime a religion threatens a parishioner with burning in hell for eternity unless they believe or practice their doctrine, they are being coercive and are therefore perpetuating religious emotional abuse.

## How Being Traumatized By The Catholic Church Impacted My Life

Gaining a deeper understanding of childhood trauma helped me realize that being indoctrinated into the toxic ideology of the Catholic Church was deeply traumatizing for me in the following ways:

- I suffered from toxic guilt and shame from being taught I was morally corrupt and inherently bad. This indoctrination undermined my ability to trust that I was a good, moral, and lovable person, which negatively influenced my self-esteem and the belief I deserved to be loved.
- I was taught my sexuality was immoral and evil and that if I honored it, I would burn in hell for eternity. This caused the loss of freely expressing and enjoying the pleasure of my sexuality and instead viewing it as something I should hide and be ashamed of instead of something beautiful I should celebrate.
- The teachings on the power of Satan caused me to have an obsessive fear that the devil would possess, torture, or hurt me. This caused me to lose a sense of safety in the world.
- I was coerced into fearing eternal damnation if I didn't surrender my natural human needs, sexuality, self-interests, sense of self, and sense of safety to the beliefs, moral code, and rules of the Church. This caused me to live in a world where I would suffer no matter what I chose. I was damned if I was true to myself since it meant I'd burn in hell for doing so, and damned if I was true to the church's teachings since I could never be happy following teachings that weren't aligned with who I was.

# Healing Religious Emotional Abuse

Looking back, I can see that I originally began healing my religious emotional abuse in 1987 when I first got sober. When you first join Alcoholics Anonymous, they recommend you choose a power greater than yourself to rely on to help you stay sober. They are extremely liberal in supporting members in finding a higher power they are comfortable with.

As long as your higher power is not you, they are fine with whatever you choose. Unlike the Catholic Church, AA didn't threaten me with burning in hell or any other punishment if I didn't believe in a particular God or ideology. In fact, you don't have to believe in any type of God to be a member of AA. The only requirement for membership in AA is the desire to stop drinking.

Reading the *Conversations with God* book series by Neale Donald Walsch in the early nineties was also instrumental in helping me get untangled from the Catholic church's indoctrination.

A common theme for people who experience religious emotional abuse is lacking a sense of belonging. This was certainly true for me. Feeling disconnected and like I didn't belong was a deeply painful and lonely experience.

Attending gay AA meetings and making gay and lesbian sober friends gave me a community where I felt I belonged. I also found a more gay-affirming church with the Church of Religious Science in the late eighties. The church I attended even had a gay and lesbian spiritual support group that met twice a month. This was another way I gained a sense of belonging.

Although the Catholic church's teachings had negatively impacted me for several decades, I'm happy to report that after many years of healing work and seeing the church for what it truly is, I've successfully deprogrammed myself from its toxic ideology. Today I find sustenance and support in a safe spiritual community where I am celebrated for who I am and what I believe in, and for that, I am truly grateful.

# Spiritual Neglect

### What Is Spiritual Neglect?

Spiritual neglect occurs when parents neglect to expose their children to religious or philosophical perspectives that help them see the good in life and the good in themselves.

Sadly, due to many survivors being raised in religions based on the fear of God and eternal damnation, spiritual neglect can be as prevalent as religious emotional abuse in our culture.

My parent's philosophy about God and life was heavily influenced by their Catholic upbringing. It was considered blasphemy to even think there could be ways to look at God and the world other than what they were taught by the Catholic Church. This is why they automatically delegated any type of religious or philosophical guidance for my sister and me to the teachings of the Church.

Sadly, instead of teaching me to see the good in myself and the world, the Catholic Church taught me just the opposite; to see the bad in myself and the evil in the world.

# Healing Spiritual Neglect

The Church of Religious Science and many other personal and spiritual development teachers and philosophies I explored have also made a profound difference in helping me see the good in myself and the good in all of humanity.

Also, finding like-minded, safe communities helped me feel good about who I was and what was possible for me. They were also instrumental in helping me heal my relational trauma since they gave me the corrective experience of feeling safe and accepted while being completely authentic.

This is the healing power of finding healthy communities where you feel safe and celebrated. The good news is no matter where you've been, what you've done, or how you feel about yourself, there's a safe community where you can find acceptance, fellowship, and belonging.

Part III and the appendix contain a list of the many safe, supportive communities you can access in-person and online.

# CHAPTER 17

---

# HOW MY ACE SCORE PREDICTED MY FUTURE

Once people know about ACEs, once they have the information, they are able to look at the context of their lives differently. They no longer feel they are to blame, or that they're stupid, or that there's something wrong with them. They understand that their bodies have experienced a normal reaction to abnormal circumstances across the span of their lives.

—Nadine Burke Harris, M.D., *The Deepest Well*

I had never heard of the Adverse Childhood Experiences (ACE) Study until I read *The Body Keeps the Score*. As I learned more about the ACE Study, I was amazed to see how accurate it was in predicting my future simply by identifying and adding up the different types of adversity I experienced growing up.

The original ACE Study was conducted by Kaiser Permanente and the CDC-Center for Disease Control, and the results were published in 1998. In it, 17,000 Kaiser Permanente health plan members agreed to answer yes or no to ten questions regarding whether they'd experienced the most common types of childhood traumas or adversities before age eighteen.

The ACE Study Asks 10 Questions About Being Raised In A Home Where There Was:

1. Emotional abuse
2. Emotional neglect
3. Physical abuse
4. Physical neglect
5. Sexual abuse
6. A parent addicted to alcohol or drugs
7. A parent who suffered from anxiety, depression, or other mental health issues
8. Witnessing a mother being physically abused by her spouse
9. Losing a parent due to incarceration
10. Parents separating or divorce

A person's ACE score can range from 0 to 10. Each type of trauma or adversity counts as one ACE, regardless of how many times it occurred. ACE study co-founders Dr. Robert Anda and Dr. Vince Felitti knew that there were many other ACEs than those they included in the original ACE study. They settled on the original 10 questions because they were identified as the most common ACEs.

## Your ACE Score Is Like A Cholesterol Score For Childhood Trauma

The higher the ACE score, the more types of adversity or trauma the person experienced during childhood. The goal of the ACE study was to see if higher ACE scores were linked to higher levels of negative health, behavioral, or social outcomes later in life.

## The Outcome of the ACE Study

The outcome of the ACE Study was staggering. Below are just a few pieces of data from the first 1998 ACE Study. Out of the 17,000 surveyed:

- 30.1% reported being physically abused (that left a mark on their body) as a child
- 23.5% reported family members abusing alcohol while growing up
- 19.9% reported being sexually abused as a child
- 18.8% reported growing up with a family member with a mental health disorder
- 12.5% witnessed their mothers being hit by their spouses while growing up
- 11% reported being emotionally abused as a child
- 4.9% reported family members abusing drugs while growing up

The first ACE Study was done in a San Diego community composed of primarily white, college-educated, middle to upper-middle-income families with health insurance. The average age of participants was fifty-seven.

The ACE Study revealed that even children from middle to upper-middle-income families experience significant adversity and trauma. In other words, trauma does not discriminate and can happen to any child regardless of socioeconomic status, race, or religion.

Subsequent ACE studies have been conducted in various communities worldwide. They have generated consistent outcomes, revealing that childhood adversity and trauma are extremely common and impact every community. Although the ACE Study proved that nobody is immune to childhood adversity, subsequent ACE studies have shown higher ACE scores in poor and marginalized communities.

## The Key Findings From the ACE Study

1. **ACEs are common and are largely unrecognized & where there's one ACE, there are usually more.** About two-thirds of the participants in the first ACE study experienced one or more types of adverse childhood experiences (ACEs). Of those, 87 percent had experienced 2 or more types of ACEs.

2. **There is a direct link between childhood trauma, depression, anxiety, obesity, addiction, chronic illness, and financial problems** in adulthood.

3. **21.5% of adults had 3 or more ACEs, and 16% had 4 or more types of ACEs.** An ACE score of 4 or higher is considered a high-risk score for developing serious negative social, behavioral, mental, and physical health outcomes in adulthood.

4. **Negative ACE-related outcomes are dose-dependent.** The more ACES you have, the higher the risk of experiencing negative physical, mental and behavioral health, and social and financial outcomes as an adult.

5. **ACEs are responsible for a large percentage of adult medicine and common public health and social problems.**

6. **Physical and sexual abuse are no more damaging for long-term physical, mental, or behavioral health or social outcomes than other types of ACEs.** The ACE study showed that it didn't matter what types of ACEs made up an ACE score. For example, an ACE score of 4 that includes divorce, physical neglect, emotional neglect, and emotional abuse will have the same long-term negative outcomes as an ACE score of 4, including sexual abuse, physical abuse, physical neglect, and being raised by a parent with a substance use disorder. This is due to the brain's inability to distinguish

between toxic stress from different types of adversity. As far as the brain is concerned, it's all toxic stress.

Source: 1998 CDC, Adverse Childhood Experiences Study

## People With High ACE Scores Use Food & Substances As A Solution

Once children with high ACE scores (four or higher) become adults, they often cope with their traumatized nervous systems and virulent inner critic by drinking, overeating, doing drugs, smoking, and other high-risk behaviors.

But for survivors, these behaviors aren't the problem; they're an attempt at a solution. This is why telling someone with a high ACE score that their eating, drinking, or smoking is bad for them isn't likely to change their behavior. In truth, these behaviors are their best attempt at regulating a brain, body, and mind chronically dysregulated by childhood trauma.

## High ACE Scores Predict Addiction, Severe Obesity & Negative Mental Health Outcomes

I was shocked the first time I saw how much higher the risk factors are for those of us with ACE scores of 4 or higher compared to people with ACE scores between 0-3 for developing addictions, obesity, and mental health disorders in adulthood.

(I have **bolded** the outcomes I've experienced)

## People With ACE Scores of 4 or Higher Are:

**10.3** times more likely to use injectable drugs

**7.4** times more likely to **be an alcoholic**

**3.5** times more likely to **become severely obese**

**3.23** times more likely to **binge drink**

**3.3** times more likely to **engage in risky sexual behavior**

**2.9** times more likely to **be a current smoker**

## People With ACE Scores of 4 or Higher Are:

**12.2** times more likely to attempt suicide

**5.13** times more likely to **suffer from depression**

**4.0** times more likely to **suffer from an anxiety disorder**

**3.0** times more likely to be diagnosed with severe mental illness

As someone with an ACE score of 6, I initially felt relieved after learning about the link between ACEs, addiction, and mood disorders since it confirmed my addictions and mental health issues were never my fault to begin with. Yet it also made me really sad. I couldn't help but wonder: *Why couldn't I have been born to more functional parents?*

After all, the ACE study proves I probably wouldn't have struggled with my weight or suffered from any addictions if I had zero or just a couple of ACEs. I know it's water under the bridge, but it's hard not to feel ripped off when you see how heavily the deck is stacked against you to experience so many negative outcomes and so much suffering compared to those with zero or just a couple of ACEs.

## Learning How High ACE Scores Are Linked to Negative Health Outcomes

At first, I was shocked to learn that high ACE scores were linked to so many negative health outcomes in adulthood. It didn't add up that experiencing adversity as a child could put a person at risk of developing a serious illness fifty years later.

But things started to make sense once I dug deeper into the science behind the ACE Study and understood the relationship between adversity, toxic stress, the nervous system, and the immune system.

I learned that children who experience one or two ACEs (i.e., one or two adverse events in childhood) for a short period of time could typically recover and grow up without experiencing any lasting harmful effects. However, it's an entirely different story for children with ACE scores of 4 or higher.

Since the fight, flight, or freeze part of children's brains with high ACE scores is bombarded with handling so much stress, it adapts by overdeveloping. This leaves fewer resources for the prefrontal cortex—the part of the brain in charge of impulse control, emotional regulation, and the ability to hold a focus, causing it to under-develop.

As a result, a child exposed to chronic toxic stress ends up with a brain stuck in a fight, flight, or freeze state to cope with their stressful environment. These states drive anxiety, agitation, hypervigilance, and dissociation. The underdeveloped part of this child's brain (the prefrontal cortex) causes them to struggle with emotional regulation, impulse control, and attention.

Over time, when a body, brain, and mind are exposed to chronic levels of toxic stress, the body triggers an overproduction of the stress hormone cortisol. Too much cortisol causes chronic inflammation, which then causes the immune system to break down, setting the body up for chronic illness later in life.

## Having A High ACE Score Is Like Driving A Car Beyond Its Operating Capacity

When I thought about how people with high ACE scores have much higher risks for negative health outcomes as they get older, I thought, *Going through life with a high ACE score is like driving a car at 100mph every day when it's designed for a maximum speed of 60. Since it's not designed to operate at such high speeds, over time, it can't help but wear out and break down.* When you run any kind of vehicle or organism beyond its maximum operating capacity on a regular basis, it's going to wear out sooner, get sick, break down, or die early.

Plus, when you add in the high-risk coping behaviors people with high ACE scores are known to engage in, it increases the risks even more for negative health outcomes in adulthood. This is why a big focus in healing trauma needs to be on accessing therapies and practices to regulate the nervous system to give the brain, body, and mind the best chance for optimal health.

## High ACE Scores & Risks of Developing Negative Health Outcomes

Once again, it was pretty shocking the first time I reviewed how much higher the risk factors are for those of us with an ACE score of 4 or higher for developing negative health outcomes in adulthood.

(I have **bolded** the outcomes I've experienced)

### Negative Physical Health Outcomes:

**4.0** times more likely to suffer from diabetes

**4.0** times more likely to suffer from chronic bronchitis, emphysema, or COPD

**3.0** times more likely to suffer from a stroke

**3.0** times more likely to **suffer from a chronic pain condition**

**3.0** times more likely to suffer from ischemic heart disease

### Autoimmune Disorders:

The risk for autoimmune diseases also increases as ACE scores rise. For every increase in the ACE score of 1 point, the risk of developing an autoimmune disease such as type 1 diabetes, lupus, rheumatoid arthritis, and many others increases by 20%. Also, studies show that those with an ACE score of 2 or higher have a 70% higher chance of being hospitalized due to their autoimmune disorder.

## Staying Healthy: Preventing ACE-Related Health Outcomes

While reviewing the above list, I'm incredibly grateful that I've had just one negative physical health outcome come, (a chronic pain condition) to pass for me. I also feel extremely fortunate to have been able to get the medical care I needed to resolve it to where it's a non-issue today.

I believe a big part of why I am not suffering from more ACE-related health issues is due to my intervening in my food, weight, alcohol, drug, smoking, and codependency issues when I was in my late twenties.

Even though I've done a lot of work to prevent negative ACE-related outcomes, I also recognize, as someone with an ACE score of 6, that to remain healthy, I must continue to make healthy lifestyle choices, stay dedicated to self-care practices, and schedule regular medical checkups to stay on top of my health.

## Calculating My ACE Score

Once I learned about the ACE Study, I was compelled to know my ACE score. Since the ten questions from the ACE survey were included in *The Body Keeps the Score,* I immediately answered each of them and, within a few minutes, calculated my ACE score to be a 5. It would be another five years before I realized I had also experienced physical neglect, which would add an additional ACE to my score, bringing it up to a 6.

## The Types of ACEs I Experienced Before Age Eighteen

1. Being raised by an alcoholic parent
2. Parents separating or divorcing
3. Being raised by a parent with a mental health disorder
4. Emotional neglect
5. Emotional abuse
6. Physical neglect

## Not Realizing Physical Neglect Was Also An ACE For Me

Identifying the first five ACEs while completing my initial ACE survey was easy since they were obvious. But it would be another five years after I calculated my first ACE score before realizing I'd missed identifying physical neglect as an ACE for me.

Since I thought physical neglect could only be counted as an ACE if you lacked food or adequate shelter while growing up, I assumed it wouldn't apply to me. But when I was reviewing the ACE study questions in the final manuscript for this book, I noticed that question five, the one that screens for physical neglect, included language in the second part of it I hadn't fully digested when I first took the ACE survey. Below is the second part of the fifth question that I've since answered yes to.

*1. Did you often feel that you had no one to protect you?, Or 2. Were your parents too drunk or high to take care of you or take you to the doctor if you needed it?*

I don't know why I didn't consider that being a passenger with my mother driving drunk on a regular basis qualified for the question "Did you feel that you had no one to protect you" or "Were your parents too drunk or high to take care of you," but now it's so obvious.

My mom and dad also failed to protect me in my teens through their lack of supervision while I was out getting drunk and high every night and developing my own alcohol and drug addictions. In addition, my dad failed to protect my sister and me by subjecting us to living with my mom's insane drunken behavior for over a decade.

Also, when I was sixteen after my dad had moved out, my mom failed to protect me by bringing strange drunk men home from the bars while I was asleep and alone in my room.

When I took a moment to think about how I could have missed how my parents neglected me by failing to protect me over and over again—I realized it's a perfect example of how those of us raised by alcoholic or dysfunctional parents frequently overlook our parent's neglect as normal since it's all we knew—It was the water we swam in.

## How My ACE Score Predicted My Future

The following ten ACE Study graphs illustrate how my ACE score of 6 predicted the negative outcomes listed below. After each graph title, I share how each specific outcome impacted my life and its status today.

**1. ACE Scores and the Prevalence of Adult Alcoholism:** I developed a severe alcohol use disorder when I was sixteen and have been in long-term recovery for several decades.

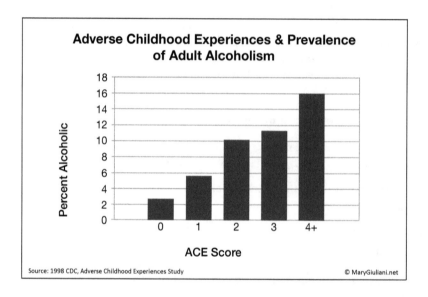

**2. ACE Scores and the Prevalence of Adult Illicit Drug Use:** I used several illicit drugs as an adult and am now in long-term recovery.

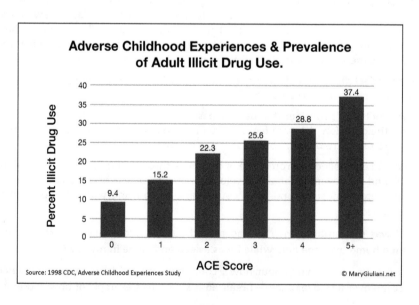

**3. ACE Scores and the Prevalence of Severe Obesity:** Since age six, I struggled with food and weight and became severely obese as an adult. At forty-two, I had gastric bypass weight-loss surgery and lost 160lbs. Between having surgery, doing family of origin & trauma healing work, and creating healthy food, exercise, and self-care plans, I have maintained a healthy weight for over two decades.

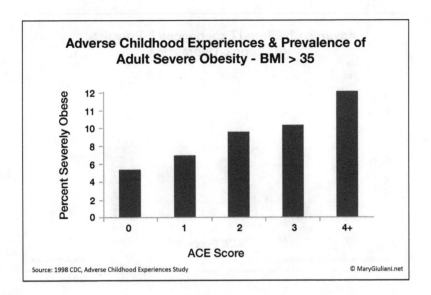

**4. ACE Scores and the Prevalence of Anxiety:** In 1994, I was diagnosed with generalized anxiety disorder and have successfully managed it with antidepressant medication, self-care, and trauma recovery practices and therapies.

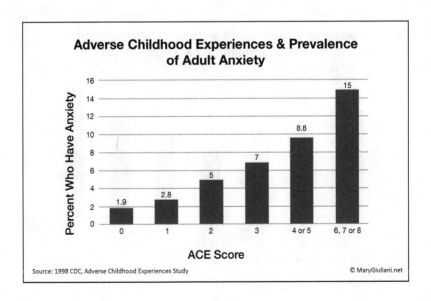

**5. ACE Scores and the Prevalence of Chronic Depression:** I was diagnosed in 1994 with dysthymia, which is persistent depression. I have successfully managed it with antidepressants, self-care, and trauma recovery practices and therapies.

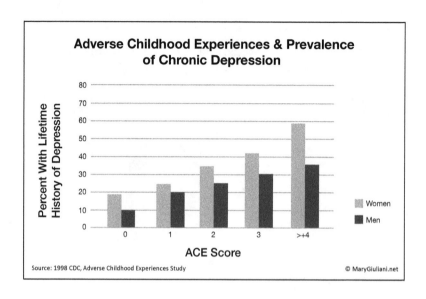

**6. ACE Scores and the Prevalence of Smoking as an Adult:** I began smoking cigarettes at age fifteen and continued until twenty-seven. I used the patch to quit and have been a nonsmoker for several decades.

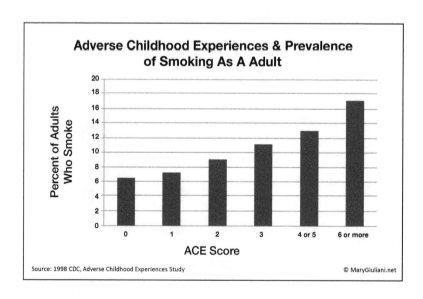

**7. ACE Scores and the Prevalence of Antidepressant Prescriptions 50 Years Later:** I've managed my anxiety and dysthymia using antidepressant medication for about 25 years. I also use self-care, family or origin work, trauma recovery practices, and therapies to manage my mental health.

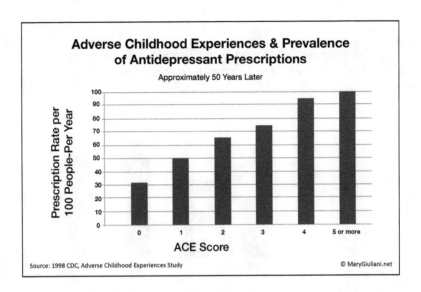

**8. ACE Scores and the Prevalence of Impaired Worker Performance:** When I was actively addicted to alcohol and marijuana, I called in sick several times a month due to hangovers. My work performance and my financial stability also suffered from my active addictions. Since I've been in long-term recovery, I've completely turned around my work performance and have been financially stable for several decades.

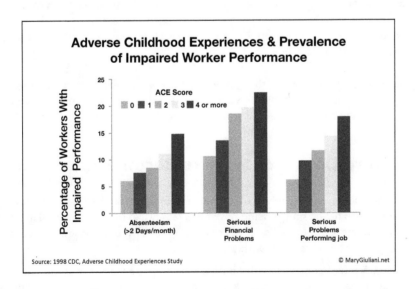

**9. ACE Scores and the Prevalence of Low School Engagement:** School was difficult for me as a child due to my impaired ability to focus, sleep deprivation, and fear of abusive bullies. In high school, I skipped school due to hangovers and my mom keeping me up, to where I came close to lacking the credits to graduate. Since I struggled so much with school, I grew to hate it and, as a result, opted out of college.

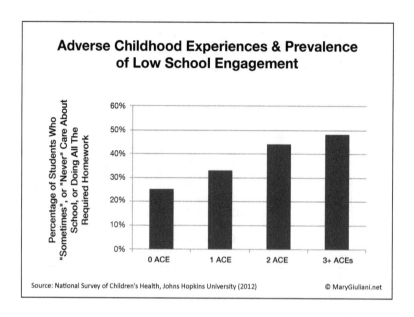

Source: National Survey of Children's Health, Johns Hopkins University (2012)    © MaryGiuliani.net

**10. ACE Scores and the Prevalence of Adult Chronic Pain:** When I was fifty-two, I developed CRPS-complex regional pain syndrome, a chronic pain condition. The burning pain in my feet became so debilitating I opted to have a spinal cord stimulator implanted in my spine for pain management. Thankfully, I've been relatively pain-free for the past ten years. I had no idea at the time that my high ACE score meant my chances of developing a chronic pain condition were 2-3 times that of someone with zero or just a few ACEs.

According to an article by W. Jackson, *Connecting the Dots: How Adverse Childhood Experiences Predispose to Chronic Pain. Pract Pain Manag.* 2020;20(3).

> Multiple studies from around the globe have shown a dose-response relationship between ACEs and later development of chronic pain. The presence of such early trauma appears to confer a two- to three-fold risk of later development of chronic pain.

# Your ACE Score Does Not Have to Become Your Destiny

It was overwhelming and depressing when I first began to process all I had learned about ACEs. It was shocking to see how much havoc simply being raised in a family like mine had caused in my life. Yet, once I took the time to learn more about ACEs, it was reassuring to learn that most of the negative outcomes are preventable or can be turned around with the right support.

My story exemplifies that someone with an ACE score of 6 can overcome the adversity from their childhood and go on to lead a healthy, happy life with meaningful relationships and a fulfilling career. The most beneficial thing I've done to prevent or turn around negative ACE-related outcomes was to get the support I needed to stop my high-risk coping behaviors and replace them with healthier alternatives and a resilience-building lifestyle.

### Interventions I've Implemented to Mitigate Negative ACE-Related Outcomes

- I quit drinking alcohol and smoking marijuana by attending AA, NA & MA meetings and working the 12 steps.
- I quit smoking cigarettes.
- I let go of unhealthy relationships and embraced connecting with healthy, growth-oriented people by attending Codependents Anonymous meetings and other positive organizations.
- I set healthy boundaries with my family members, friends, and employers.
- I manage my anxiety and dysthymia with an antidepressant and self-care.
- I manage my physical health by reaching a healthy weight with weight-loss surgery and maintaining it through healing my trauma and having a structured food, exercise, and self-care plan.
- I manage my stress levels and self-regulation by implementing trauma-healing therapies and recovery-oriented practices and maintaining healthy, nurturing relationships.

### Why I No Longer Suffer from Any Significant Negative ACE-Related Outcomes

If I hadn't gotten help to make each of these interventions happen and been focused on building resilience and engaging in healthy relationships, there's no doubt that many more of the negative outcomes of a high ACE score would have come to pass for me.

I'm extremely grateful that I no longer suffer from any of the previous or predicted negative outcomes for someone my age with an ACE score of 6.

For this reason, I can't stress enough that to prevent future negative ACE-related health and social outcomes, survivors must stay committed to intervening in existing high-risk coping behaviors and embracing a trauma-healing and resilience-oriented lifestyle.

### You Can Heal

One of the most hopeful messages I got while learning about childhood trauma was that it's treatable and that I could heal. Therefore, having a high ACE score doesn't mean you're destined for a life filled with pain and suffering.

If you're willing to get into action about your healing, you can expect to feel better and see positive changes in your life. Just like anything you make a commitment to, the more you dedicate yourself to working on healing your trauma, the better your life will get and the more satisfaction and fulfillment you will experience.

# Taking the ACE Questionnaire

Completing the ACE questionnaire was a game-changer for me. It really opened my eyes to how much I had been impacted by the adversity I'd experienced growing up. It made me have much more compassion for myself and reaffirmed why finding trauma-based therapies to heal was so important.

Even if you didn't have a difficult childhood, taking the ACE questionnaire will still be helpful since it will give you a better idea of what types of adversity and/or household dysfunction cause children to develop C-PTSD, which will help you become an advocate for preventing and healing it.

# ACE QUESTIONNAIRE

**Directions:** Add a "1" to each question if your answer is yes and leave blank if the answer is no. Add the total number of yes answers to arrive at your ACE score.

## While you were growing up, during your first 18 years of life:

**1.** Did a parent or other adult in the household often swear at you, insult you, put you down, or humiliate you?
Or
Act in a way that made you afraid that you might be physically hurt?
If yes enter 1 ___1___

**2.** Did a parent or other adult in the household often push, grab, slap, or throw something at you?
Or
Ever hit you so hard that you had marks on your body or were injured?
If yes enter 1 _____

**3.** Did an adult or person at least 5 years older than you ever touch or fondle you or have you touch their body in a sexual way?
Or
Try to or actually have oral, anal, or vaginal sex with you?
If yes enter 1 _____

**4.** Did you often feel that no one in your family loved you or thought you were important or special?
Or
Your family didn't look out for each other, feel close to each other, or support each other?
If yes enter 1 ___1___

**5.** Did you often feel that you didn't have enough to eat, had to wear dirty clothes, and had no one to protect you?
Or
Your parents were too drunk or high to take care of you or take you to the doctor if you needed it?
If yes enter 1 _____

**6.** Were your parents ever separated or divorced?
If yes enter 1 _____

**7.** Was your mother or stepmother: Often pushed, grabbed, slapped, or had something thrown at her?
Or
Sometimes or often kicked, bitten, hit with a fist, or hit with something hard?
Or
Ever been repeatedly hit over at least a few minutes or threatened with a gun or knife?
If yes enter 1 _____

**8.** Did you live with anyone who was a problem drinker or alcoholic or who used street drugs?
If yes enter 1 _____

**9.** Was a household member depressed or mentally ill, or did a household member attempt suicide?
If yes enter 1 _____

**10.** Did a household member go to prison?
If yes enter 1 _____

**Add up your YES answers:** ___2___ **This is your ACE score**

Source: CDC-Centers for Disease Control and Prevention, 1998

## How Resilience Factors Can Offset the Negative Outcomes of a High ACE Score

When I first learned having an ACE score of 6 meant my chances of experiencing serious negative health, behavioral and social outcomes were between 2-12 times greater than those with zero or just a few ACEs, I was pretty freaked out.

But after I took a deeper dive into understanding how ACEs and the risk of negative health outcomes worked, I discovered that my ACE score alone wasn't the most accurate way to assess my health risks. I learned that a more accurate way to assess my risks was to include my resilience score and also take into account the number of positive childhood experiences (PCEs) I had growing up.

## What's Your Resilience Score?

Studies show that resilience and positive childhood experiences can offset high ACE scores' negative health and social outcomes. The below questionnaire is designed to assess the strength of your resilience based on what you experienced growing up. To determine your resilience score, answer the questions below:

# RESILIENCE QUESTIONNAIRE

**Directions:** Choose one of the five answers for each question:

      1          2              3            4           5

**(Definitely true)  (Probably true)  (Not sure)  (Probably not true)  (Definitely not true)**

1.  I believe that my mother loved me when I was little. *DT* 1
2.  I believe that my father loved me when I was little. 3
3.  When I was little, other people helped my mother and father take care of me, and they seemed to love me. 5
4.  I've heard that when I was an infant, someone in my family enjoyed playing with me, and I enjoyed it, too. 3
5.  When I was a child, there were relatives in my family who made me feel better if I was sad or worried. 3
6.  When I was a child, neighbors or my friends' parents seemed to like me. 2
7.  When I was a child, teachers, coaches, youth leaders, or ministers were there to help me. 2
8.  Someone in my family cared about how I was doing in school. 1
9.  My family, neighbors, and friends often talked about making our lives better. 5
10. We had rules in our house and were expected to keep them. 1
11. When I felt bad, I could almost always find someone I trusted to talk to. 4
12. As a youth, people noticed that I was capable and could get things done. 3
13. I was independent and a go-getter. 5
14. I believed that life is what you make it. 2

**How many of the 14 questions were answered as "Definitely True" or "Probably True"?**

___6___  **This is your Resilience score**

Source: This questionnaire was developed by the early childhood service providers, pediatricians, psychologists, and health advocates of Southern Kennebec Healthy Start, Augusta, Maine, in 2006 and updated in February 2013. Two psychologists in the group, Mark Rains and Kate McClinn, came up with the 14 statements with editing suggestions by the other members of the group. The scoring system was modeled after the ACE Study questions. The content of the questions was based on a number of research studies from the literature over the past 40 years, including that of Emmy Werner and others. Its purpose is limited to parenting education. It was not developed for research.

## How Positive Childhood Experiences (PCEs) Can Offset A High ACE Score

PCEs are considered protective factors known to offset negative ACE-related mental and physical health and social outcomes. According to Dr. Christina Bethell's research, the following seven positive childhood experiences can offset the negative outcomes of a high ACE score.

# POSITIVE CHILDHOOD EXPERIENCES QUESTIONNAIRE

**Directions:** Up until you were 18 years old, answer yes or no to the following statements:

1. You were able to talk to your family about your feelings  N
2. Your family stood by you during hard times  Y
3. You participated in community traditions  Y
4. You felt a sense of belonging in high school  N
5. You felt supported by a friend  N
6. There were 2 adults (not parents) who took an interest in you  N
7. You felt safe and protected by an adult in your home  Y

**How many of the 7 statements can you answer as a yes?**

_3___ **This is your Positive Childhood Experiences score**

Source: Dr. Christina Bethel

Resilience research shows that our brains are plastic and can heal through positive childhood experiences (PCEs) and resilience-building practices such as eating nutritious foods, getting adequate hydration, sleep and exercise, being in nature, and connecting with safe friends.

Early intervention for food, smoking, substance misuse, and other high-risk- behavior also mitigates the risks of negative health outcomes associated with a high ACE score.

## My ACE, Positive Childhood Experiences, & Resilience Scores

After answering the questions from the ACE, Resilience, and Positive Childhood Experiences Questionnaires, I calculated my ACE score to be 6, my Resilience score to be 5, and my PCE score to be a 2.

According to the ACE study, an ACE score of 4 or higher is considered a high ACE score. This is due to the ACE study proving that people with ACE scores of 4 or higher have much higher rates of negative health and social outcomes in adulthood than those with zero or lower ACE scores.

However, research has also shown that the more positive childhood experiences-PCEs and the higher the resilience a child has, the more they can offset the risk of experiencing negative health and social outcomes from a high ACE score.

## What Do Your ACE, PCE and Resilience Scores Mean?

Although I have not found any hard or fast rules to measure PCE or resilience scores in terms of their exact ability to offset specific negative ACE related outcomes due to a high ACE score, the value I've found in completing the PCE and resilience questionnaire has been twofold.

1. Completing the Positive Childhood Experiences and the Resilience Questionnaires have helped me identify which areas in my life I received support in and which ones I didn't while growing up. This has directed me to focus on shoring up my resilience in the areas where I didn't receive support as a child.

2.    Learning I have a ACE score of 6 (which is high,) a PCE score of 2 (which is low) and a Resilience score of 6 (which is medium) has made me aware that I have a much higher risk of experiencing negative health and social outcomes as I age. I've put this knowledge to use by making healthy lifestyle choices, staying committed to self-care, and making sure I get in for regular checkups with my doctor to stay on top of my health.

## Handling Negative ACE-Related Health or Social Outcomes

Once you have added up your ACE, PCE, and resilience scores, it's important to look at what, if any, negative ACE-related health, behavioral, or social outcomes have come to pass for you and then look at what actions you can take to eliminate or mitigate them. Doing so will automatically improve your ability to avoid additional negative ACE-related outcomes down the road.

Since I had already intervened in several of my ACE-related negative outcomes by getting into recovery with substances, smoking, food, weight, anxiety, depression, and codependency, I didn't need to focus on these issues.

The primary focus of my trauma healing has been on finding ways to regulate my nervous system, minimizing stress in my life, healing the relational aspects of my trauma, as well as implementing trauma-based self-care and resilience-building practices.

## What To Do If You Have an ACE Score of 4 or Higher

If you have an ACE score of 4 or higher, you're likely dealing with nervous system dysregulation since it is the most common symptom of C-PTSD. This can manifest as anxiety, depression, relationship difficulties, addictions, guilt, shame, chronic illness and pain, and other symptoms I've discussed throughout this book.

The first thing to remember is these symptoms are not your fault. However, if you're interested in experiencing more fulfillment and joy in your life, it's your responsibility to heal or manage them. The good news is complex trauma is treatable; therefore, if you're willing to get into action about your healing, you can experience significant improvements in your life. I am a living example of this.

The first step to getting on track with healing is to gain an in-depth understanding of the nature of C-PTSD. The second step is to learn what treatments, practices, and support systems are available to give yourself the best chance at optimal healing and recovery.

To accomplish both of these steps, you'll need to read this book in its entirety. When you get toward the end of Part III, you'll be directed on how to map out your trauma healing and recovery journey. You'll also find dozens of resources in the appendix to support you throughout your healing journey.

# THE ACE STUDY REVEALED CHILDHOOD TRAUMA IS THE GRAVEST HEALTH CRISIS IN THE U.S.

When the CDC calculated the costs to the various sectors of our society to manage and treat those suffering from the negative outcomes of childhood abuse and neglect throughout their lives, they were stunned to realize it exceeded even the astronomical costs of cancer and heart disease combined!

I was completely blown away when I read the data the CDC compiled below about how much pain and suffering could be prevented if we focused on preventing and healing childhood trauma.

### How Addiction, Depression, Domestic Violence & Suicide Would Plummet By Preventing Childhood Trauma

1.    Depression would drop by more than **50%**

2.    Alcoholism would drop by **66%**

3.    Suicide rates would drop by **75%**

4.    IV drug use would drop by **75%**

5.    Domestic violence would drop by **75%**

What's truly astonishing as well as totally heartbreaking is even though the ACE study has shown for over twenty years that preventing child abuse and neglect is the single most effective way to prevent mental illness, drug and alcohol abuse, smoking, severe obesity, diabetes, heart disease, cancer, stroke, domestic violence, and suicide, it has not prompted any major campaigns or initiatives to prevent childhood trauma or to heal the long-term effects it causes for millions of people.

This tragedy illustrates how powerful ignorance, shame, secrecy, and social taboo are when it comes to adults facing the fact that children are being neglected and abused far more often than most people realize or are willing to admit. It's also a call to action for us all to do what we can to help prevent and heal childhood trauma.

# WANT TO HELP PREVENT & HEAL CHILDHOOD TRAUMA? TAKE THE ACE QUESTIONNAIRE

Whether or not you believe you experienced adversity or trauma growing up, the benefit of learning your ACE score is in how it helps identify how what you experienced as a child may be affecting your mental, physical or behavioral health as an adult and what you can do to heal. To take the ACE questionnaire, see the previous section of this chapter.

The first step to overcoming the tragedy of childhood trauma is to understand that it's not about blaming or shaming parents. It's about facing the truth that children have essential emotional, physical, and relational needs. When these needs go unmet, there are predictable negative outcomes, and trauma is one of them. The good news is trauma is preventable and treatable.

However, it can't be prevented or treated unless we are willing to face the fact that it exists. By taking steps to prevent and heal childhood trauma, we give ourselves, those we love, and those we come in contact with the best chance to thrive vs. being relegated to a life of struggle and survival.

One of my intentions in writing this book is to raise awareness about ACEs and help people understand that if they want to help prevent and heal childhood trauma, they can start by taking the ACE survey and asking their family members and friends to take it too.

Even if you haven't experienced any major adversities growing up, by taking the ACE questionnaire you'll become aware of what types of adversity drive the chronic toxic stress that causes children to develop C-PTSD. And being aware of how trauma develops and impacts people throughout their lives will empower you to pass this vital information on to help prevent trauma and support survivors in healing.

To support your family and friends in becoming trauma informed you can send them to the below link to get their ACE Score by completing the ACE Questionnaire. https://marygiuliani.net/adverse-childhood-experience-ace-questionnaire.

It takes a village to prevent and heal C-PTSD. I'm committed to being part of the solution, and I hope you will be too. If you've chosen to join me I want to thank you in advance for your support by taking the ACE Questionnaire and sending the above link to your friends and family to take it as well.

# CHAPTER 18

———

# LEARNING DRINKING & SMOKING MARIJUANA WERE A NORMAL RESPONSE TO AN ABNORMAL ENVIRONMENT

Ask not why the addiction but why the pain?

—Gabor Maté, M.D.

As I have shared throughout my story, addiction has been a persistent theme throughout my life. The toxic shame I've carried, believing I was weak and a failure for having addictions has been equally as damaging as the addictions themselves.

My need to compulsively use food to self-soothe began when I was just five years old. I added alcohol, marijuana, and cigarettes to the mix of my self-soothing strategies when I was sixteen.

One of the most tragic things I've found about addiction is how misunderstood and mischaracterized it is in our culture. My intention with this chapter is to shed light on the direct link between complex PTSD and addiction. I'll also discuss the chronic brain disease nature of addiction and the many life-changing insights I've learned about how genetics, biology, neuroscience, and childhood adversity interact and manifest as addiction.

## How Common Addiction Is

If there's one thing I've learned while researching alcohol and drug addiction, it's how common it is. Sadly, over 20 million Americans suffer from alcohol and substance use disorders. Of the 20 million, 16 million (or 80%) are addicted to alcohol. The harsh reality is that 8.4% of adults (almost one in ten) in our country suffer from a serious addiction or struggle with drugs and/or alcohol.

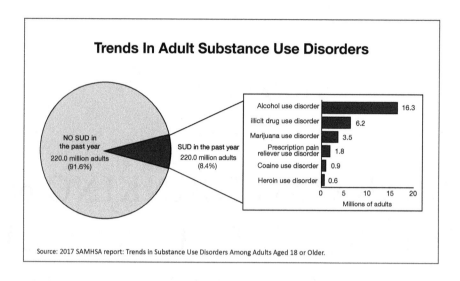

Source: 2017 SAMHSA report: Trends in Substance Use Disorders Among Adults Aged 18 or Older.

## How Many Lives Are Lost Per Year to Addiction and Obesity

It was shocking to learn that in the United States, one of the richest countries in the world, we lose 549,000 people every year to addiction. These addictions include alcohol, drugs, and the comorbidities of obesity due to food addiction.

This means that over 1,500 people die every day due to addiction. This is comparable to experiencing the loss of life from a 9/11 three times a week, every week. When I broke down the annual death rate in the U.S. into the smallest increments of time, I was shocked to learn that sixty-two people die every hour of every day due to addiction. This means one person dies every minute due to addiction in our country. This doesn't even account for the millions of family members left heartbroken due to losing those they love to alcohol, drugs, or obesity-related causes.

According to the National Institute of Health, out of these 549,000 annual deaths, 300,000 are due to obesity-related causes. According to the CDC, 140,000 are alcohol-related, and 109,000 are due to drug-related causes. Close to 70% of deaths due to drug related causes are opioid-related. Although the opioid addiction epidemic is tragic in its own right, what I find just as tragic, if not even more so, is that alcohol claims 50% more lives than opioids, yet its scourge is barely noticed or acknowledged.

I believe this is partly because, in the U.S., the vast majority of adults drink alcohol regularly. It's been an acceptable drug that's been embedded in our rituals, traditions, and culture for hundreds of years. In fact, it's the only drug when you say you don't do it; people often ask you why, and some even ask if you have a "problem" with it. Once you answer them, they almost always feel the need to tell you they don't drink that much. I don't know if it's to convince me, themselves, or us both that they don't have a drinking problem. What I do know is broaching the topic of addiction seems to trigger some pretty interesting responses in people.

The multibillion-dollar alcohol industry also has a huge stake in keeping Americans in the dark about how one in ten customers will become addicted and that 140,000 die each year from consuming their product.

## 50% of Americans Believe Addiction is a Choice

Why is it that when we lose one person every minute of every day due to alcohol, drugs, and obesity, we don't respond as we did with the 3,000 people we lost on 9/11? I believe it is because we viewed the people we lost on 9/11 as victims since it wasn't their fault they were killed by terrorists. In contrast, half of the U.S. population believes addiction is a choice, and thus it's the addict's own fault they died.

This isn't just my opinion. It's based on a 2019 study about people's views on addiction conducted by Pew Charitable Trusts. According to that study, half of the U.S. population believes that it's the alcohol, drug, or food addict's own fault they died because they made a free choice to kill themselves slowly, or sometimes quickly, through engaging in their addiction. Below is an excerpt from an article by Judith Grisel, Ph.D., and Paul DiLorenzo regarding this tragic misunderstanding.

### The American Misunderstanding of Addiction Continues

For the Association and the National Institutes of Health. The behavioral manifestation that we call addiction results from a constellation of complex causes, including genetic risks, developmental experiences, social and cultural environments, and interactions among these factors. Labeling the multifaceted disorder, a disease is not an attempt to justify bad behavior. Instead, it reflects our best science. Alterations in brain activity — often beyond the scope of individual influence, let alone control — enhance probabilities for illegal and illogical actions.

## How the Stigma of Addiction Has Taken Millions of Lives

If 50% of Americans believe addiction is a choice, then it makes sense that half of the U.S. population wouldn't have compassion for those who suffer from it. It also makes sense why they wouldn't support initiatives that could help prevent addiction and help those with substance use and eating disorders get into treatment.

During my research for this book, I was shocked to learn that only 7% of people suffering from alcohol or drug addiction seek treatment. The main reason is due to the stigma of addiction. Simply identifying as someone with an addiction puts you at risk of being passed over as a friend, a mate, or even as an employee. It's no wonder so many find it hard to admit they have an addiction. Who wants to sign up to be considered weak, irresponsible, or untrustworthy and potentially lose friends, a mate, and even a job?

What happens to the 93% of those suffering from addiction day in and day out who don't seek treatment? According to a study by the National Institute on Alcohol Abuse and Alcoholism (NIAAA), 25% will get sober or become moderate drinkers or drug users without treatment (through AA or rehab programs).

This still leaves over 68%, or 13 million people, struggling with substance addictions. What's happening to them? All I know is what I went through while in active addiction, which was pure, unadulterated hell.

## Discovering Addiction Is a Trauma Response

The first thing I noticed about Dr. Gabor Maté was his empathy and compassion for people suffering from addiction. In fact, he was the first authority figure and doctor I'd ever seen view addiction through the lens of it being a natural adaptation to cope with the pain of underlying childhood trauma.

He made a profound difference in my having a deeper level of compassion for myself by helping me see that my struggle with addiction wasn't because I was weak, irresponsible, or defective but because I'd been traumatized.

It made sense why Maté was so compassionate toward those suffering from addiction. He'd worked for twelve years in the downtown eastside of Vancouver, Canada, an area with more IV drug users per capita than any other area in the world. His patients suffered from hard-core IV drug addiction, alcoholism, mental illness, and HIV.

After experiencing so much contempt and judgment from my own father and our overall culture, who believe addiction is a choice, it was so comforting to learn from Maté that addiction is a survivor's best attempt to cope with a brain, body, and mind profoundly dysregulated by trauma.

Listening to Maté's book *In the Realm of Hungry Ghosts: Close Encounters with Addiction,* where he cites dozens of studies proving addiction is a physiological and psychological trauma response, not only changed my view of addiction, it profoundly changed my view of myself.

## My Dad's View on Alcoholism

My dad's view on alcoholism was in stark contrast to Maté's. One year during a family holiday dinner, when the topic of alcoholism came up, my dad chimed in, "I don't believe alcoholism is something you inherit or it's a disease. People who can't handle their liquor are just weak. They're just drunks, that's all."

I was so hurt and angry after hearing him make such insensitive remarks knowing full well how I'd struggled with alcohol. Given that I'd been in recovery for over a decade, he could have said how proud he was of me for getting sober and turning my life around. But instead, he felt the need to slam people like me who, in his mind, don't have the "strength" to drink moderately as he and other people do. I walked away from that gathering feeling really sad for having a dad who, one more time, was so out of touch with how hurtful his remarks could be.

## How Trauma Drives Addiction

According to Maté, people turn to addictive substances or behaviors as a solution to cope with emotional pain rooted in childhood trauma. In the below excerpt from his book *In the Realm of Hungry Ghosts: Close Encounters with Addiction,* he discusses the relationship between childhood trauma and addiction.

> Those who grew up in homes where loving care was inconsistent, unstable, or absent do not develop the crucial neural wiring for emotional resilience.
>
> When you don't have love and connection in your life when you are very, very young, then those important brain circuits just don't develop properly— and their brains are then susceptible when they do the drugs.
>
> Drugs make people with dysregulated brain waves feel normal and even loved. As one patient said to me, "When I did heroin for the first time, it felt like a warm, soft hug, just like a mother hugging a baby."

Maté cites several peer-reviewed studies *In the Realm of Hungry Ghosts,* revealing that brain circuits responsible for impulse, stress, and emotional regulation are all impaired in people who struggle with addiction.

Maté also states that although substance addiction begins as a response to helping soothe the pain of trauma after the addiction gets started and takes hold, it changes the brain and takes on the characteristics of a brain disease. These characteristics include tolerance, overwhelming cravings, and the inability to moderate or stop despite life-damaging consequences. However, addiction always begins as an attempt to solve the problem of emotional pain due to what we didn't get when we were very small.

This is why Maté repeatedly states in his talks that addiction isn't the problem. The actual problem is the unbearable emotional pain due to unhealed C-PTSD. The addiction is an attempt at a solution. Thus, when we address and solve the real problem, the emotional pain due to unhealed childhood trauma, we'll solve the problem of addiction.

As I continued studying the link between C-PTSD and addiction, I discovered another doctor that holds a similar philosophy as Maté and who is getting phenomenal results treating patients in his opioid addiction treatment center.

## Is It Addiction, Or Is It Ritualized Compulsive Comfort-Seeking?

I had another major aha moment when I read an article about a doctor redefining addiction and providing a revolutionary approach to treating it.

**Addiction doc says: It's not the drugs. It's the ACEs...adverse childhood experiences.**

Source: Jane Ellen Stevens. 5-2-17, Acestoohigh.com.

He says: Addiction shouldn't be called "addiction." It should be called "ritualized compulsive comfort-seeking."

He says: Ritualized compulsive comfort-seeking (what traditionalists call addiction) is a *normal* response to the adversity experienced in childhood, just like bleeding is a normal response to being stabbed.

He says, "The solution to changing the illegal or unhealthy ritualized compulsive comfort-seeking behavior of opioid addiction is to address a person's adverse childhood experiences (ACEs) individually and in group therapy; treat people with respect; provide medication assistance in the form of buprenorphine, an opioid used to treat opioid addiction; and help them find a ritualized compulsive comfort-seeking behavior that won't kill them or put them in jail.

This "he" isn't some hippy-dippy new-age dreamer. He is Dr. Daniel Sumrok, director of the Center for Addiction Sciences at the University of Tennessee Health Science Center's College of Medicine. The center is the first to receive the Center of Excellence designation from the Addiction Medicine Foundation, a national organization that accredits physician training in addiction medicine. Sumrok is also one of the first 106 physicians in the U.S. to become board-certified in addiction medicine by the American Board of Medical Specialties.

Sumrok, a family physician and former U.S. Army Green Beret who's served the rural area around McKenzie, TN, for the last 28 years, combines the latest science of addiction and applies it to his patients, most of whom are addicted to opioids — but also to alcohol, food, sex, gambling, etc. He sees them in the center's two outpatient clinics: his clinic, which the Center for Addiction Science has taken over as its rural clinic, and another that opened recently in downtown Memphis.

Sumrok has pieced together the ingredients for a revolutionary approach to addiction. It's an approach that's advocated by many of the leading thinkers in addiction and trauma, including Drs. Gabor Maté, Lance Dodes, and Bessel van der Kolk. Surprisingly, it's a fairly simple formula: Treat people with respect instead of blaming or shaming them. Listen intently to what they have to say. Integrate the healing traditions of the culture in which they live. Use prescription drugs, if necessary. And integrate adverse childhood experiences science: ACEs.

"My patients seem to respond really well to this," he says.

Reading this article gave me an immediate sense of relief. It was due to finally hearing someone speak the truth about why I ate, drank, and used drugs the way I did. It wasn't because I was hedonistic, irresponsible, defective, or due to being genetically predisposed to addiction.

It was due to my being a trauma survivor who was doing the best she knew how to soothe her pain. It felt so validating to hear a leading doctor in the addiction field state that there wasn't anything wrong with me. In fact, I learned my compulsive need to seek comfort through food and substances was a normal response to living through the hell of my childhood.

It was also exciting to see that his approach to effective treatment involves treating people with respect, addressing their adverse childhood experiences both individually and in a group setting, providing medication assistance where necessary, and helping them find a ritualized compulsive comfort-seeking behavior that won't kill them or put them in jail—All of which are sorely lacking in the majority of today's treatment centers and 12 step programs. My hope is that the results he's been getting with this approach will speak for themselves and be adopted on a much broader scale.

## The Direct Link Between Opioid Misuse, Deaths & High ACE Scores

I've watched several programs on the opioid addiction epidemic we've been grappling with in the U.S. and am continually disheartened that childhood trauma, complex PTSD, or ACEs is rarely if ever, mentioned as a root cause underlying it. I certainly agree that pharmaceutical companies played a big role in making these highly addictive drugs available. However, if we don't get down to what makes one person unable to stop taking them and another easily able to take or leave them, we won't solve the root cause driving this crisis.

We have science-based data proving the link between opioid misuse and high ACE scores, yet there seems to be a disconnect in our overall society to linking the two. An excerpt from the below study, *Adolescent Opioid Misuse Attributable to Adverse Childhood Experience*\* speaks to this issue.

> There was a significant graded relationship between number of ACEs and recent opioid misuse among adolescents. More than 70% of recent adolescent opioid misuse in our study population was attributable to ACEs.
>
> Our results are consistent with previous population attributable fractions (PAF) estimates for illicit drug use in adults: 56%–64% of drug use outcomes were associated with childhood adversity.[17] The high PAFs for individual ACEs highlight emotional abuse and neglect's considerable contributions to adolescent opioid misuse at a population level. These forms of childhood maltreatment are often underappreciated as important risk factors for negative health outcomes.[39]
>
> Source PubMed on 5-11-20" Elizabeth A. Swedo, MD,[1,2] Steven A. Sumner, MD,[2] Sietske de Fijter, MS,[3] Luke Werhan, MPA,[3] Kirkland Norris, MPH,[4] Jennifer L. Beauregard, Ph.D.,[1,5,6] Martha P. Montgomery, MD,[1,3,7] Erica B. Rose, Ph.D.,[1,8,9] Susan D. Hillis, Ph.D.,[2,10] and Greta M. Massetti, PhD

I was so happy to see that the researchers from this study not only provided data on a direct link between high ACE scores and opioid misuse but also highlighted how emotional abuse and neglect are underappreciated high-risk factors for negative health outcomes, with one of them being opioid misuse.

## Addiction Is Not Limited To Alcohol, Drugs, or Food

In our culture, addiction is most often associated with people who have alcohol or drug problems, yet we fail to point out that there are dozens of other addictions. People who compulsively work, eat, shop, clean, watch porn, play video games, constantly stay busy, or are always on their phones aren't even considered to be practicing an addiction. In fact, some are even celebrated for their behavior, such as those who compulsively work, clean, and use social media. Dr. Gabor Maté speaks to this in his article *Beyond Drugs: The Universal Experience of Addiction*.

> Most addicted people use no drugs at all. Addiction cannot be understood if we restrict our vision of it to substances, legal or illicit.
>
> Addiction is manifested in any behavior that a person craves, finds temporary relief or pleasure in but suffers negative consequences as a result of, and yet has difficulty giving up. In brief: craving, relief, pleasure, suffering, impaired control. Note that this definition is not restricted to drugs but could encompass almost any human behavior, from sex to eating to shopping to gambling to extreme sports to TV to compulsive internet use: the list is endless.
>
> "I'm not going to ask you what you were addicted to," I often say to people, "nor when, nor for how long. Only whatever your addictive focus, what did it offer you? What did you like about it? What, in the short term, did it give you that you craved or liked so much?" And universally, the answers are: "It helped me escape emotional pain... helped me deal with stress... gave me peace of mind... a sense of connection with others... a sense of control."

Such answers illuminate that the addiction is neither a choice nor a disease but originates in a human being's desperate attempt to solve a problem: the problem of emotional pain, of overwhelming stress, of lost connection, of loss of control, of a deep discomfort with the self. In short, it is a forlorn attempt to solve the problem of human pain. Hence my mantra: "The question is not why the addiction, but why the pain?"

And the source of pain is always and invariably to be found in a person's lived experience, beginning with childhood. Childhood trauma is the template for addiction — any addiction. All addictions are attempts to escape the deep pain of the hurt child, attempts temporarily soothing but ultimately futile. This is no less true of the socially successful workaholic, such as I have been, than of the inveterate shopper, sexual rover, gambler, abject street-bound substance user, or stay-at-home mom and user of opioids.

Not only is the urge to escape pain shared by all addicts, substance users or not, the same brain circuits are involved in all addictions, from shopping to eating to dependence on heroin and other opioids. The same brain circuits, the same brain systems involving pleasure and reward and incentive, the same neurochemicals — not to mention the same emotional dynamics of shame and lack of self-worth, and the same behaviors of denial and dishonesty and subterfuge.

It is time to realize, then, addiction is neither a choice nor an inherited disease but a psychological and physiological response to painful life experiences. It can take many forms, but whatever form it takes:

- it employs the same neurological pathways and emotional patterns;
- the damage it does extends well beyond the suffering imposed by drug use specifically;
- to ostracize the drug addict as somehow different from the rest of us is arrogant and arbitrary,
- to treat the addiction, which is a symptom, without treating the pain that underlies it is to deal in effects rather than in causes and therefore dooms many to ongoing cycles of suffering.

## Love Addiction

When a survivor is in the grip of an addiction to drugs or alcohol, it's typically obvious. But what is often less obvious is survivors who stay in abusive or other types of dysfunctional or unfulfilling relationships even though it's hurting them. This can account for why some sibling survivors grow up to struggle with substance or food addictions, and others develop addictions to dysfunctional or abusive relationships.

Although many people don't see someone who stays in an abusive, dysfunctional, or unfulfilling personal or professional relationship as practicing an addiction, when you look at what constitutes an addiction by reviewing Gabor Maté's definition, you may see these types of relationships in a different light.

Addiction is manifested in any behavior that a person:

- Craves, finds temporary relief or pleasure from
- Suffers negative consequences as a result of engaging with it
- Yet has difficulty giving it up

With this definition of addiction in mind, it becomes clear that continuing to engage in abusive (emotionally or physically) or unfulfilling personal or professional relationships could also be considered addictions.

Maintaining a relationship with emotionally and/or physically abusive or neglectful spouses, family members, friends, or bosses can be another form of addiction for those suffering from untreated C-PTSD. We often form and stay in these types of relationships for the same reasons we become addicted to substances or other compulsive behavior. They satisfy the same goal, which is to numb or distract us from the emotional pain (conscious or unconscious) of untreated C-PTSD.

If we witnessed conflict-ridden, abusive, dysfunctional, or unfulfilling relationships between our parents growing up, when we find similar types of people as adults, we often feel attracted to them since they feel like home to us. Although it can feel wonderful in the beginning, once the honeymoon is over and the relationship becomes abusive, neglectful, or dysfunctional, it's often difficult for survivors to leave even though the relationship is hurting them.

Just like people who struggle with substance addictions, the first step in recovery is coming out of denial, and the second step is reaching out for help. See the appendix for support groups if you are struggling in your relationships.

## How the ACE Study Revealed the Link Between Trauma and Alcoholism

Upon first seeing the below graph illustrating that the risk of someone with an ACE (Adverse Childhood Experiences) score of 4 or higher is 700% more likely to become an alcoholic than someone with a 0 ACE score, I sat back in my chair and just sighed.

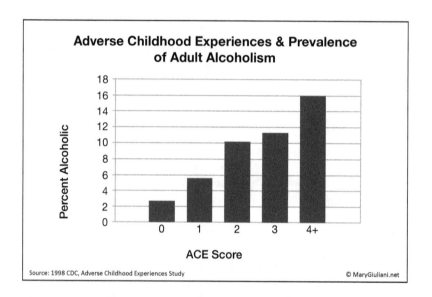

Although I hadn't had a drink for close to twenty years and was no longer struggling with alcohol, it still made me really sad to see how the toxic stress I was forced to live in for so long growing up in my family had set me up for so much pain and suffering with alcohol.

But when I took a moment and looked at the graph again, I noticed a sense of relief. Understanding why I felt the need to turn to alcohol helped me realize that I wasn't weak or a failure. Instead, I was just someone trying to find a solution to cope with the unbearable pain of living with unresolved childhood trauma.

## How Active Addiction Is In & Of Itself Traumatizing

Another critical aspect of addiction is to recognize how it perpetuates trauma. Practicing a serious addiction is engaging in a relationship with a substance or behavior you can't predict or control, and that causes life-damaging consequences.

Just like childhood trauma, being in the throes of addiction makes you feel powerless and trapped in a dynamic that's hurting you, keeping the cycle of trauma alive until you find healing and recovery.

In addition, active addiction creates fertile ground for injuries, accidents, fights, and other violent activities and crimes. It can also drive antisocial behavior, resulting in ethical, legal, and financial consequences that are traumatizing for survivors, their families, friends, and those they come in contact with.

## Addiction Is A Chronic Brain Disease

> Addiction is a chronic disease of the brain, and it's one that we have to treat the way we would any other chronic illness: with skill, compassion, and with urgency.
>
> —U.S. Surgeon General Vivek Murthy, MD, 2016

My intention in this section of this chapter is to provide a user-friendly explanation of how once a substance addiction takes hold, it operates as a chronic brain disease. I also share the many life-changing insights I had while discovering the various aspects of how alcohol and drugs change the brain, the nature of insurmountable cravings, and the gaslighting phenomenon that accompanies cravings in people suffering from addiction.

Once I understood on a deep level the mechanism of substance addiction from a brain disease standpoint, it changed how I viewed addiction, how I viewed myself, and, most importantly, how I approached my recovery.

### How Understanding The Brain Science of Addiction Can Save Lives

I believe if just a fraction of the 50% of Americans who believe addiction is a choice took the time to learn that copious use of alcohol and drugs changes the brain, and once enough brain changes have taken place, the ability to stop or moderate use can become neurobiologically impossible, millions of lives would be saved. This is not just my opinion; it's a scientific fact.

According to Dr. Nora Volkow, head of the National Institute on Drug Abuse, "Recent studies have shown that repeated drug use leads to long-lasting changes in the brain that undermine voluntary control." Dr. Gabor Maté also states in *The Myth of Normal: Trauma, Illness & Healing in a Toxic Culture,* "Scans have shown similar deleterious changes in the brains of non-substance addicts as well, such as inveterate internet gamers. The compulsive intake of foods that trigger the brain's reward apparatus can also produce such effects."

The inability to "just say no" to overusing alcohol, drugs, food, or other behavioral addictions is akin to losing your brakes while driving down a mountain. Although the driver has an intense desire to slow down or stop, they simply don't have the ability to because their brakes have failed.

Millions of lives could be saved if more people understood the true nature of addiction because the view of it would change from being a character flaw, a choice, or a personal failure to a chronic brain disease. When people struggling with addiction see that they are not bad or flawed but are suffering from a chronic brain disease, they will be more likely to seek treatment. In turn, the more people who seek treatment, the more lives will be saved, and fewer children will be traumatized due to being raised by parents with addictions.

### The Mechanics of Addiction As A Brain Disease

The American Society of Addiction Medicine defines addiction as a treatable, chronic medical disease involving complex interactions among brain circuits, genetics, the environment, and an individual's life experiences.

A survivor's initial attraction to drinking or using drugs is to regulate unbearable emotions due to the toxic environment they were raised in and how their brain, body, and mind have been impacted by childhood trauma.

However, once a person continually engages in copious use of substances, over time, significant brain changes take place. Once enough brain changes have taken place, a threshold is crossed into addiction. At this stage, substance use becomes and acts like a chronic brain disease.

Reading Bucknell University Professor Judith Grisel's book, *Never Enough: The Neuroscience and Experience of Addiction,* gave me a whole new perspective on understanding the causes of substance addiction, where cravings come from, and how dependence forms. Grisel outlines the risks and characteristics of substance addiction in the below excerpt from her book *Never Enough: The Neuroscience and Experience of Addiction*

### The Brain Disease Characteristics of Addiction

- Tolerance
- Craving
- Dependence
- Inability to stop using the substance despite negative consequences

### The Risk of Substance Addictions

According to studies Grisel cites in *Never Enough,* the risk of addiction is split between two factors:

- 50% of the risk for addiction is due to genetic influences
- 50% of the risk for addiction is related to environmental influences, such as high ACE scores and copious use in adolescence

### Genetic Influences for Substance Addiction

1. People genetically predisposed to addiction are 3-5 times more likely to develop an alcohol use disorder.
2. There is a 40% chance of having a problem with addiction if both parents or a parent and a grandparent have a history of alcohol or drug addiction.
3. That risk would be 20% if just one parent and no grandparents had an addiction.
4. There is only a 5% chance (of having a problem with addiction) if your family has no history of substance addiction.
5. This data has been validated with identical twins being raised by biological parents versus biological twins being separated and adopted by addicted and non-addicted parent

### Environmental Influences for Addiction:

1. Copious alcohol and drug use in adolescence. 90% of adults who qualified for an AUD or SUD started drinking in adolescence and qualified for a SUD by the time they were twenty-five. The earlier a child starts drinking or using drugs, the higher the chance of addiction.
2. A catalyzing environment. Childhood abuse, neglect, or lack of positive role models.

### How Genetics Combines with the Environment to Cause Addiction

1. Studies show that those with a high genetic and environmental risk of developing an alcohol use disorder (AUD) have about 50% of the volume of beta-endorphins in their blood than those with low genetic risk have.

   Beta endorphins contribute to humans experiencing a natural sense of well-being by soothing stress and facilitating social connections. Therefore, people with low levels of beta-endorphins lack a sense of safety and connection. Sadly, they have likely felt this way since they were children.

   Given that alcohol remedies this natural deficit, it makes sense that when people predisposed to an AUD or substance use disorder (SUD) ingest alcohol, opiates, or other addictive substances or engage in addictive behaviors, they experience a sense of safety, connection, and well-being that they may have never experienced before.
2. Our genetics and behaviors interact with our environment to form the basis of our decisions. Some people are more sensitive to stress, making it harder to cope with an unhealthy relationship or a fast-paced job. Some people experience many adverse

childhood events or one traumatizing event as an adult and turn to alcohol to self-medicate.

3. Even those with a high genetic risk for substance abuse must first be driven by a nonhereditary factor to do it. The catalyst that leads to alcohol abuse is very often an environmental factor, such as childhood trauma, copious use during adolescence, the end of a marriage, work-related or financial stress, or a traumatic event (such as a violent crime, car accident, or natural disaster) or a combination of these factors. In addition, 20% of those suffering from anxiety or depression are shown to develop an AUD.

4. There is a caveat in the above factors. Even if a person has none of the hereditary or environmental risk factors, studies show that with enough exposure to any drug of abuse, brain changes will ensue, making the person vulnerable to developing the hallmarks of addiction: tolerance, dependence, and craving.

It's just that the above three factors make the ground much more fertile for developing an addiction. It's not necessary to have all of the above-catalyzing factors to become addicted, but once a threshold is reached, it's like breaching a dam that's impossible to rebuild. However, if the biological predisposition is very high, use starts during adolescence, or certain risk factors are present, less exposure will cause addiction.

Learning that having a high ACE score and a parent and grandparent who suffered from alcoholism made it likely that I have 50% fewer beta-endorphins than normal levels helped explain why I felt such joy and bliss the first time I drank alcohol and smoked marijuana. Clearly, my brain was getting what it needed to remedy my beta-endorphin deficits.

When I thought about it, between my genetic predisposition, beta-endorphin deficits, ACE score of 6, and copious drug and alcohol use in adolescence, it would have been surprising if I hadn't developed addictions!

It was as if my brain, body, and mind were exposed to the perfect storm for addiction to bloom and thrive. Understanding this gave me pause for a big dose of self-compassion. It has also helped me be gentle with myself when I struggle with food or other issues around impulse control and self-soothing. Today I know there's nothing wrong with me. I'm simply doing the best I can with the genetic and environmental cards I've been dealt.

## The Neurobiology of Intense Cravings

Once addiction takes hold, it's not about satisfaction or pleasure; it's about runaway, cue-enhanced wanting.

— Oliver J. Morgan

I don't think I've found a better author or book to explain the mechanics of intense cravings and how they keep the cycle of addiction spinning than Oliver J. Morgan in his book *Addiction, Attachment, Trauma, and Recovery: The Power of Connection.*

I didn't realize it at the time, but as early as sixteen, I was training my brain and mind to assign an extremely high value (salience) to using alcohol and marijuana to relieve stress and provide pleasure, connection, and fun on-demand. My early onset and copious use of alcohol and marijuana wired my brain to constantly remind me that this was, hands down, the best solution for relieving stress, having fun, and feeling connected.

The reason I loved how partying with my friends made me feel was because of the massive amounts of dopamine and beta-endorphins (the feel-good chemicals) alcohol and weed produced in my brain. The problem with using such high quantities of alcohol and marijuana over an extended period of time was that the idea of making healthier choices to relax and have fun, such as physical activity or an alcohol-free lunch with a friend, would never enter my mind. They simply couldn't hold a candle to the relief and pleasure that drugs and alcohol gave me.

As Morgan discusses in *Addiction, Attachment, Trauma, and Recovery,* I had sensitized the neural structures in my brain to expect, want, and eventually need this intense dopamine and beta-endorphin high, which set me up to crave this level of relief and pleasure all the time.

When these substances were missing, I felt restless and irritable, and I couldn't find any satisfaction unless I was drinking and using. This is what prompted me to begin drinking and using every day. This daily-use pattern continued from when I was seventeen until I got sober at twenty-seven.

In *Addiction, Attachment, Trauma, and Recovery,* Morgan discusses the mechanism of how intense cravings to continually use substances develop.

## Incentive Salience and Neural Sensitization

### The Nature of Cravings

The dopamine system can become hyperreactive to drug cues, situations, and environments, which in turn heightens both incentive salience (assigning a high value) and intensified drive for acquiring and using alcohol and drugs, although not necessarily pleasure.

The cues and contexts trigger pulses of wanting or swelling urges to use that are temporary, often unexpected, and occur outside conscious awareness. But they're powerful, nonetheless.

Users often experience combined salience and neural sensitization as a state of needing. As in, "I need a drink" or "I need another hit of heroin." Needing is an extreme pathological form of intense wanting, triggered by cues and rewards.

Neural sensitization can become enduring and long-lasting. Perhaps even permanent. It's believed to be the culprit in fostering cue-driven compulsion and intense desire to take drugs and can even initiate those urges that seem to come out of nowhere and leave the struggling addict defenseless.

Incentive salience and neural sensitization are the twin mechanisms, the signature response identified for compulsive urges to take drugs and for the vulnerability to persistent risk of relapse, even after persistent periods of curtailed use or abstinence. Addiction, they suggest, is not so much about satisfaction or pleasure as it is about runaway, cue-enhanced wanting.

I had a major aha moment when I read the last sentence of the above excerpt: *Addiction, they suggest, is not so much about satisfaction or pleasure as it is about runaway, cue-enhanced wanting.*

This sentence totally captures the essence of what it was like for me to be in the throes of an intense craving state. It perfectly describes how once enough brain changes have taken place, salience becomes heightened, which means a much higher value is assigned to one's drug of choice.

Additionally, neural sensitization sets in, meaning that the brain responds with a higher level of intensity to cues and triggers, resulting in compulsive, overwhelming cravings to use one's substance of choice. Due to these brain changes, cravings can become overpowering, making them extremely difficult, if not impossible, to overcome.

I believe if more people understood the brain science behind what causes overpowering cravings and that these types of cravings exemplify what makes addiction a chronic illness and not a choice, it might help more people understand that those who suffer from addiction need to be treated with care and compassion just as those who suffer from chronic illnesses such as diabetes, asthma or heart disease.

It could also help those who feel hopelessly defeated by their addictions see they are suffering from a chronic illness vs. a moral failure which would likely motivate many more to seek treatment.

## Knowing My Vulnerabilities Helps Protect Me From Relapse

Understanding the brain science aspect of how cues and triggers work with addiction has helped protect my sobriety since it's given me the information I need to steer clear of them. For example, I know that one of my strongest triggers is being with a spouse who drinks. Therefore, I know I can't be in a romantic relationship with someone who drinks alcohol or uses drugs. I learned this lesson the hard way.

This is why it's no mystery to me why I've been able to stay sober from alcohol for thirty-two out of the past thirty-five years. During this time period, all of my long-term romantic relationships have been with non-drinkers—except for one who began drinking after we'd been together for three years, and I ended up joining her.

Another trigger that puts me at risk for relapse is stress. I have to be very careful about the level of stress I expose myself to. Since I know high levels of stress can trigger intense cravings for me, I make sure I'm very careful when making personal and professional decisions by being mindful of the potential stress they may bring into my life.

Gaining a deeper understanding of the neurobiology of cravings as they relate to addiction has been extremely helpful. It's shown me that humans are simply organisms that are at risk of becoming sensitized to the brain disease of addiction under certain conditions. This has helped me not personalize my struggle with addiction as if it's a personal failure or a sign of weakness. The beauty of gaining this understanding is it has helped me prevent relapse by better managing my recovery.

## How the Brain Processes Mind-Altering Substances

Another life-changing moment was learning how the brain processes mind-altering substances. Neuroscientist Dr. Judith Grisel discusses this topic in her book *Never Enough: The Neuroscience and Experience of Addiction*.

### Law of Pharmacology: What Goes Up Must Come Down

The brain automatically adapts to every drug that alters its activity by producing an opposite state. There's no way around it. What goes up must come down.

All drugs are counteracted by an adaptive brain: Our brain and body are always adjusting to reach a stable internal state. It's akin to its setpoint or homeostasis. Human survival depends on staying at baseline.

Therefore, whatever state a drug induces, the opposite state will begin to kick in to reverse the drug's effect to bring your body and brain back to their setpoint or baseline.

### How Drugs Impact The Brain: The A and B Process for Drugs of Abuse

- **The A Process** is what the drug does to the brain.

- **The B process** is what the brain does to maintain homeostasis. This means the brain returns to the baseline state it was in before you took the drug. The brain's receptors become desensitized during the B process, which means they don't produce as much dopamine.

After repeated use, you don't get much of a rush and don't get high, but you feel terrible when you don't do your drug of choice. Then the only reason to continue to use the drug or behavior is to not feel terrible or just to return to feeling normal

### Caffeine's A & B Process

When you drink coffee, there's an initial increase in energy. But then, to bring you back to baseline, the brain produces a decrease in energy that makes you feel tired. When you're a regular coffee drinker, you need coffee in the morning because your brain has adapted to the regular flood of caffeine. Once you build a tolerance, you automatically don't feel good when you stop using it (mild withdrawal). With caffeine, a more severe withdrawal can include fatigue and headaches.

### Alcohol's A & B Process

When you drink alcohol regularly, you automatically build a tolerance and need more to experience the desired effect. Once you build a tolerance, you automatically don't feel good when you stop drinking (mild withdrawal). The withdrawal is always the opposite of what the drug did for you when it worked. With alcohol, mild withdrawal causes you to feel tense, irritable, anxious, or just an overall lack of well-being.

### Grisel then goes on to make some profound statements:

- A regular coffee drinker doesn't drink coffee because she is tired. She's tired because she drinks coffee.

- People who drink alcohol on a regular basis don't have a drink because they have had a rough day; their day is filled with tension and anxiety because they drink too much.

## How This Played Out in My Life

While I was in active addiction, I didn't understand that my compulsion to have a "feel good" experience from the drug was becoming more and more impossible due to my tolerance building and my dopamine levels continually dropping. Hence, my brain convinced me I would reach that "feel good" high by continuing to drink or use. But at best, the only thing I was able to get relief from was the despair of feeling like crap most of the time.

## My Aha Moment!

After understanding how alcohol, drugs, and caffeine impacted my brain, body, and mind, I finally understood why they'd been such a struggle for me. When I read Grisel's explanation that the brain's response to every drug of abuse, including caffeine, is to produce its opposite state, I was shocked.

This made me realize that right from the beginning, no matter what drug you're taking, you take one step forward to where you feel better or high, and then your body automatically takes one step back to counteract the drug with its opposite effect. Once I understood this concept, I thought,

*So, what's the point of even doing drugs (including caffeine) if your body*
*automatically begins working on producing the opposite effect?*

## Understanding the Mechanism of Addiction

Grisel's statement that "regular alcohol drinkers don't have a drink because they have had a rough day, but instead their day is filled with tension and anxiety because they drink so much" really hit me. This is why the only way anyone who regularly uses drugs (whether it be alcohol, marijuana, caffeine, or opiates) can feel "normal" or just less crappy is to continue to take the drug.

**Grisel goes on to make the most profound statement of all:**

> Once you have built up a tolerance to any of these drugs, getting high, if it occurs at all, is increasingly short-lived, which makes the purpose of using the drug primarily to stave off withdrawal.

When I took this in, it took away any illusion that doing any drug could ever make me feel better. I realized it was simply a setup to stave off withdrawal so I could feel less crappy. I don't know about you, but I think I'd rather pass on signing up for anything where the main goal is to feel less crappy!

## Being Gaslit By Cravings

When I first began drinking and using drugs, they did deliver the goods. This is why my brain gave me intense cravings to get that feeling back. I never forgot how great my early days of partying felt. What I didn't understand until recently is that while I'm in an intense craving state to drink or use, my brain becomes a master at gaslighting me into believing that drinking or using will deliver the same amazing, totally fun, over-the-top experience I had in the good old days even though it's a total lie.

I think most people who have relapsed can attest that the fantasy of believing they'll feel that over-the-top high or relief once they get that first hit or drink never matches the reality of how they feel when they actually do it. The stark reality is that once long-term use begins and the brain adapts, the boat of that initial high has sailed, and the alcohol or drug simply can't get you to where you want to go. The problem is your brain still believes it can. This is where the phenomenon of what I refer to as "neuronal gaslighting" comes in.

When I asked myself why I continued to use alcohol and marijuana day after day and year after year without any real joy, I realized I was being gaslit by a brain that was still chasing the notion that I could capture the initial feeling or at least some of the initial joy I'd experienced in the good old days when being a partier worked for me.

The problem is that once a certain level of tolerance builds, your brain simply can't deliver much of a high. The best you can hope for is the relief of feeling somewhat normal or less crappy due to being in a state of mild withdrawal. As Grisel states, once tolerance has built, the only value in using alcohol or any mind-altering drug is to stave off withdrawal!

Another downside to building a tolerance to alcohol or drugs is that there will be a big drop in dopamine when you stop using them altogether. This is experienced as feeling like crap, coupled with an intense craving to drink or use whatever your drug of choice is. This dynamic is what keeps those who struggle with alcohol or drugs in the insane loop of addiction.

## Finding Healthy Ways to Have Fun, Self-Soothe, and Feel Good

Once I let go of the illusion that alcohol or drugs could make my life better, I knew I needed to focus on finding healthier ways that actually worked and could provide a sustainable sense of well-being.

Connecting with like-minded people has been the healthiest way for me to have fun and experience a sense of connection and well-being. I've also found that reminding myself that I deserve to find healthy ways to self-soothe when in emotional or physical pain has been helpful.

In my early recovery, I sometimes judged myself as being weak, just for thinking I needed something outside myself to feel better. Today I realize that it's completely healthy and normal to want to feel good or to need to soothe my emotional or physical pain through connecting with other people or other healthy outlets.

## Early Recovery from Addiction

The trick I found while in my early recovery was to surround myself with others who were in the same type of recovery. This is where Twelve-Step meetings were a lifesaver. Since I no longer had alcohol or marijuana to help me stay regulated, I instead connected with people at my AA and CoDA meetings. By completely throwing myself into my program, I developed many close girlfriends.

This made socializing much safer, easier, and more fun. Also, since we were all fully committed to working on our recovery programs, we enhanced each other's growth.

## Why Do People Relapse After Going through So Much Hell with Addiction?

The brain and mind never forget the exquisite pleasure and soothing you experienced at the beginning of your drinking or using days. This is where drinking and using cues and triggers come in.

A drinking or using cue can be triggered by a certain mood or a memory of a person, place, or time when you had a wonderful experience drinking or with your drug of choice. At the beginning of sobriety, triggers seem to be everywhere.

Unfortunately, triggers or cues elicit an automatic spike, followed by a sharp drop in dopamine and beta-endorphins in the brain, which sets off a powerful craving to seek out a drink or your drug of choice. Once you give in, the fix never feels as good as you imagined it would. So, you end up disappointed and ashamed for falling for it one more time. This often triggers the cycle of continued drinking or using with the hope of attaining the ever elusive high while simultaneously escaping the shame of relapse.

## How Trauma Triggers Can Put Us At Risk For Relapse

Trauma triggers are especially dangerous for relapse because they cause the brain to become dysregulated. When your brain is dysregulated, the prefrontal cortex—the rational part in charge of impulse control, emotional regulation, and thinking through the drink, drug, or snack—can go partially or completely offline.

It wasn't until I discovered I'd been suffering from C-PTSD that I realized that both of my relapses (one with marijuana and one with alcohol) were close to the end or right after a long-term romantic relationship had ended.

Going through the intense emotional pain of losing a partner, which for me was the only real family I had, triggered deep feelings of loss not only over losing my partner but also over never having experienced the safety, love, and connection I longed for but failed to receive from my family as a child or as an adult.

Since I wasn't aware I was suffering from trauma, I had no idea that the emotional pain I experienced after the end of my romantic relationships was significantly magnified by the deep pain from my unhealed childhood trauma. Now that I understand how vulnerable to relapse I can be when facing any type of major loss, I know I must protect my sobriety by surrounding myself with ample support during difficult periods.

## Other Triggers That Put Us at Risk for Relapse

A brain sensitized by addiction doesn't need a trauma trigger to experience a strong craving to drink or use. Sometimes hearing a familiar song you listened to while using or running into an old party buddy can be a trigger. It may be finding yourself in a specific location, smelling marijuana, or being at a party or concert. It can be the time of year, being around people drinking or using or someone offering you a drink or a drug.

Interestingly, even experiencing intense positive emotions, such as a job promotion, a wedding, or being on vacation in a beautiful setting, can trigger cravings. Also, experiencing intense negative emotions, high levels of stress, or being in an emotionally or physically abusive relationship can trigger cravings. Any type of major loss, such as a relationship breakup or divorce, a job loss, a death in the family, the loss of a pet, or a scary diagnosis, can also trigger a craving.

## Willpower Is No Match for a Traumatized Brain Battling Addiction

Since studies show that 75% of people with addictions have a history of childhood trauma and trauma impacts a survivor's ability to control their emotions and impulses, it's critical to address trauma and addiction recovery simultaneously.

Pushing the idea that people struggling with addictions should work on being stronger or developing their willpower is deadly advice, given what we know about the compromised brain capacities of those with a history of childhood trauma. If willpower alone could overcome urges for those struggling with addiction or self-destructive behaviors, the problem of addiction wouldn't be so widespread.

When overwhelming cravings are coupled with severely compromised impulse control, many people with addictions simply don't have the neurobiological capacity to resist urges to continue drinking or using their drug of choice. This is where Antabuse was a lifesaver for me when I struggled to get sober again after a relapse with alcohol.

As I learned more about childhood trauma's impact on the brain and how common impulse control deficits, cravings, and triggers to drink or use can be for survivors with addictions, I realized I couldn't completely depend on my willpower to keep me in long-term recovery. To bolster my recovery, I use additional strategies, such as setting up my environment and my relationships in ways that support my recovery.

Becoming aware of how I could set my environment up to stay sober and the types of support available to deal with my addictions and recover from relapse have been critical for my recovery. The great news is there are all types of programs that provide support, including Twelve-Step and non-12-Step groups, in and outpatient rehabs, medication-assisted treatment programs, and harm-reduction programs, just to name a few.

In my early recovery, I found that skipping the kinds of events where I used to drink or use or where people I'd partied with I knew would be was extremely helpful for me in staying sober. I know myself well enough to know I can't hang out with my old party buddies without succumbing to joining them. If there was an event I wanted to attend where alcohol was being served, I learned early on in AA I could protect my sobriety by asking a sober friend to go with me.

## Managing Intense Cravings

Many people with a history of childhood trauma find that once they start drinking or taking drugs, they suddenly feel "normal" or feel a sense of aliveness that they've never felt before. For many, the pleasure or well-being they experience is so intense it compels them to return to it over and over again.

For some, it's a transcendent or peak experience. I know this was certainly true for me. I absolutely fell in love with the feeling alcohol and marijuana gave me the first time I tried them.

I felt a level of joy, aliveness, and connection with my friends that I'd never felt before. I couldn't wait until the weekends because I knew I would get to re-experience the over-the-top joy and bliss that partying with my friends gave me.

Even today, when I pass by an outdoor beachfront bar on a hot, sunny day and see a group of friends having a grand time drinking ice-cold beer, I find myself reminiscing and longing for the good old days when I could have a blast partying with my friends.

Now that I'm well-schooled in the neurobiology and psychology of addiction, I know that allowing myself to dwell in these romantic fantasies is a dangerous setup that can trigger my brain to develop a powerful craving to drink or use, which puts me at high risk for relapse.

Today I know exactly what to do when I notice myself wishing I could drink or use. My first line of defense is to take myself to the memory of hitting bottom and the despair I felt. I remind myself that my brain is gaslighting me into believing drinking will be blissful like it was when I was sixteen. I then remind myself that it's a lie that will lead only to the insanity of active addiction. I also remind myself how wonderful my life is as a sober woman today and what I would lose if I gave drugs or alcohol another try.

These strategies are usually enough to end any delusion that partying with alcohol or drugs could ever be fun for me again. However, if I'm still feeling tempted, I use the following mantra:

*Drinking or using drugs is like dropping a nuclear bomb on my life*

Seeing the mushroom cloud with all I hold dear getting blown up usually does the trick of squashing any fantasy that maybe this time, drinking or using could be different. In fact, this is hands down the best mantra I've ever come up with to shift me out of a craving state.

If by chance, this mantra doesn't help shake the craving, I always have the option of using my emergency stash of Antabuse to keep me away from alcohol.

## How Survivors Are Attempting To Meet A Normal Human Need Via Substances

The Benjamin Franklin quote, "When the well is dry, we know the worth of water," captures the essence of what makes alcohol, drugs, food, and other addictive behaviors so rewarding for survivors.

Drinking or doing drugs for many trauma survivors is akin to the relief a tall glass of water provides after being parched from an all-day hike on a hot afternoon after running out of water. The feeling of relief is intense and satisfying because you're giving your brain and body what it needs.

It wasn't until I learned that I'd been traumatized that I understood that my metaphorical well was dry. And this is precisely why food, alcohol, and drugs held so much value to me. This brings to mind the following quote by Gabor Maté:

> Humans have needs, and if they are met, they will behave in predictable ways, and if they are not met, they will behave in predictable ways. It's not our behavior that defines our nature but our needs that define our nature. The behavior reflects the degree to which those needs are or are not met.

What Maté describes above is what was happening with me. Due to being traumatized as a child, I couldn't get my neurobiological, physical, emotional, or relational needs met. My drinking and using behaviors were simply an attempt to meet these needs.

The problem with trying to get our emotional or relational needs met with chemicals or compulsive behaviors is that they can't completely deliver what we actually need. This is why we're left still feeling empty.

Healing from trauma and recovering from addiction involves learning how to get our neurobiological, emotional, physical, spiritual, and relational needs met in healthy ways

## Long-Term Recovery Is Not Only Possible But Probable If You're Willing to Do the Work

After reading this chapter, it may seem that my view on how trauma impacts a person's ability to get and stay sober is bleak, given how cravings can be so strong and impulse control can be so weak with survivors.

I've shared the challenging parts of my recovery and the brain science of addiction because it wasn't until I understood its mechanics and worked with my vulnerabilities that I achieved long-term sobriety.

Setting my environment up and putting structures in place to bolster my recovery has proven that it's not only possible for a survivor to get and stay in long-term recovery, but it's also probable if you're willing to show up and do the work.

## How to Get and Stay in Long-Term Recovery

I cover all of the ways I've been able to stay clean and sober and recover from relapse in Chapter 32, "Alcohol and Drug Addiction Recovery Options for Survivors."

In addition, I share how I've been able to stay in recovery from compulsive eating and maintain a healthy weight for over twenty years in Chapter 33, "Food Addiction and Weight-Loss Recovery Options for Survivors."

In the appendix, you'll find all the books, groups, podcasts, and websites that have helped me maintain my long-term recovery.

# CHAPTER 19

---

# HOW FOOD SAVED MY SANITY FROM AN INSANE ENVIRONMENT

*Addiction is a normal response to abnormal circumstances.*

—Gabor Maté, M.D.

From the time I was just five years old, I learned to use food to soothe my anxiety, handle my grief, lift my mood, and numb the chronic emotional pain I was experiencing from living in a chaotic, alcoholic home. I've gained and lost hundreds of pounds throughout my first forty years. The most common weight-loss approaches I took were various diets, exercise routines, Twelve-Step groups, self-help books, and medically supervised weight-loss programs.

The problem with each of these methods was they never addressed the root cause of why I needed to turn to food to cope with my life in the first place. Therefore, every time I lost weight, I ended up gaining all of it back, and the cycle repeated itself.

When I turned forty and reached my top weight of 310 pounds, I knew I needed to do something different since it was obvious what I'd been doing wasn't working. Since I was heading toward midlife, I began to worry that my excess weight could cause me to suddenly drop dead of a heart attack, become diabetic, develop chronic pain, or a whole host of other serious health issues that are common due to being severely obese.

Since I hadn't been able to get my weight under control with diets, exercise, therapy, or Overeaters Anonymous, I decided to look to medical science for answers. I was encouraged to discover several peer-reviewed studies proving for people who were 100 pounds or more overweight that gastric bypass surgery provided a much better chance of reaching and maintaining a healthy weight for the long term versus traditional diet, exercise, and self-help approaches. That was when I decided weight-loss surgery would be the smartest choice in handling my problem with food and weight.

My gastric bypass weight-loss surgery took place in August 2002. The good news is I lost 160 pounds within two years. The even better news is I've been able to maintain my weight loss for the past twenty years.

The saga of my four-decade struggle with food and weight took a dramatic turn in 2017 when I learned that I had undiagnosed and untreated childhood trauma. It was then that I understood what had been driving me to turn to food to cope in the first place.

## How Your ACE Score Can Account for Your Struggle with Food & Obesity

It was while reading *The Body Keeps the Score* that I came across the ACE-adverse childhood experiences study for the first time. It was astounding to learn that children exposed to various types of adversity had much higher rates of addiction, obesity, anxiety, depression, and several chronic health issues in adulthood.

As I dove deeper into the science behind the ACE Study, I discovered some revealing information about how high ACE scores (4 or higher) can account for struggles with food and weight.

It was so validating when I found the graph below from the ACE Study showing that the chances of struggling with severe obesity increase by 240% when you have an ACE score of 4 or more compared to an ACE score of zero. Just understanding what could be behind my forty-year struggle with food and weight was a huge relief for me. Learning about the link between childhood adversity and obesity sparked a desire to dig deeper into what had made me turn to food.

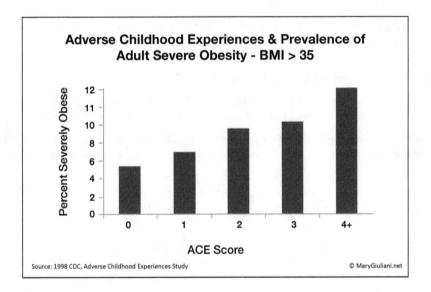

Initially, I thought I used food to soothe myself when I was sad, lonely, or angry. However, as I dug deeper and discovered the nuances of attachment trauma, I realized that food played a much deeper role than I originally thought.

After reading *Addiction, Attachment, Trauma, and Recovery: The Power of Connection* by Oliver J. Morgan, I came to realize that my use of food was primarily an attempt at a relationship for soothing and regulation that I hadn't been able to receive from my mother. Although my dad contributed to my use of food by offering me treats to soothe my distress, the primary reason I turned to food was as a substitute relationship for the deep hunger I had for a calm, present, attuned mother, which my mom was simply incapable of providing.

Although I know that my mom deeply loved me and tried her best, due to her own struggle with anxiety, depression, difficulty in her marriage, alcoholism, and her own unresolved trauma, she simply didn't have the capacity to be present and calm enough to attune to me to meet my basic attachment needs. Unlike my mom, food was always available to soothe my pain, lift my mood, and help regulate my emotions.

Over time, as my mother's drinking worsened, not only was she unavailable to help keep me emotionally regulated, but she became the source of most of the stress I was attempting to cope with. This required me to soothe myself even more with food.

In the below excerpt from *Addiction, Attachment, Trauma, and Recovery,* author Oliver J. Morgan discusses the link between early attachment trauma and addiction.

> Attachment is the ground out of which the self emerges, and it is our best defense against adversity, stress, and psychopathology.
>
> While human connection is essential for development and buffers us from life's travails, disconnection creates fertile ground for the emergence of addiction and other troubles later in life.
>
> I view addiction in large measure as a disorder of attachment and human connection. Unfulfilled interpersonal needs can be shifted toward bonding and relationship building with a drug, an activity, or a behavior that partially fulfills the role as a substitute.
>
> All that's required is for the drug or activity is for it to "have what it takes" in order to fill the role of substitute. The drug or activity must be able to facilitate comfort or relief, reward, analgesia, or diversion.
>
> It brings something of value to the relationship. Unmet attachment needs can be met, even if only partially by a relationship with addiction.

## The Importance of Understanding the Role Food Played for Me

Clarifying that I developed a substitute relationship with food versus an addiction is an important distinction to make. It speaks to why I found it necessary to use food in the first place.

Many people mistakenly believe those who overeat, drink, and do drugs addictively are irresponsible hedonists whose sole motivation is to use food or substances to experience pleasure or euphoria.

What I've noticed about the subject of addiction is how rare it is to hear people attempting to understand why people use food, substances, or other addictive behaviors in the first place. By asking what the substance or behavior does for a person, you can get down to what problem they're trying to solve.

When I understood that I was using food as an attempt to soothe the pain of my unmet attachment needs, it helped me get clear about what was necessary for me to recover. I realized I needed to focus on healing my relationship with myself. I also needed to gradually and safely learn how to form healthy relationships with fellow humans.

## ACE Study Co-Founder Dr. Vincent Felitti on Obesity & High ACE Scores

While researching the link between high ACE scores and obesity, I discovered some remarkable research by Dr. Vincent Felitti, the co-founder of the ACE Study. Interestingly, the ACE Study was born out of the research Felitti had done with patients from his weight-loss clinic at Kaiser Permanente in the mid-nineties.

Although many of Felitti's patients lost a significant amount of weight, he was perplexed why many would suddenly drop out of the program and quickly regain their weight.

In an attempt to understand this phenomenon, he decided to launch a research study on these patients. After interviewing several hundred patients, he discovered that 55% of the patients reported a history of sexual abuse. He also found that many of his patients had histories of other types of childhood adversity, including emotional and physical abuse, emotional and physical neglect, domestic violence, divorce, and being raised by a parent addicted to alcohol or drugs or who suffered from anxiety, depression or other mental health issues.

After realizing that he'd stumbled upon a clear link between childhood adversity and later issues with obesity, he eventually met and partnered with Rob Anda, MD, MS, from the CDC, where the official ACE Study was conceived of and launched in the late nineties.

## The ACE Study Revealed What Drives Severe Obesity

The ACE Study found that survivors with four or more ACEs overeat and become obese for two primary reasons.

1.  **Food is used as a drug for its psychoactive benefits, such as:**

    - **As a sedative** to help with anxiety and provide soothing, calming benefits.
    - **As a stimulant** to lift a survivor out of a depressed mood and provide increased energy or well-being.
    - **As a pain reliever** to numb uncomfortable, emotional pain.

2.  **Being overweight is experienced as a solution versus a problem since an obese body (consciously or unconsciously) provides:**

    - **Sexual protection:** One of Dr. Felitti's patients famously said, "Overweight is overlooked, and that's what I need to be." This speaks to how survivors feel safe in an obese body since it reduces or *says no* to sexual advances.
    - **Physical protection:** A large body can provide a sense of personal power and protection from the threat of being assaulted. Many survivors felt utterly powerless to protect themselves from abusive caregivers, siblings, classmates, or other adults as children. Therefore, having a large body can help a survivor feel powerful and safe in the world.
    - **Social protection:** Sadly, people tend to expect less from obese people in our culture. Therefore, being obese provides social safety from being judged, shamed, or ridiculed. This is due to there not being as much pressure or expectations for obese people to take risks in their personal and professional life.

## The Neuroscience of Childhood Trauma and Obesity

After reading *The Body Keeps the Score* and dozens of other books on C-PTSD's impact on children's brains, nervous systems, and minds, several more puzzle pieces fell into place about why I struggled with food and weight.

Below are the various ways my brain and nervous system were changed by childhood trauma, how it impacted my behavior with food, and how it affected my weight.

**Chronic Anxiety and Tension:** The fight, flight and freeze areas of a traumatized child's brain overdevelop, causing chronic tension and anxiety. A child dealing with chronic stress and anxiety will naturally seek ways to calm themselves down. Without a calm, attuned caregiver to help them calm down, a child will seek whatever means are available or modeled.

In my case, my mother was extremely anxious, angry, or intoxicated, and my dad was emotionally and often physically absent. This is what made food a soothing, calming solution for my emotional distress when my parents couldn't be there for me.

**Emotional Reactivity:** Due to the brains of traumatized children being hypersensitive to external stimuli, they can become easily hijacked by situations that non-traumatized children don't react to. Due to becoming upset more easily and staying upset longer, I found the need to self-soothe more often. Hence, I began self-soothing with food and gaining weight when I was just six years old and continued to do so into adulthood.

**Pleasure Center Deficits:** Due to trauma-related pleasure center deficits, I required more food to feel full and satisfied, which resulted in binge eating and weight gain.

**Impulse Control Deficits:** Due to the impulse control area of my brain under-developing, I had difficulty resisting food cravings, resulting in my overeating and gaining weight.

## How Compulsive Eating Changes The Brain

According to research by Dr. Nora Volkow, head of the National Institute on Drug Abuse, drugs and food manipulate the brain in many of the same ways. Volkow said that compulsive eaters crave food with more intense desire than the average person, but when they get their hands on a bite, it's rarely as satisfying as they expect it to be. That may be the reason why people keep eating well past the point of fullness or pleasure.

Learning that my brain had been changed not just by being exposed to the toxic stress of growing up in my crazy family but also due to my compulsive eating helped me to make sense of why I had so much difficulty resisting the impulse to overeat.

Realizing my struggle with food and weight was never my fault to begin with, but was due to how childhood trauma and compulsive eating had changed my brain gave me pause for a huge dose of self-compassion. Although I accept full responsibility for my healing and recovery, just knowing my struggle with food and weight wasn't my fault, and there is nothing inherently wrong with me helped me release the huge burden of guilt and shame I'd carried about them.

## Learning to Manage Food and My Weight Through a Trauma-Informed Lens

When I learned that childhood trauma is, at heart, relational trauma, I realized that I needed to focus on healing my ability to connect in safe, healthy relationships. The beauty of healing relational trauma is that instead of turning to food for soothing, you learn how to turn to healthy relationships. As I have shared throughout this book, connecting with safe people was what I had longed for all along. Food became a substitute for the soothing I needed but couldn't get from my family.

## Structure Has Played A Crucial Role in My Reaching & Maintaining a Healthy Weight

Given my trauma history, I don't have the luxury of relying on willpower alone to reign in my impulse to eat when I'm not hungry. This is why putting structures in place around food, exercise, and self-care has played a critical role in my success in reaching and maintaining a healthy weight.

This isn't to say that trying to improve willpower or impulse control is futile. In fact, I've made progress in both of these areas. However, I'm aware that when I get stressed, my willpower can become unstable, which puts me at risk for weight gain. This is why using external structures has played a vital role in my maintaining a healthy weight for so long.

The main structure that has worked for me for over two decades is what I call my *weight loss formula*. It includes food, exercise, and self-care plans that are enjoyable, satisfying, and sustainable as a lifestyle for the long term. My *weight loss formula* also includes tracking my food, exercise, sleep, and weight through my phone, a smartwatch, a smart scale, and various apps.

I don't track my food when I'm within my ideal weight range. However, if my weight starts to trend up more than 3-5 pounds for a week or longer, I start logging my food and exercise to get back within my ideal weight range and am typically able to do so within a week or two.

The reason I'm able to get back on track so quickly is that I've developed specific protocols to implement when my weight begins to trend up. This allows me to quickly course correct and get back down to my ideal weight range in a relatively short period of time.

Developing my *weight loss formula* has been a lifesaver for me. As a result, I no longer worry about regaining the weight I've lost (like I used to) since I know exactly what to do when I gain a few pounds to get back on track and get down to my ideal weight.

I've been fine-tuning my *weight loss formula* for the past twenty years to where it's easy, satisfying, reliable, and predictable. As the saying goes, the proof is in the pudding; I've maintained my entire 160lb weight loss for twenty years by using my *weight loss formula*.

After struggling for almost forty years with food and weight, achieving this level of stability and freedom with food, weight, and my body are true miracles for me.

## For Details on How To Reach & Maintain A Healthy Weight

For details on all the steps necessary to develop your *weight loss formula* and other options to manage food and weight issues, see chapter 33. "Food Addiction and Weight-Loss Recovery Options for Survivors."

# CHAPTER 20

---

# IS IT MENTAL ILLNESS OR MENTAL INJURY?

If Complex PTSD were ever given its due, the DSM would shrink to the size of a thin pamphlet.

—John Briere, Ph.D.

## My Journey with Mental Health

As a child, I obsessed, ruminated, and worried a lot. I never knew I had an anxiety disorder or any type of depression until I saw my first psychiatrist when I was thirty-five. Before that, I just thought I was a worrywart. My mom was a worrywart too, so I reasoned it was a family personality trait.

Even after eight years of sobriety and a ton of personal growth work, I was still a chronic worrier and struggled with ruminating. When I thought about how far I'd come from being in the depths of despair with my addiction to alcohol, drugs, and food, I figured if I could overcome all three of these struggles, I could certainly figure out how to let go of worrying.

In 1994 I read a book about how anxiety and depression are genetically based and cause a chemical imbalance in the brain. The book then went on to talk about how antidepressants could help rebalance my brain chemistry to normal levels, thereby resolving my struggle with worry and rumination.

During this period, I noticed that most of my sober friends were on antidepressants. I asked them how the meds were working for them. It was encouraging to hear that they all seemed pretty satisfied with how the meds helped them manage their anxiety and depression.

Between being sick and tired of being unable to get all the worrying and ruminating to stop and thinking that maybe I did have an inherited chemical imbalance in my brain, I decided to see a psychiatrist.

By the end of my first appointment, my psychiatrist diagnosed me with generalized anxiety disorder and dysthymia and prescribed an antidepressant to treat it. He said these conditions ran in families, and I likely inherited them from my mother. It felt so good to hear him say that my anxiety and depression weren't my fault, and that antidepressant medication could help me. I hadn't realized how much I'd been judging myself for not being "strong enough or smart enough" to overcome my worrying on my own. It felt so good to finally have hope!

Within a week of being on meds, I noticed a slight decrease in my worrying. Within two weeks, it had decreased even more. Within a month, I rarely worried at all, no longer woke up anxious and felt better than I'd ever felt. It was like a miracle! It was so obvious that my brain chemistry was off and that this drug was helping balance it. I was so relieved to finally not be so anxious and obsessed all the time. My only regret was that I hadn't started on these meds twenty years sooner!

## ACE Study, Depression, Anxiety, and Antidepressants

It would be almost twenty-five years after being diagnosed with generalized anxiety disorder and dysthymia before I would learn about the link between childhood trauma, anxiety, and depression. After learning about the ACE Study and seeing the below graph illustrating the link between anxiety, depression, and high ACE scores, I was amazed to see that one more time, the long shadow of childhood trauma had reared its ugly head.

### The ACE Score & the Prevalence of Chronic Depression

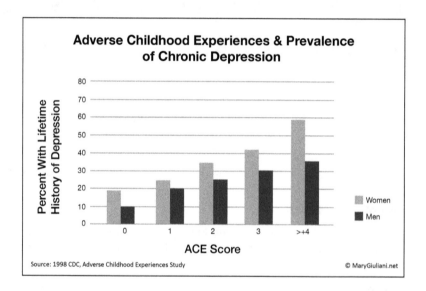

### The ACE Score & the Prevalence of Anxiety Disorders

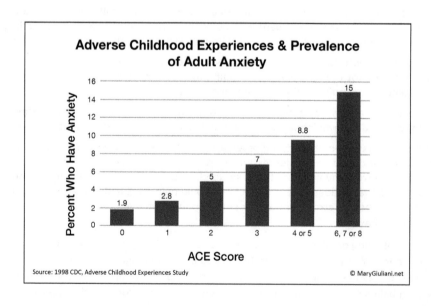

## The ACE Score & the Prevalence of Antidepressant Prescriptions

It was shocking to see that 100% of people with an ACE score of 5 or more are projected to need the support of antidepressant medication by the time they're fifty. Obviously, this is due to how dysregulating C-PTSD is for survivors' brains and how antidepressants help keep them emotionally regulated.

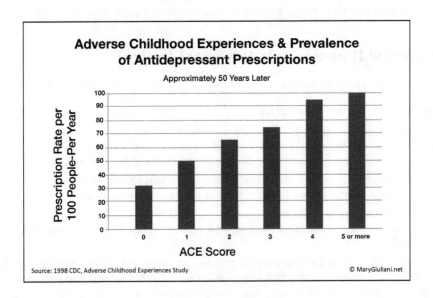

Source: 1998 CDC, Adverse Childhood Experiences Study                    © MaryGiuliani.net

## The Stigma of Needing To Be on an Antidepressant

Over the past twenty-five years, I twice attempted to get completely off my antidepressant medication, with disastrous results. In both cases, I weaned myself off extremely slowly over the course of several months. Once I was completely off, all seemed fine for about six weeks. However, once something stressful came up, the anxiety returned with a vengeance.

Once it started, within a few weeks, it became so severe that I felt like I was coming out of my skin. The second time I got off of my meds, not only did the anxiety come back, but a serious depression accompanied it. I'd never experienced this level of depression before. My bed felt like a magnetic force field pulling me into it. It was a major effort just to get out of bed to take on the day. Sometimes the pull to stay in bed all day was so strong I couldn't help but surrender to it. It was a very scary and difficult period.

After working so hard to get off my meds, I hesitated to jump back on them when the anxiety and depression began increasing. After attempting to hold on for a few weeks to see if the anxiety and depression would decrease, it became so unbearable that I simply had to resume my medication. Once back on it, I felt better within a week and was completely fine within two.

Although I wasn't aware of it at the time, I now realize that one of my motives for discontinuing my meds was due to my internalizing the stigma associated with needing to be on an antidepressant to manage my mental health. I had unknowingly bought into the narrative that being unable to overcome my anxiety on my own and needing to be on medication for it meant I was weak or defective.

Instead of recognizing that my brain had been changed by the toxic stress I was exposed to in childhood and that someone with an ACE score of 6 is likely to need antidepressant medication to stay regulated, I blamed myself for not being strong or emotionally healthy enough to regulate my mental health on my own.

Today I realize just like taking insulin to manage blood sugar doesn't make a person with diabetes weak or a failure, my taking an antidepressant to regulate my nervous system doesn't make me weak or a failure, either.

It feels so good to no longer judge myself for using an antidepressant to help regulate my nervous system. Today I'm truly grateful that these medications exist because the quality of my life is immeasurably better due to being on them.

I do want to mention that just because antidepressants have worked for me doesn't mean I think other people with C-PTSD or who have other mental health issues should be on them. All medications have side effects, and some antidepressants' side effects can be significant. This is why it's critical that you talk to a psychiatrist or mental health practitioner about starting, stopping, or changing any psychotropic medication.

# ACEs & Mental Illness: Or Is It Mental Injury?

In 2019 I saw Michelle Esrick's amazing documentary *Cracked Up: The Darrell Hammond Story,* which chronicles *Saturday Night Live* comedian Darrell Hammond's decades-long attempt to deal with his traumatic childhood during which he suffered severe physical and emotional abuse.

According to an excerpt from the movie's website, "Behind the scenes, Darrell suffered from debilitating flashbacks, self-injury, addiction, and misdiagnosis, until the right doctor isolated the key to unlocking the memories in his brain that had been kept locked away for over 50 years."

In the film, Hammond describes a life-changing moment when his doctor tells him, "I don't want you to call what you have a mental illness. I would like you to call it a mental injury."

After I witnessed this scene, I felt an immediate sense of relief since I totally identified with it. The relief came from hearing someone call a thing what it actually was. Why did I resonate so deeply with this scene?

When I thought about what I experienced growing up, with my mom's drunken tirades and the emotional and physical abuse she directed at my dad, I realized that what I had witnessed for nearly a decade was pure domestic violence.

I then remembered what I read in psychotherapist Terrance Real's book *US: Getting Past You and Me to Build a More Loving Relationship,* where he shares a transcript where he's counseling a mother who verbally abuses her spouse in front of their five-year-old daughter.

> Therapist-Children have no boundaries...they're wide-open systems. When she (the mother's five-year-old daughter) hears you scream at William (her husband), it goes into her as if you were screaming at her. I would do the same trauma work with her as a kid who had been sworn at.

This made me realize that when I'd witnessed my mom rage at my dad for almost a decade, the same rage going into him was also going into me. This is why I don't view my anxiety disorder and dysthymia as inherited mental illnesses; I see them for what they truly are: mental injuries resulting from being exposed to a decade of domestic violence.

## The Relationship Between Childhood Trauma & Serious Mental Illness

Another paradigm-shattering moment during my journey in learning about childhood trauma was discovering a SAMHSA-Substance Abuse and Mental Health Services Administration study on the direct link between C-PTSD and serious mental illness.

> Childhood trauma is a significant risk factor for serious mental illness, with meta-analyses showing that people with histories of childhood trauma are about three times as likely to be diagnosed with serious mental illness in adulthood as those without such histories.
>
> Serious mental illnesses include major depression, schizophrenia, bipolar disorder, and other mental disorders that cause serious impairment." The current paper focuses primarily on these diagnosable conditions, as well as on "psychosis" and "psychotic symptoms," and is based on a literature review of research published between 2012 and 2017

In addition, the below charts also shed light on the connection between high ACE scores, the rates of antipsychotic prescriptions, and the rates of people suffering from hallucinations.

## ACE Scores and the Prevalence of Antipsychotic Prescriptions

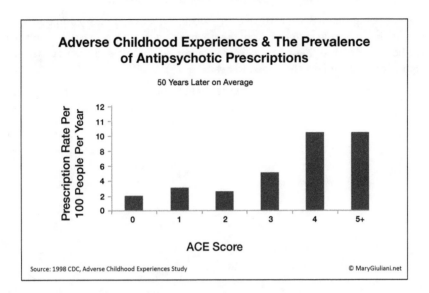

## ACE Scores & the Prevalence of Hallucinations

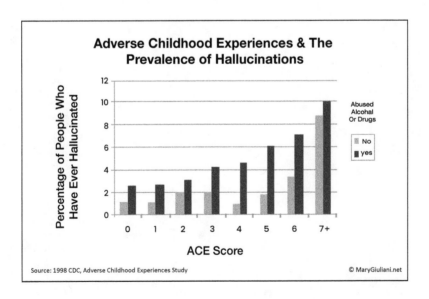

## The Direct Link Between Mental Health Disorders & Childhood Trauma

Just like the ACE study proved a direct link between childhood trauma and addiction and severe obesity, childhood trauma is also directly linked to significantly higher rates of depression, anxiety, and serious mental illness. Additionally, the very reason many people use and become addicted to mind-altering substances is out of desperation to find relief from the discomfort and pain of having to live with anxiety, depression, or other mental health issues. This was certainly true for me.

Just like my alcohol, drug, and binge eating disorder diagnoses', my dysthymia and generalized anxiety disorder diagnoses were merely symptoms of what I was really suffering from, which is complex PTSD.

I believe if more people understood that the majority of addictions and mental health disorders are born out of childhood trauma, it would help fight the stigma and shame we have in the U.S. about being labeled with them and help us have more compassion for those who suffer.

Since the fear of being shamed as untrustworthy, weak, defective, or crazy and then being ostracized is the number-one reason people suffering from mental health and addiction issues don't seek treatment, helping those who suffer realize these struggles are trauma symptoms and are not their fault, they may feel safe enough to get the support they need to heal.

And the more people seek treatment for mental health issues, the less their children, spouses, and coworkers are traumatized, and the more progress is made in breaking the chain of trauma.

# CHAPTER 21

---

# HOW TRAUMA THREW A WRENCH INTO MY CAREER

There is the life that most of us live, and then there is the life we have buried deep inside us, the life we know we're supposed to be living.

—Holly Whitaker

I realized I wasn't alone in my history of lacking meaning and fulfillment in my work when I learned from a 2022 Gallup poll that only 21% of employees are engaged in their work. Many factors can play a role in employee disengagement or workplace apathy; however, one thing I've learned from experience and my research on C-PTSD is unresolved trauma is definitely one of them.

The search for deep meaning and purpose in my work began soon after I got sober in my early thirties. I consumed as many books, workshops, and retreats as possible to guide me on my quest. Over several decades, I tried one strategy after another to experience the meaning and purpose I desired. When it seemed like I'd finally found a way toward accomplishing my goal, I'd hit one roadblock or another and find myself, one more time, back to square one.

It wasn't that I lacked clarity about my passion. I'd been pursuing my passion for personal growth since I discovered my mom's self-help books lying around the house and secretly read them as a ten-year-old girl. Having my own life transform due to all the personal development work I'd done ignited a passion in me to support others in doing the same so they, too, could live lives they loved. This is the very reason I became a life coach.

It wasn't until I learned I'd been suffering from childhood trauma and could look at my career through a trauma-informed lens that I was able to connect the dots as to why I'd struggled for so long with my work. Once I understood that childhood trauma is relational trauma, and it impacts emotions and the stress-response system and causes difficulty in close relationships, I gleaned a better understanding of why managing employees and working with coaching clients had been so difficult for me.

While looking back on my childhood, I could see how a significant aspect of my early relational trauma was how my mother taught me to feel responsible for her and other people's feelings and well-being. I was shamed as a bad or selfish daughter if I didn't comply with her requests to do things for her or others. If I set a boundary or said something that upset her, I was made to feel it was my fault for hurting her feelings.

After I understood how trauma triggers worked, I could see how interacting with my employees and coaching clients triggered a post-traumatic stress response in my body and mind. I realized these trauma triggers had transported me into experiencing the same intense feelings and sensations in my body I felt when I was a little girl after my mom had become upset with me.

But instead of feeling responsible for my mom's feelings, it was my employees' and coaching clients' feelings I felt responsible for. I was often plagued with guilt or shame if I failed to meet their needs. Like my mom, I feared they would shame or abandon me if I didn't comply with their requests. Sometimes I ruminated for days on how to handle conflicts or issues. Over time it became exhausting.

What I found odd at the time was I thought I'd already worked through these issues since I'd done so much work on healing my family of origin and codependency issues. I was fully aware on a cognitive level that I was not responsible for my employees' or clients' feelings, well-being, or outcomes. Yet I still couldn't shake how triggered, upset, and stressed out I got by interacting with them.

## Facing a Minefield of Trauma Triggers

After learning more about childhood trauma, I realized that running a networking organization with over six hundred members, working with individual coaching clients, and managing several full-time employees, was like walking through a minefield of trauma triggers. Since I never knew when one would go off, I was often hypervigilant at my networking meetings, and with my employees and coaching clients.

When triggered, my stress-response system jolted me into a fight, flight, freeze, or fawn state. Sometimes I'd shut down or go into a shame spiral (a freeze state) and just want to disappear. Other times, to assuage an upset client or staff member so they wouldn't shame or leave me, I shifted into people-pleasing (a fawn state) and made decisions that weren't always in my best interest. When faced with conflict, I often turned to my old standby, food, to numb my painful feelings (a flight state).

Since I didn't realize that childhood trauma was triggering stress responses that drove these feelings, bodily sensations, beliefs, and behaviors, I attempted to solve them through talk therapy or by processing them with my partner or friends. Since my attempts at healing were all cognitive-based, I was never able to heal the parts of the trauma that continued to live in my stress-response system and in my body. This is why they never got resolved, and I continually got triggered.

Over time I developed an approach-avoidance dynamic with my networking and coaching businesses. On the one hand, I still had a passion for helping people grow and develop so they could go on to live their best lives. Yet, on the other, managing my business, employees, and coaching clients were so triggering, stressful and overwhelming that the idea of continuing with it left me deeply conflicted.

I hated the overwhelm and stress of running my business and fantasized about finding a way to earn a living doing something less stressful. Yet another part of me didn't want to give up. I still had hope I could figure out how to heal the issues that kept stressing me out and getting in the way of me being able to enjoy my work.

## Finding Refuge in Less Stressful Work

In 2002, after finally getting sober after a two-and-a-half-year relapse with alcohol, I was at a turning point in deciding the best path to take to earn a living. Although the stress of dealing with my girlfriend insisting that she should be able to drink while living with me had played a part in my relapse, it wasn't the only factor. I also knew that spending a decade as a stressed-out, overworked entrepreneur had also played a role.

Although relapsing on alcohol was a living hell, I came to realize that there was a silver lining surrounding it. By relapsing, the universe had done for me what I couldn't or wouldn't do for myself. It helped me drive my business so far into the ground that it made it unsalvageable, to where I had no choice but to let it go. This freed me up to find less stressful work that was more in alignment with my recovery.

Although I hated the idea of having to get a real job, I knew protecting my sobriety had to come first. I was fortunate to be able to parlay my sales, advertising, and marketing skills into working as a sales executive in the advertising and online marketing industry.

At first, it was exhilarating to make more money than I'd ever made, work far fewer hours, and receive awards and prizes for being a top-producing account executive. However, after the initial high wore off, I couldn't help but acknowledge that the deep meaning and purpose I longed for in my work was sorely lacking.

In my heart, I knew that sharing my story of being raised in a chaotic, alcoholic home and overcoming life-threatening addictions to alcohol, drugs, and food could help a lot of people. Yet I was conflicted.

The only way I could see being able to live my purpose would be to launch my own business. Since the stress of running my last business had contributed to my relapse with alcohol, it felt too risky to even consider. So, one more time, I felt stuck in the conflict between longing to live my purpose and fearing that the stress of doing so could put my sobriety at risk—which meant putting my very life at risk.

## Finding the Path to Meaningful Work

I'd been hosting my transformational talk show *Mary Giuliani LIVE* on Facebook Live for about eight months when I began reading *The Body Keeps the Score*.

Once I realized that my most difficult struggles in life were due to living with untreated C-PTSD, I felt an intense desire to learn as much as I could about it. As I learned more about how trauma had impacted me and the different methods I could use to heal, I felt compelled to dedicate my entire focus to learning about C-PTSD. It was then that I decided to put my talk show on hiatus.

## Noticing the Signs

After being deeply immersed in studying childhood trauma for several months, I noticed something different about how I felt and operated in my day-to-day life. I was unusually excited to wake up each morning, knowing I would get to continue reading the latest book on childhood trauma or get to watch a webinar or interview on trauma that I'd signed up for. I also noticed how happy I was while researching various aspects of C-PTSD, even though I knew I wouldn't be paid for doing so

Then, it hit me. These were the signs I'd learned about in the many "finding your purpose" books I'd read that offered clues to tell you when you were on track with living your purpose.

Another oddity was noticing that the very things I used to consider my worst liabilities (e.g., something you wouldn't want a potential employer to know about you, like having a history of alcohol and drug addiction and severe obesity) were actually assets in my work with trauma survivors. Who knew that some of my most difficult and embarrassing struggles would become my greatest assets? If this isn't a sign that you're on track with living your purpose, I don't know what is!

When I looked back over the entire arc of my life, I realized that a big part of my work over the years had been on healing various aspects of the trauma I experienced growing up. Although I didn't know I'd been doing trauma-healing work until my mid-fifties, I now realize I was inadvertently healing cognitive and relational aspects of my trauma through my romantic relationships, with the therapists and coaches I'd worked with, and with the 12-Step work I did.

When I thought about it, the vast majority of the personal growth work I've done over the years has always been about healing the wounds from my childhood.

Suddenly it hit me. Healing childhood trauma has always been my life's work. I just didn't have a name for it until I learned what I'd been struggling with was trauma!

## What Changed After I Learned I Had C-PTSD?

One of the greatest gifts of learning I'd been suffering from childhood trauma was how it brought to light that my addictions to alcohol, drugs, and food were an attempt to medicate the pain of C-PTSD. Learning this helped me replace the shame I'd been carrying for believing I was weak and a failure for struggling with them with compassion and understanding.

Another gift of learning I had trauma was how it made me aware that I needed special brain and body-based trauma therapies to fully heal. This discovery was a mixed bag. On the one hand, I was ecstatic that I'd finally found the missing piece I needed to experience the healing that had eluded me for so long. On the other, it brought to light that every single therapist and psychiatrist I'd seen over the past thirty years had failed to diagnose me with what I was actually suffering from, resulting in my never being provided access to the body and brain-based trauma treatments necessary to fully heal.

Had I been diagnosed correctly and been provided trauma-based therapies and treatments; I would have healed much sooner and been spared years of unnecessary pain and suffering.

It was then that I realized if the mental health community had failed to diagnose and treat me for C-PTSD, there had to be millions of other survivors who had also been misdiagnosed and were unknowingly suffering from symptoms of untreated trauma.

This sparked a compelling desire in me to share with fellow survivors what I'd learned about the direct link between obesity, addiction, and childhood trauma so they, too, could heal the root cause of their issues vs. spinning around in symptom-based approaches. This, ultimately, is what inspired me to write this book.

## Owning The Value In Sharing My Story

As a first-time author, I initially had concerns about how well a book would do about the link between childhood trauma, obesity, and addiction and how to heal. But when I took a moment to look over the course of my life, I thought:

> Who better to be a messenger of hope and healing for people who are or who have struggled with food, weight, alcohol, and drugs than me? Due to my passion and commitment to healing my trauma and recovering from addiction, I've achieved long-term recovery from all of these struggles, and I'm living a life I love.

My story is not only a testament that you can recover from complex trauma, addiction & severe obesity, but it's also a testament to what opens up in a survivor's life when they heal the root cause of their problem instead of staying distracted spinning around in symptom relief.

Before knowing that C-PTSD was the root cause of these struggles, 95% of my time was consumed with managing my trauma symptoms. This left me with an underlying feeling that life was passing me by. That's because, deep down, I knew it was.

I knew sharing my story of how I'd recovered from addiction, obesity & being raised in an alcoholic family could help a lot of people and was desperately needed, yet my unhealed trauma kept me stuck. It wasn't until I learned the true cause of all these struggles was C-PTSD, and I began my trauma healing journey that the doors to finally sharing the gift of my story with the world opened up.

## Once I Kept the Focus on My Healing, My Purpose Found Me

The funny thing about my life-purpose journey is that my purpose had been right under my nose all those years. Yet, it wasn't until I understood I was suffering from childhood trauma and learned what was necessary to heal that I was able to place the final piece into my life-purpose puzzle.

The ironic thing about finally getting clear about my purpose and following it is that instead of searching for clarity on what it was or how I could align it with my work (like I'd been doing for years), once I stopped the search and just kept the focus on my healing, my purpose ended up finding me.

## Overwhelm & The Slide Into Terminal Ambiguity

Although it was wonderful to finally have clarity in knowing that my purpose is to help trauma survivors heal and go on to live rich and rewarding lives—what I wasn't clear about was what role

I wanted to play in fulfilling it. After looking at my skills, experience, and passion, I came up with several ideas I thought I'd be good at, enjoy, and could use to make the difference I wanted to make in the world.

After several rounds of going over my options, I began to feel overwhelmed. I knew that to protect my health and recovery, I needed to keep my stress level to a minimum. This made it difficult to figure out what role would best suit me or how big of a project I could take on.

I knew if I allowed myself to stay stuck in overwhelm, it would turn into what I call *terminal ambiguity*: a pattern of being stuck in "not knowing what to do," which I've fallen into before. The danger of terminal ambiguity is it's a surefire way for me to give up and stay permanently stuck.

## Using My "One Small Thing" Strategy To Break Free From Overwhelm Paralysis

The best way I've found to break out of *terminal ambiguity* is to use my "one small thing" strategy. I learned about using this strategy while working with my therapist, Sharon. It was during a period when my dad needed more help due to dementia setting in, and my sister and I were struggling with what we could do to help him.

I felt overwhelmed and triggered due to feeling like I'd be seen as a selfish daughter and a bad sister if I honored my own needs. Yet, I felt like my sister would never be satisfied with the level of help I felt okay offering. I wanted to contribute, but I also felt it was important to honor my needs as well. It felt like I was in a no-win situation.

After explaining my dilemma to Sharon, she said: "You and your sister don't need to shoulder the entire burden of your dad's care. Take a look at his needs and determine what each of you can do and what other resources you can access. Then choose your one small thing."

Feeling perplexed, I said, "It seems like just doing my one small thing won't be enough."

"Mary, doing your one small thing is enough," Sharon replied with conviction, "But my sister is doing so much more," I told her. Sharon paused, looked up at me, and said with a slight, sarcastic smile and a twinkle in her eye, "Well, there's a special place in heaven for her."

At that moment, I felt a huge energetic shift in how I saw the situation. Suddenly I felt totally assured that my contribution was enough no matter how much my sister chose to do. It felt like a huge burden had been lifted.

I realized that just because my sister chose to do more than I did, it didn't mean I needed to do more to be considered a good enough or noble enough sister or daughter. It helped me own that I can choose what's right for me. And once I got clear about what was right for me to do, it miraculously became easy to choose my one small thing.

What changed? Sharon gave me permission to be true to myself. And that made it easy to choose my one small thing. It also helped me recognize that my one small thing was enough, even if other people were doing more.

My "one small thing" strategy helped me realize that if I help just one person make progress in healing their trauma and recovering from their struggle with addiction, food, and weight, it's enough. What's so powerful about this philosophy is since I know it's doable, I know I will do it. It brilliantly gets me out of overwhelm-paralysis and into action so I can make the difference I'm called to make.

Now, instead of beating myself up for not doing more, being more, helping more people heal, and then feeling overwhelmed, guilty, ashamed, and quitting before I even get started, I keep bringing myself back to focusing on doing my "one small thing."

## What Is My One Small Thing?

1. **As an author:** I share my story of being raised in a chaotic, alcoholic home, how it impacted my brain, body, and mind, how I coped, and who I became as a result. I also share what I've done to recover from complex trauma, achieve long-term recovery with alcohol, drugs, food, and obesity,

and how healing my trauma has given me the gift of self-compassion, self-acceptance and the ability to experience the joy of connecting in close relationships. It's also given me the gift of making the difference I'm called to make by helping fellow survivors heal and thrive.

2. **As a speaker:** I speak about the link between childhood trauma, addiction, obesity, difficulties with relationships and work, and how to heal and go on to live deeply rich and rewarding lives. I also speak about the tragic toll stigma plays for those who suffer, or have suffered with addiction and obesity and what steps we can take to end it, thereby helping those who suffer feel safe to seek support and/or treatment.

3. **As a trauma recovery and resilience coach:** I provide a safe, compassionate space that supports adult survivors to move from surviving to thriving in a life they love by healing their trauma on a body, brain, mind, behavioral and relational level.

The wonderful thing about helping survivors heal and thrive as an author, speaker, and coach is that I can do the work I love while honoring my need to keep a healthy balance between my work and personal life.

Being able to do the work I love while minimizing the stress I take on is something I'd only dreamed about until I discovered and healed my C-PTSD. This is one more gift of healing trauma and what's possible when you never give up on yourself or your dreams.

# CHAPTER 22

---

# MAKING PEACE WITH MY PARENTS

Before we can forgive one another, we have to understand one another.

—Emma Goldman

Before I had done a lot of healing around my childhood trauma, it was difficult to acknowledge many of my parents' redeeming qualities. It wasn't until I understood how childhood trauma had impacted me and had fully processed the hurt, sadness, and anger, and had grieved the losses that I could turn to acknowledge the good my parents had contributed to my life. This chapter is about the many positive ways my parents helped me become the woman I am today and what I've done to find peace in my relationships with them.

## What I'm Grateful to My Mother For

I'm most grateful to my mom for how she inspired me to become passionate about personal growth and evolution. The reason I even began reading personal-growth books when I was a child was that she was so interested in them.

Up until I was about seven or eight, I could always count on my mom to be there to hold me when I cried or reassure me when I was upset. Before she got into daily drinking, she was full of enthusiasm and was often the life of the party. I loved how she'd always make birthdays and holidays special for us during these years.

I'm also grateful for how she inspired and encouraged me to get into singing since she also had a passion for music and singing. She frequently played records and always sang along. I admired her beautiful voice. I also loved when she would coach me on how to sing.

When I began singing, playing guitar, and writing songs, she was my biggest fan. She especially loved the album of original songs I recorded. She played it for all her friends and was so proud of me.

Even though her unhealed trauma and addiction to alcohol caused so much pain and suffering for my family and me, I never doubted that she loved and cherished me, and for that, I'm truly grateful.

Sadly, as the years rolled by and alcoholism ravaged her body and mind, I needed to distance myself from her since it was too painful to be in her presence. Although I stayed in touch with her, I could handle only small doses of time in person or over the phone.

She was diagnosed with advanced colon cancer when she was seventy and passed away two years later. I had mixed feelings about her death. The truth was I had lost my mother to the disease of alcoholism and untreated C-PTSD forty years before she actually died when I was just nine years old. I'd been grieving her loss for many years before she actually died. When she finally did die, I felt relieved for her that the suffering she'd endured for most of her adult life was finally over.

I also felt relief for myself. It had been extremely difficult dealing with the ongoing stress and chaos of having a mother who would call at unexpected times while drunk or never knowing when I might get a call from a bar or a psych ward to ask me to pick her up. Just never knowing when the call was coming was highly stressful and draining.

I also felt a deep sadness for the constant river of pain and suffering that ran through my mom's life. In many ways, it felt like I'd witnessed a wasted life. A part of me feels shame for even saying this. But in truth, that's what it felt like witnessing her going through so much pain and suffering for so many decades.

Tragically, her life was so ravaged by the long shadow of unhealed trauma that the only way she could cope was to numb the pain with alcohol. Who's to say that if I'd been born in her time and experienced what she did and had to face coping with chronic depression, anxiety, toxic shame, and deep and enduring loneliness—I wouldn't have struggled in the same ways she did.

If there's any redeeming value in all my mother's suffering, it inspired me to get and stay sober because I knew I could never bear the pain she endured for so many decades.

## What I'm Grateful to My Father For

I'm most grateful to my dad for instilling a sense of adventure, agency, and a strong work ethic in me. I also love that he embraced my being a tomboy and didn't treat me differently because I was a girl. He helped me to embrace my power and develop new skills by allowing me to help him with home improvement projects, work with hand and power tools, and troubleshoot how to repair and install things around the house.

He also loved adventure and taught me how to ride a dirt bike, drive a stick shift, play Ping-Pong and billiards, set up a campsite, and tow an RV.

He modeled the ability to make a good living through his various jobs tending bar in some of the most exclusive yacht clubs and restaurants in Orange County, California. In addition, he modeled entrepreneurship, launching two of his own businesses and owning rental property.

It's no surprise that I followed in his footsteps by also becoming an entrepreneur, owning rental property, and enjoying home improvement projects.

Although my dad was never emotionally warm, I know he loved and was proud of me in his own way, and I'm grateful for that.

Sadly, he started showing signs of dementia at eighty-four and was eventually diagnosed with Alzheimer's. Since he could no longer care for himself, my sister and I moved him from his home in Palm Desert to an assisted living facility in San Clemente, CA. Today he's ninety, and although his cognitive health continues to decline, his physical health is good.

## Forgiving My Parents

For me, forgiveness is about making a conscious, deliberate decision to release any feelings of anger or resentment I have toward someone who hurt me. To get to the point of being ready and able to forgive my parents, I first needed to acknowledge and fully feel the emotional pain and trauma I experienced due to being raised by them. I then needed to take the time to heal my trauma on the nervous system, cognitive, and relational levels. Finally, I needed to grieve the many losses I'd sustained due to my trauma.

Skipping grieving the losses from childhood trauma and moving into premature forgiveness of parents is a common exit many survivors unknowingly take. I know because before I knew I had C-PTSD, I had done so myself. Tragically, prematurely forgiving one's parents before fully processing and integrating your feelings can bring a survivor's trauma healing to a screeching halt.

It's an easy exit to be lured into for several reasons. First of all, who wants to lean into pain? The natural impulse for humans is to avoid any hint of it. Also, many religious practitioners, gurus, and even therapists tout forgiveness as the "noble" or enlightened thing to do to be a "good" person or to find peace and serenity.

The tragedy of prematurely forgiving parents before you have fully processed, grieved, and discharged your losses is that it can stall the trauma-healing process, leaving you to suffer indefinitely from C-PTSD symptoms.

Once I had covered a lot of ground in healing my losses on a cognitive, nervous system, emotional, and relational level, I could extend compassion and forgiveness to myself for all the ways I'd adapted and coped. This helped me have the desire to understand the trauma my parents had experienced as children.

By looking at what happened to my parents, it became clear that they were once innocent children raised in families that traumatized them too, but unlike me, they didn't know what C-PTSD was and were never given the opportunity to heal. Sadly, they had to endure the symptoms of unhealed trauma for their entire lives.

Once I understood what happened to my parents, I could see how they'd inadvertently passed their trauma down to me because of how they were parented and how they operated in their marriage. By first doing my own trauma-healing and grief work and then seeking to understand what happened to my parents, I was able to have compassion for them and forgive them.

## Forgiveness with Boundaries

It's important to understand that just because you decide you're ready to forgive your parents or anyone for that matter, it doesn't mean you're agreeing to allow them into your life or will let them continue to abuse or neglect you. It's completely okay to choose to have no contact with them if you feel you need to protect yourself from further abuse or neglect.

When we forgive our parents, we're not saying we condone what they did or failed to do for us or that we'll forget what happened. Forgiving our parents is about freeing ourselves from the need to harbor feelings of hurt or resentment toward them.

It's also important to mention that since some types of trauma are so egregious, it's entirely understandable to forgo forgiving your parents. Also, forgiving your parents isn't a prerequisite for healing trauma.

If you choose to have any type of relationship with them, it's important to remember that you get to decide how you would like to define it. This includes the frequency of visits or calls, the topics you are and are not willing to discuss, and the consequences they can expect if they don't respect your needs or boundaries.

If your parents continually disrespect your boundaries or abuse you in any way, you may decide that the only way you can keep yourself out of harm's way is to have no contact with them. This is not only okay but absolutely necessary for your healing.  If we continue to tolerate engaging in relationships that are verbally or physically abusive or that lack mutual respect, we are setting ourselves up to be continually traumatized.

If you find it difficult to set boundaries or move away from abusive or toxic relationships, please seek the support you deserve by contacting a trauma-informed therapist or coach or begin attending a Codependents Anonymous or other support groups to help you do so.

And always remember that the real purpose of forgiveness is to enhance your well-being, not your parents' or anyone else's.

# CHAPTER 23

---

# GAINING A NEW, COHERENT NARRATIVE: A LIFE THAT FINALLY MAKES SENSE

The degree of recovery matches the degree in which the survivor's story is complete, coherent, and emotionally congruent, and told from a self-sympathetic perspective.

—Pete Walker, M.A.

Soon after learning I was suffering from C-PTSD, I noticed that I'd started to feel better even though I hadn't begun any trauma-based treatment or therapies. Once I dug deeper into understanding childhood trauma and learned what the healing process entailed, I discovered why.

Learning I'd unknowingly been suffering from C-PTSD for over five decades gave me access to a new level of awareness that was logical and helpful in making sense of why I'd struggled for so long. When I understood that *a trauma survivor needs to gain a new coherent narrative about their life to heal*, I understood why I seemed to magically feel better. It was because understanding what had happened to me had been automatically rewriting my self-narrative—the story I tell myself about who I am and what happened to me.

Gaining clarity on what was behind so many of my struggles was like experiencing a huge emotional release and completion. The narrative in my head told me: *Okay, now I see why it all played out the way it did*. It felt so good to finally be done with constantly trying to figure out why I was the way I was and how to get better. In many ways, I felt like I could finally exhale.

Before this realization, there was an underlying frustration with tolerating what seemed like a lifetime of struggles that never completely went away. It gets exhausting to continually search for answers and constantly try new things, hoping maybe this time I will solve my struggle with food, weight, relationships, or my career.

Once I learned that the root cause of all these issues was C-PTSD, I experienced a total shift in how I saw and held myself. A whole new level of self-compassion opened up for me once I realized what had happened to me and how I had been impacted.

I was able to just be there for myself versus constantly pushing myself to overcome whatever challenge was in front of me. Also, when I finally had a story that made sense as to why I'd struggled so long, it was like a new level of peace and calm came over me.

Also, when I understood the root cause that had been driving so many of my struggles and learned that those struggles were never my fault to begin with, a huge amount of shame lifted. I felt calmer and more grounded. Miraculously, I simply felt like I was okay.

And when I combined my new narrative about why I'd struggled for so long with the comforting balm of self-compassion, my life and my trauma-healing journey became much easier. This is the healing power of a new, coherent narrative.

## What Is A New, Coherent Narrative?

Trauma expert and psychotherapist Pete Walker touches on the therapeutic value of gaining a new, coherent narrative in *Complex PTSD: From Surviving to Thriving*:

### The Power of Narrative:

There is also growing evidence that recovery from complex PTSD is reflected in the narrative a person tells about her life. The degree of recovery matches the degree in which the survivor's story is complete, coherent, and emotionally congruent, and told from a self-sympathetic perspective. In my experience, deep-level recovery is often reflected in the narrative that highlights the role of emotional neglect in describing what one has suffered and what one continues to deal with.

Looking back, even though I'd made some significant headway in self-compassion and self-acceptance before I discovered that trauma was the root cause of my issues with addiction and weight, I still felt the need to hide my past from most people I met unless I knew they were truly safe and wouldn't judge me over it. This speaks to how my self-narrative about my addiction and obesity history was still mired in toxic shame.

## The Transformative Power Of A New Compassionate Narrative

The reason I feel so comfortable sharing such intimate details of my life in this book is that my narrative has changed from worrying I'll be judged as being weak and a loser for struggling with addiction and weight to understanding that using food, alcohol, and drugs were a sane response to being raised in an insane environment.

As a result, my concern about what people think about my past struggle with alcohol, drugs, food, and weight is pretty much gone. This is why when I hear Dr. Gabor Maté pose the question during so many of his talks, "Ask not why the addiction, but why the pain?" I resonate so deeply with it. It's because he's modeling the power of holding a new, compassionate narrative for people who struggle with addiction.

While writing this chapter, I realized that this entire book is essentially a macro version of creating and sharing a new, compassionate narrative about my life. And by extension, it offers survivors who struggle with addiction, weight, mental health, or other C-PTSD symptoms the opportunity to adopt a new compassionate narrative about their lives.

This is what makes the process of writing this book so healing. The more I explore and share what I've discovered on my trauma-healing and recovery journey, the more my life makes sense. And the more my life makes sense, the more regulated I become. This is the transformative power of gaining a new, compassionate narrative.

# CHAPTER 24

---

# POST-TRAUMATIC GROWTH: THE ALCHEMY OF HEALING TRAUMA

Once you reach a certain threshold on your trauma-healing journey, you come to realize that healing trauma is essentially practicing alchemy. Metaphorically you've actually turned lead into gold!

—Diane Poole Heller, Ph.D.

I experienced a whole new level of hope when I heard attachment and trauma therapist Dr. Diane Poole Heller share some of the silver linings survivors can look forward to as a result of healing their trauma.

### How the Life Force Opens Up through Healing Trauma

The life force energy tends to open up for survivors who have been dedicated to healing their trauma. The reason so much energy gets opened up by healing trauma is due to all the energy that's been used to hold our defenses in place, which then gets released through trauma work. This energy is then freed up to move us in a much more expanded and energized way.

Also, healing trauma requires us to develop many new levels of awareness and capacities that we can now repurpose into new creative projects. This is not to minimize the devastation of trauma but to acknowledge all the ground a survivor has gained on an emotional, physical, social, and spiritual level.

One of the other hidden gifts in healing trauma is how in order to heal, it requires us to build resilience. This is why you can never go back once you've healed your trauma. You can never go back to your old "normal" after healing trauma since you have moved from a highly constricted state to a highly expanded state. What this means is you become so much bigger, so much more mature, so much more transcendent, and as a result so much less ego identified.

After feeling so drained by all the struggles that unhealed trauma had created throughout my life, the idea that something could actually give me energy was extremely appealing. I would soon learn that an indicator of a phenomenon known as post-traumatic growth includes the life force energy opening up.

Post-traumatic growth is why I believe so many people who have made it to the other side of healing their trauma relate to Maya Angelou's book titled *Wouldn't Take Nothing for My Journey Now.* This title beautifully captures the essence of how experiencing trauma can become the catalyst that causes us to grow and transform in ways that would never have happened had we not experienced such trauma. This has certainly been true for me.

## What Is Post-Traumatic Growth?

The term post-traumatic growth-PTG was coined by Richard Tedeschi and Lawrence Calhoun in the 90s. The term describes how some survivors of traumatic events experience positive change due to overcoming adversity, trauma, or other major life crises. It can manifest in several different ways.

Although not all survivors experience PTG, studies estimate that approximately 50% will. Below are seven types of post-traumatic growth, along with examples of how I've experienced each type.

**1. Increased strength and confidence to face challenges:** Overcoming being raised in an extremely toxic and dysfunctional family—as well as overcoming struggles with anxiety, addiction, severe obesity, toxic shame, relationship issues, chronic pain, and business challenges—have all increased my confidence in my strength to face new challenges. The narrative I have today regarding facing adversity is, *If I've been able to overcome all of these challenges, I can overcome just about anything.*

**2. New opportunities open up:** As a result of discovering and healing my trauma, a whole new range of opportunities has opened up to help me forge healthy, like-minded relationships and experience a deep sense of meaning and purpose in my work.

**3. Greater capacity for intimacy:** Had I not been traumatized as a child; I likely would not have been in enough pain to be motivated to dig as deeply into understanding and healing my psyche. As a result, I have gotten to know, love, and accept myself on a very deep level. This has been the catalyst for how deep, meaningful, and intimate I can be in my relationship with Maria. It is also why I've been able to develop close, intimate friendships with fellow survivors. Since unhealed childhood trauma is synonymous with disconnection and loneliness, being able to experience this kind of connection and intimacy today is one of the most precious gifts of healing trauma and one I cherish and am truly grateful for.

**4. Spiritual awakening:** Discovering and recovering from trauma has given me an entirely different view of humanity and life. I've come to recognize how truly innocent and vulnerable we are as a species. I've also become aware of how deeply connected we are and how much we need each other to thrive, survive, and experience true fulfillment.

**5. Greater appreciation for life:** I know the pain of being stuck in toxic guilt and shame, hopelessly addicted to drugs, alcohol, and food, and living with severe obesity. This is what makes the liberation I've experienced from healing my trauma and being in recovery from my addictions so sweet. Being a survivor who managed to recover and thrive has not only humbled me but given me a deep appreciation for life.

**6. A much richer inner life:** A big part of healing trauma is excavating the pain of childhood emotional abandonment and self-abandonment. It has also involved learning to be there for and honor my authentic self. Being true to myself has given me the courage to take the necessary risks to live my purpose and help fellow survivors do the same. All of these experiences have been deeply satisfying and have given me a much richer inner life.

**7. A willingness to share all of me:** The most liberating gift I've received by healing my trauma has been releasing the shame I'd carried over my addiction and obesity history. As a result, I'm more passionate than ever about being an open book about sharing my trauma healing and recovery journey. Having the freedom to share all of me and knowing by doing so, I'm helping others heal their trauma is one of the greatest gifts I've received by healing my trauma. This is why healing our trauma is the gift that keeps on giving.

## What Makes Some Grow From Their Trauma & Others Stay Stuck?

What can survivors do to give themselves the best chance to experience PTG?

1. **Developing a strong support system** by gaining the support of a safe community and a trauma-informed therapist, and/or coach is critical in experiencing PTG.

2. **Integrating your traumatic experiences** through trauma-based therapies, practices, and treatments naturally leads to PTG.

# PART III

# THE TRAUMA HEALING & RECOVERY JOURNEY

# CHAPTER 25

---

# WHERE TO BEGIN YOUR TRAUMA-HEALING & RECOVERY JOURNEY

*Our traumas can either teach us or run us, depending on how we handle them.*

—Terrance Real

## Now What?

After spending over a year reading everything I could get my hands on to understand what C-PTSD is and what the most effective therapies and practices are to heal, I found myself struggling with where to start my healing journey.

Given I'd already done so much psychological and spiritual work before learning I had trauma, I thought maybe a specific body or brain-based trauma therapy would provide the targeted healing I needed, and my treatment would end in a relatively short period of time.

However, as I dug more deeply into learning about childhood trauma, I discovered it had impacted many more areas of my life than I'd initially realized. This was when I knew I needed to take a broader look at how to best approach my healing journey.

## Getting Educated About Childhood Trauma

Since we can't heal something we don't understand, getting educated about the various aspects of complex PTSD is extremely important before embarking on your trauma-healing journey.

This includes learning how C-PTSD has impacted you on a brain, body, mind, emotional, relational, and behavioral level and what's necessary to heal.

Given that we're all at different stages of understanding what childhood trauma is, how it has impacted us, and how much ground we've already taken on our healing journeys, it's important to recognize what stage you're at in your healing process and what healing work you may have already done. This can help you decide what aspect of trauma you feel is the best area to begin studying or working on.

After you're done reading and completing the exercises in the remainder of this book, the books I recommend you read that have been the most helpful in gaining a comprehensive understanding of C-PTSD and what is necessary to heal include:

- *The Body Keeps the Score: Brain, Mind, and Body in the Healing of Trauma,* by Dr. Bessel van der Kolk
- *Complex PTSD: From Surviving to Thriving,* by Pete Walker
- *Healing the Fragmented Selves of Trauma Survivors: Overcoming Internal Self-Alienation,* by Janina Fisher, PhD

For those who have or are currently struggling with addiction, the below books that address the direct link between addiction and trauma have been the most helpful for me.

- *Trauma and Addiction: Ending the Cycle of Pain Through Emotional Literacy,* by Tian Dayton, PhD
- *In the Realm of Hungry Ghosts: Close Encounters With Addiction,* by Gabor Maté, M.D.

Even if you haven't struggled with addiction, I still highly recommend Tian Dayton's book *Trauma and Addiction: Ending the Cycle of Pain Through Emotional Literacy* since it covers the topic of emotional illiteracy (the inability to feel or identify feelings), how common it is in survivors, and what's necessary to heal. I also recommend you read *In the Realm of Hungry Ghosts: Close Encounters With Addiction,* by Gabor Maté, M.D., whether or not you've struggled with addiction since it provides an in-depth look at the nature of addiction and how it is not limited to alcohol and drugs.

I started with Van der Kolk's book and then read Walker's, Maté's, Dayton's, and Fisher's books. I include in the appendix a list of close to one hundred books I've read or listened to related to healing complex trauma. Reviewing these titles may help you clarify what specific symptom or area of C-PTSD is next for you to explore or heal on your trauma-healing journey.

Ninety-five percent of these books are available in paperback or audio format. Today I listen to practically all my books through Audible. I love listening vs. reading books since I can do so while driving, exercising, cleaning the house, or doing other activities that don't require my full attention. As a result, I get through two to three times as many books per month, which has dramatically sped up my healing process.

# What Are The Best Approaches For Healing Complex PTSD?

When first starting out on my trauma healing journey, it was really helpful to review what some of my favorite practitioners and experts in the trauma field recommended on what goals and approaches were best to take to heal.

### Bessel van der Kolk's Goals & Approaches For Healing Complex PTSD

Dr. Bessel van der Kolk outlines his goals and approaches for healing trauma in *The Body Keeps The Score:*

#### Goals of Healing C-PTSD

1. Finding a way to become calm and focused
2. Learning to maintain that calm in response to images, thoughts, sounds, or physical sensations that remind you of the past
3. Finding a way to be fully alive in the present and engaged with the people around you
4. Not having to keep secrets from yourself, including secrets about the ways you have managed to survive

These goals are not steps to be achieved, one by one, in some fixed sequence. They overlap, and some may be more difficult than others, depending on the individual circumstances.

### Three Approaches To Healing C-PTSD

1. Top-down: by talking, (re-) connecting with others, and allowing ourselves to know and understand what is going on with us while processing the memories of the trauma.

2. By taking medicines that shut down inappropriate alarm reactions or by utilizing other technologies that change the way the brain organizes information.

3. Bottom-up: By allowing the body to have experiences that deeply and viscerally contradict the helplessness, rage, or collapse that result from trauma.

   Which one of these is best for any particular survivor is an empirical question. Most people I have worked with require a combination.

When reviewing Van der Kolk's three approaches, I could see how I'd addressed healing my childhood wounds with primarily the top-down approach before knowing I had trauma. I'd relied on cognitive types of talk therapies through various therapists, coaches, my Twelve-Step groups, and by reading many self-help books. I'd also used the second approach, taking antidepressant medicines to shut down inappropriate alarm reactions.

At this point, I'd never used the second part of the second approach, which is utilizing other technologies that change the way the brain organizes information.

Nor had I used the third approach, the bottom-up approach—known as the body-based approach—in which we allow the body to have experiences that deeply and viscerally contradict the helplessness, rage, or collapse resulting from trauma.

Understanding these three approaches gave me enormous hope for my healing possibilities because I knew there were new approaches I could try.

## Pete Walker's Approach to Healing Complex PTSD

According to Walker, author of *Complex PTSD: From Surviving to Thriving,* "recovery is progressive." There are seven progressive steps to focus on for healing C-PTSD. Although we often work on many levels of recovering at the same time, recovering is, to some degree, progressive.

1. It begins on the cognitive level when psychoeducation and mindfulness help us understand that we have C-PTSD. This awakening then allows us to learn how to approach the journey of deconstructing the various life-spoiling dynamics of C-PTSD.

2. Still, on the cognitive level, we take our next steps of shrinking the critic. Some survivors will need to do a great deal of work on this level before they can move down to the emotional layer of work which is learning how to grieve effectively.

3. The phase of intensely grieving our childhood losses can last for a couple of years. When sufficient progress is made in grieving, the survivor naturally drops down into the next level of recovery work. This involves working through fear by grieving our loss of safety in the world. At this level, we also learn to work through our toxic shame by grieving the loss of our self-esteem.

4. As we become more adept at this type of deep-level grieving, we are then ready to address the core issue of our C-PTSD, the abandonment depression itself.

5. The final task here involves releasing the armoring and the physiological reactivity in our body to the abandonment depression via the somatic work discussed in this chapter.

6. This work culminates with learning to compassionately support ourselves through our experiences of depression.

7. Finally, as we will hear in the next chapter, many survivors need some relational help in achieving the complex tasks involved in deconstructing each layer of our old pain-exasperating defenses.

Walker's progressive list of steps to heal C-PTSD was helpful in that it assisted me in understanding the process, seeing which steps I'd already accomplished, and identifying which ones I still needed to take.

## Janina Fisher's Approach To Healing Complex PTSD

According to psychotherapist and trauma expert Dr. Janina Fisher, *In Transforming the Living Legacy of Trauma: A Workbook for Survivors & Therapists,* "Resolution of the past requires transforming our relationship to what happened. And this is achieved through the development of the following skills."

1. Expanding the window of tolerance until both the implicit memories and the day-to-day stresses of life after trauma can be experienced as within our capacity. We do not have to like trauma-related feelings, past or present—we do need to feel a sense of being able to tolerate them. If we have the bandwidth to stay present, manage our impulses and emotions and keep our thinking brains online, we do not have to reexperience overwhelming feelings or go numb.

2. Recognizing as implicit memory the feeling and bodily states that can still be triggered even after successful treatment, whether or not we have the images or the narrative of an event.

3. Learning to recognize triggering stimuli and to accurately label triggered states as responses to the past—*This is a feeling memory or a body memory. This is triggering.*

4. Refraining from searching for proof beyond a reasonable doubt what happened and not trying to remember every detail of what you know at your core has happened.

5. Identifying distressing feelings or symptoms as survival strategies rather than as problems or defects to be eliminated.

    For all of these reasons, I have focused attention in this book on helping you notice when your body and brain are remembering dangers from the past. And when we can finally appreciate what it took to adapt to that dangerous environment and to parents who were incapable of safe attachment.

    Then it becomes possible to live fully in the present, despite traumatic triggering and trauma-related conditioning. It becomes possible to have a healing story. A story that makes meaning of what happened and that attests to how we have survived it.

What I appreciate most about Fisher's approach to healing trauma is how much emphasis she puts on helping survivors notice bodily sensations and mood or state shifts as a possible implicit (non-verbal) body or feeling memory and how simply "noticing" it helps regulate the nervous system.

Additionally, I love how she de-shames survivors' use of food, substances, and other compulsive behavior by helping us see it as our best attempt to survive and cope with the unbearable pain of a body, brain, and mind dysregulated by childhood trauma.

I also appreciate how she encourages survivors to take pride in themselves for finding a way to fight their way back (even if it wasn't pretty) from the brink of total destruction to a healthy, normal life—and by doing so, shift from a shame-based narrative to a healing story about how we were able to survive our childhood.

## Anna Runkle: The Crappy Childhood Fairy's Five Steps to Healing Complex PTSD

Although Anna Runkle isn't a licensed trauma therapist, she is a C-PTSD survivor and coach who has done a remarkable amount of work healing her own trauma. She has also worked with thousands of survivors to heal their trauma through her online platform, where she shares videos and offers courses and coaching programs on how to heal C-PTSD.

Anna has outlined five key steps to healing C-PTSD. Each step targets an essential area for survivors to build a solid foundation for long-term trauma recovery.

### Anna Runkle's Five Key Steps to Healing Complex PTSD

1. Undersanding that your C-PTSD symptoms are normal responses to abnormal circumstances during your developmental years
2. Noticing when you are dysregulated and learning the steps to get regulated
3. Learning how to connect with people
4. Facing and resolving self-defeating behaviors
5. Shedding the trauma identity, owning your true self, and sharing your gifts

What makes Runkle's five steps unique is she is the only trauma coach or practitioner I've found who includes facing and resolving self-defeating behaviors as a critical step in healing trauma.

## Self-Defeating Behaviors Are Extremely Common Among Survivors

Since every traumatized child must find a way to cope with the toxic stress of their environment, unless they resolve their C-PTSD as an adult, they'll likely still be using the same or similar adaptations they learned in childhood to cope with stress or trauma symptoms.

The more obvious self-defeating behaviors are using alcohol, drugs, food, or other compulsive behaviors such as work, spending, gambling, or pornography to numb painful feelings or regulate moods. Self-defeating behaviors can also be more subtle, such as isolating at home to avoid the discomfort of being with people, avoiding the vulnerability of taking risks, or remaining in jobs you're overqualified for to avoid failure.

Other self-defeating behaviors can include overworking, over-caretaking, and engaging in unfulfilling or abusive personal or professional relationships are also common self-defeating behaviors among survivors. Toxic intensity, adrenaline-seeking lifestyles, and chronic unemployment can also be ways survivors engage in self-defeating behaviors.

Unless the issues driving these behaviors are addressed, survivors risk limiting or stalling their ability to heal and recover from their trauma. The first step in addressing stopping or moderating self-defeating behavior is to use self-compassion. The second step is to get curious about what the behavior does for you. Once you uncover what you get by engaging in the behavior, you can look at finding healthier ways to get your needs met.

The good news is that millions of trauma survivors have successfully overcome self-defeating behaviors, which means you can too. I go into detail about how I've overcome several self-defeating behaviors with substances and food in Chapters 32 and 33.

If you don't have a problem with food or substances but struggle with another self-defeating behavior, the recovery principles and the suggested steps to recover in chapters 32 and 33 are the same regardless of the behavior. To utilize these chapters with your issue, simply switch out the word food or alcohol with whatever substance or behavior you are struggling with.

## The Power of Having a Framework to Guide You On Your Trauma-Healing Journey

One of the biggest obstacles I've experienced in life is lacking an adequate framework to guide me when attempting to accomplish an important goal. A framework is akin to having a map and a container with clear objectives and steps we can take to reach a goal. Without a framework, we risk getting lost or stuck, putting us at risk of stalling and giving up.

This is why utilizing the frameworks by the above trauma healing experts has been so helpful. Combining all of these frameworks has been the most beneficial for me.

## Addressing All The Ways Trauma Has Impacted You Is Essential for Optimal Recovery

As I've discussed throughout this book, healing from complex PTSD is not about dealing with traumatic memories. It's about recovering from how trauma has impacted your nervous system, body, brain, mind, behavior, and relationships in your day-to-day life.

- If you focus on healing the emotional issues related to your trauma but neglect to focus on healing your dysregulated brain, body, and nervous system, you'll suffer from symptoms such as body pain, headaches, unexplained illnesses, or gastrointestinal issues.
- If you stay in abusive or unfulfilling personal and professional relationships, the toxic stress or dissatisfaction you'll experience by engaging in them will continually traumatize you and compromise the resolution of your C-PTSD symptoms.
- Continuing to engage in addictions to alcohol, drugs, or other self-destructive behaviors, prevents you from healing the issues it is attempting to medicate and will compromise the resolution of your C-PTSD symptoms.
- If you continually engage in other self-defeating behaviors such as over-caretaking, overworking, remaining chronically unemployed, or isolating at home to avoid the discomfort of being with people—you'll keep these aspects of your trauma alive and compromise the resolution of your C-PTSD symptoms.

The bottom line is you need to address each area of your life that's keeping your trauma alive. This isn't to say you need to take on healing everything at once. It's just a reminder that you will not experience the maximum recovery and resolution of your C-PTSD symptoms until you address each area where trauma has impacted you.

I've found prioritizing the areas in my life which are causing me the most stress or pain are the best ones to initially focus on resolving or healing.

## Choosing a Trauma-Informed Practitioner or Company

A critical piece of advice I learned when beginning my trauma-healing journey was to make sure that whomever I chose to work with provided trauma-informed care (TIC).

### What Does Trauma-Informed Care Mean?

Trauma-informed care (TIC) means that a provider or company is aware of the prevalence of childhood trauma and adversity and understands the impacts of trauma on a person's physical, emotional, behavioral, and mental health throughout their life.

A trauma-informed therapist, coach, company, or organization understands that the nervous system of a person with unhealed trauma is functioning in an altered way. They're aware that a safe environment is essential to a survivor's recovery. They understand that a survivor's behavior is not who they are but is simply an attempt to soothe a dysregulated brain, mind, and body.

TIC providers should also be strengths-based and provide a nonjudgmental approach. This approach is designed to build resilience and prevent inadvertent re-traumatization.

According to the Substance Abuse and Mental Health Services Administration (SAMHSA), the six principles of trauma-informed care are:

1. Safety

2. Trustworthiness and transparency

3. Peer support

4. Collaboration and mutuality

5. Empowerment, voice, and choice

6. Awareness of cultural, historical, and gender issues

When you don't choose TIC-oriented providers, you risk inadvertent retraumatization as well as not receiving trauma-based treatments to address healing the brain, body, and mind aspects of your trauma.

## A Word About Trauma Treatment Focused On Re-Experiencing Past Trauma

In the following excerpt from *Transforming the Living Legacy of Trauma: A Workbook for Survivors & Therapists,* psychotherapist and trauma expert Dr. Janina Fisher points out that for trauma to be resolved, the treatment must remain in the present vs. re-experiencing the past.

> For decades experts have believed that the experience of resolution could only be gained by remembering the traumatic events and reexperiencing the unresolved emotions until they felt "over." A logical belief, to be sure, but it was a treatment approach that often produced the opposite effect on trauma survivors. Shame instead of relief, an increase in overwhelming feelings, and self-hatred, and impulses to attack their bodies or end their lives.
>
> In the 40 years since the inception of the trauma field, experts in the field and survivors have learned the hard way that re-experiencing the past is equally or more likely to contribute to a failure of resolution.
>
> Now we know that for trauma treatment to be effective, no matter what methods we employ, survivors do not need to re-experience or even remember the past; however, they have to be able to experience some kind of clear physical and emotional sense that "it" is over and that they are still here.
>
> We must be able to acknowledge the past and reflect on its legacy without re-experiencing it. Even when trauma responses keep demanding our attention, we have to learn how to access other places in our minds and use the resources of our bodies and minds to change the physical responses that keep us traumatized. If the goal of trauma treatment is to be here instead of there, as Bessel van der Kolk tells us, any therapeutic approach must directly or indirectly keep the emphasis on the present.

I hadn't realized until I read the above excerpt that the myth of needing to reexperience the emotions of past trauma to resolve it is still so prevalent in our culture. Movies and television shows that depict a protagonist resolving a past trauma through a dramatic re-experiencing scene are perfect examples of what keeps this myth alive.

Fisher does a great job of helping survivors understand that as long as the therapy they're engaging in acknowledges the past while staying connected to the present, it can benefit their healing.

## Healing Requires Patience While We Step Outside Our Comfort Zone

Healing childhood trauma often involves a two steps forward, one step back dynamic. This is why it's essential to be as compassionate and patient with yourself as possible while you hold the big picture for your journey as you stretch outside your comfort zone.

## Building a Safe Support System Is Key To Your Recovery

According to the below excerpt in *The Adverse Childhood Experiences Recovery Workbook,*

> What heals the traumatized brain? A guiding principle is that mature love, not time, is the healing agent. Love, sometimes called by its other names, such as caring, respect, acceptance, compassion, loving-kindness, gentle friendliness, or concern, changes the brain and body in beneficial ways. Love softens traumatic memories, and memories of being loved that we access or create help us tolerate suffering.

Since love is the primary healing agent for healing trauma, we must prioritize putting ourselves in environments where love is in abundant supply. This is why building a supportive base of safe, loving people around you while stepping out of your comfort zone is critical for your recovery. Knowing you have safe people you can trust and turn to for help to process your pain is essential for your recovery.

A solid support system can also provide built-in accountability. Knowing your therapist, coach, team, and friends will ask how it is going (it being what you said you were committed to doing) is remarkably effective in keeping your commitments.

## Taking Baby Steps Is Healing In and of Itself

Healing trauma is a journey, not a destination. Therefore, the most important thing you can do is start with baby steps and trust the process. I've found that just being on the path of recovery and putting one foot in front of the other is calming and healing.

The most important step you can take is to simply begin with one baby step. One of the easiest steps you can take is to educate yourself about C-PTSD by reading or listening to the many books or podcasts listed in the appendix. Visiting websites or watching movies recommended in the appendix are also excellent baby steps you can take right away to start your healing journey.

Reaching out to join a group, seeing a therapist or coach, or finding fellow survivors online or through in-person groups are also excellent steps you can take to begin your trauma healing journey.

The main thing is just to take one baby step today. Then take another tomorrow. Then continue with a baby step the day after that and every day after that. Before you know it, days become weeks, weeks become months, and months become years, and one day you will realize you have completely transformed your life. This is the power of baby steps.

## Understanding the Window of Tolerance

When first learning about childhood trauma, I frequently came across the term *window of tolerance*. The term window of tolerance was coined by developmental psychiatrist Dan Seigel, M.D. It is described as the zone of nervous system arousal in which human beings function most effectively.

Since an unstable nervous system is a hallmark of childhood trauma, it's important to understand what the window of tolerance is, know what it feels like to be in and out of it, and how to get and stay within it. Staying within the window of tolerance is also known as staying regulated.

When you're regulated or in your window of tolerance, you are present, grounded, flexible, curious, and can respond to the demands of everyday life without much difficulty. You might feel stress or pressure, but since you can regulate your emotions, you're able to remain calm, cool, and collected and can function well.

When you move out of your window of tolerance, you become either hyperaroused or hypoaroused. *Hyper* means "to go up," and *hypo* means "to go down." Hyperarousal indicates the nervous system has upregulated into a fight or flight state. In this state, becoming hypervigilant, overwhelmed, anxious, angry, or aggressive is common. Also, the body may have the impulse to fight, run away, or avoid uncomfortable situations.

## The Window Of Tolerance

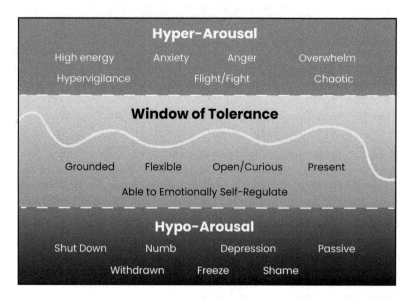

Source: Dan Siegel, M.D.

Hypoarousal means the nervous system has downregulated into a freeze or fawn state. Being depressed, withdrawn, numb, frozen, passive, ashamed, or focused on appeasing or pleasing others is common in this state. The body may shut down or have the impulse to hide while in this state.

Unfortunately, trauma is known to shrink the window of tolerance. This means it takes less stress for a survivor's brain and nervous system to get thrown off balance or dysregulated (go into hyperarousal or hypoarousal) and more time to get re-regulated.

Hyperarousal or hypoarousal, or dysregulated states are not voluntary. These are actual nervous system reactions to a real or imagined threat that were set during early childhood based on the connection or lack thereof with the primary caregiver, combined with the level of stress experienced while growing up.

*The Window of Tolerance* image above illustrates the different states of nervous system arousal that humans can fluctuate between throughout the day. It also cites the symptoms that identify which state a person is in.

Since chronic nervous system dysregulation is a hallmark for people suffering from C-PTSD, one of the primary goals in healing is to stabilize the nervous system and expand the window of tolerance. To accomplish this, a survivor must access trauma-based therapies and practices that focus on healing the brain, body, and mind aspects of their trauma.

## Working With Your Window of Tolerance

The following info-graphic provides a more detailed view to help you understand how the window of tolerance works and can also help you identify what state you are in.

Understanding what state I'm in at any given moment has been invaluable for healing my trauma. Just knowing when I am hyper or hypo aroused is regulating in and of itself. Also, knowing what state my nervous system is in informs what practices or therapies I can focus on to achieve more consistent regulation. And the more I practice getting regulated, the more my window of tolerance expands, which is a main goal of healing C-PTSD.

In upcoming chapters I go into much more detail about how to regulate your nervous system, which means getting back into your window of tolerance.

# How Trauma Can Affect Your Window of Tolerance

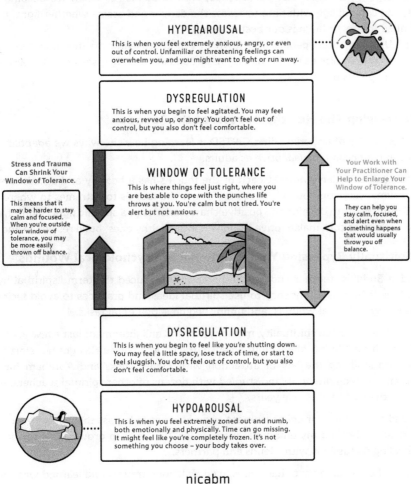

**HYPERAROUSAL**
This is when you feel extremely anxious, angry, or even out of control. Unfamiliar or threatening feelings can overwhelm you, and you might want to fight or run away.

**DYSREGULATION**
This is when you begin to feel agitated. You may feel anxious, revved up, or angry. You don't feel out of control, but you also don't feel comfortable.

Stress and Trauma Can Shrink Your Window of Tolerance.

This means that it may be harder to stay calm and focused. When you're outside your window of tolerance, you may be more easily thrown off balance.

**WINDOW OF TOLERANCE**
This is where things feel just right, where you are best able to cope with the punches life throws at you. You're calm but not tired. You're alert but not anxious.

Your Work with Your Practitioner Can Help to Enlarge Your Window of Tolerance.

They can help you stay calm, focused, and alert even when something happens that would usually throw you off balance.

**DYSREGULATION**
This is when you begin to feel like you're shutting down. You may feel a little spacy, lose track of time, or start to feel sluggish. You don't feel out of control, but you also don't feel comfortable.

**HYPOAROUSAL**
This is when you feel extremely zoned out and numb, both emotionally and physically. Time can go missing. It might feel like you're completely frozen. It's not something you choose – your body takes over.

nicabm
www.nicabm.com
© 2017 The National Institute for the Clinical Application of Behavioral Medicine

## Developing Healthy Fight, Flight, Freeze, and Fawn Responses to Danger

In the below excerpt from *Complex PTSD: From Surviving to Thriving*, Pete Walker explains that to recover from complex trauma, we must develop the healthy employment of the four F (Fight, Flight, Freeze, and Fawn) responses:

> People who experience good enough parenting in childhood (or who have successfully improved or resolved their trauma) arrive in adulthood with a healthy and flexible response repertoire to danger.
>
> In the face of real danger, they have appropriate access to all four F choices, as shown below:

- **Fight:** Easy access to the fight response ensures good boundaries, healthy assertiveness, and aggressive self-protectiveness if necessary
- **Flight:** Untraumatized people also easily access their flight instinct and disengage and retreat when confrontation would exacerbate their danger.
- **Freeze:** Untraumatized people also freeze appropriately and give up and quit struggling when further activity or resistance is futile or counterproductive. Additionally, the freeze response is sometimes our first response to danger as when we become still, quiet, and camouflage with time to assess the danger and assess whether fight, flight, continued freeze, or fawn is our best option.
- **Fawn:** Untraumatized people also fawn in a non-groveling manner and can listen, help, and compromise as readily as they assert and express themselves and their needs, rights, and points of view.

## Set Goals To Develop The Healthy Aspects of the Four Fs

One of the key principles of understanding C-PTSD is learning how the ways we *adapted* as children to cope with our trauma become *maladaptive* as adults.

It was refreshing to understand that each of the four Fs has a healthy and a maladaptive purpose. To cope with trauma, survivors found it necessary to use the four Fs to extremes to where they became maladaptive. Setting goals to develop the positive characteristics of a specific fight, flight, freeze, or fawn response is a great way to turn maladaptive responses into healthy ones, build resilience and heal trauma.

## Beware of Spiritually Bypassing Your Emotional or Psychological Wounds

John Welwood, a Buddhist teacher and psychotherapist, introduced the term "spiritual bypass" in the early eighties. It is defined as a tendency to use spiritual ideas and practices to avoid facing unresolved emotional issues, psychological wounds, and unfinished developmental tasks.

I began my journey through spirituality, metaphysics, and enlightenment just a few years after getting sober. It started with the Church of Religious Science (the church Louise Hay got her start as a minister), then morphed into studying the law of attraction with Esther Hicks and Abraham for over twenty years. In addition, I've been drawn to and studied with dozens of other spiritual teachers, practices, and philosophies over the past twenty-five years.

I never looked at my thirst for enlightenment as an attempt to bypass the pain of my childhood since I was also working on healing my emotional wounds via Twelve-Step groups, therapy, journaling, and having deep, healing discussions with friends and partners.

However, once I discovered that I had unresolved childhood trauma and learned what was necessary for my healing, I could see how being drawn to philosophies, such as "there's nothing more important than you feel good," can be counterproductive to resolving trauma. This is because to heal trauma, you must fully lean in and feel your emotional pain to digest and integrate it.

My spiritual journey helped me in many ways and yet fell short in others. The law of attraction was an excellent tool for regulating mild to moderately distressing emotions in my day-to-day life. Whenever I felt sad, angry, or frustrated, I used one of my law of attraction processes to shift myself into a better-feeling place.

Part of my life-coaching work involved teaching the law of attraction classes based on the Abraham processes for five years. I was also an Abraham student for twenty years before becoming a teacher. As a result, I got really good at shifting my state.

Becoming adept at using the law of attraction also helped me develop a powerful sense of agency. I attribute my many successes as an entrepreneur and in my advertising and marketing sales career to combining the law of attraction practices with other personal and professional training.

Where the law of attraction and other spiritual philosophies fell short was with my struggle with anxiety, sleep, triggers that caused difficulty in my intimate and professional relationships, and my addictions to food and substances. It also fell short in helping me resolve some pretty intense shame and guilt. For these issues, deeper trauma-based brain, body, and mind healing work was necessary.

## The Salvation Fantasy Can Make Survivors Easy Targets for Exploitation

Pete Walker describes a phenomenon that survivors frequently get seduced by called the "salvation fantasy." It involves a survivor having a fantasy about or fixation on finding a person, product, type of therapy, or some other external source that can completely save, fix, or cure whatever they may be suffering from or struggling with. Many survivors go to extraordinary lengths and spend money they don't have to pursue their salvation fantasies of being 100% fixed, saved, or cured.

I never thought I'd been seduced by a salvation fantasy until I gained a better understanding of what it was. Contemplating this idea made me recall an experience I had several years earlier during my personal growth journey. I'd spent an entire day at a personal growth/business-oriented conference. When I arrived home, I confessed to my partner that I'd spent $7,000 on a few personal-development programs pitched to me that day.

This was the type of conference where several speakers talked about their business or personal growth expertise and shared their programs. At the end of each presentation, there was a back-of-the-room-sale structure where you could only get in on the program's significant discounts and bonuses if you purchased them on the spot.

Although my partner was shocked and concerned that I'd spent so much, I justified my purchases as a prudent way to "spend money to make money." Looking back, I believe now that the salvation fantasy was alive and well for me during that conference, as well as during some of the other "investments" I had made over the decades.

I now recognize that trauma survivors can be much more vulnerable to charismatic and influential leaders who promise that their program, service, product, group, party, church, or organization will save them from their conscious or unconscious pain. I believe this vulnerability lies in the known psychological and neurobiological aspects of childhood trauma.

Given that most trauma survivors missed out on having a nurturing, attuned, guiding parent, many have an internal and frequently unconscious longing to be guided, supported, and protected by a strong parental figure or family. I certainly know I did.

Also, it is well documented that survivors suffer from emotional regulation and impulse-control deficits due to the brain changes that trauma causes. Sadly, these two aspects of childhood trauma make survivors extremely vulnerable to predatory hucksters.

Although I was already aware that my history made me vulnerable to being drawn to purchase the support of strong leaders, I still found a way to justify my purchases. However, after that particular extravagant purchase, I promised myself and my partner that I wouldn't spend over $200 without calling her in advance.

Gaining a deeper understanding of C-PTSD has helped me see on a deeper emotional level how holding on to a salvation fantasy puts so many survivors at risk of being seduced by charismatic business, spiritual, political, and religious leaders.

## The Salvation Fantasy of Being 100% Healed or Saved from Trauma Symptoms

When I started on my trauma-healing journey and discovered how I could approach my healing, I set my sights on doing whatever I could to experience a full recovery. However, after reading *Complex PTSD: From Surviving To Thriving,* I realized that I was caught in a salvation fantasy around being completely healed or saved from my trauma.

Although there's nothing wrong with having the goal of experiencing the maximum amount of recovery from trauma, there's a difference between experiencing the most recovery possible and being saved or completely cured by a healing modality, teacher, or healer.

I've found that entertaining the idea that I can be completely healed or saved from all the ways trauma has impacted my life is a setup for disappointment. I'm not saying that healing trauma isn't possible because I've experienced profound healing that has dramatically improved my quality of life. My point is that healing childhood trauma is more about adopting a healing and self-care-oriented lifestyle that builds and maintains your capacity to meet each moment with improved regulation versus being 100% cured—with the expectation you'll never experience a trigger again.   Since stress is part of being human, it's normal to cycle through fight, flight, freeze, and regulated nervous system states. It's being able to meet our dysregulated states with presence and healing practices that create a container for us to better hold them and make it easier to find our way back to regulation.

In many ways, the C-PTSD healing journey is like managing your fitness on physical, emotional, and spiritual levels. I've found as long as I take care of my brain, body, mind, stress levels, and relationships, my trauma symptoms are minimal to practically invisible. However, if I don't stay on track to take care of these areas, I start experiencing symptoms.

As a result of being actively engaged in healing my trauma, I've experienced a dramatic, positive shift in how I feel emotionally, physically, and spiritually. This isn't to say that I don't get triggered and occasionally slip into old, maladaptive coping mechanisms because I do. But this happens much less often, it is much less intense, and I'm able to pivot and get back on track much quicker than before.

Although managing your trauma recovery is an ongoing process, I'm here to say that you can create a life you absolutely love if you stay committed to your healing and self-care.

## Taking 100% Responsibility for Our Healing and Recovery

Obviously, it's not our fault that we were abused or neglected as children. And we're also not to blame for the long shadow of challenges we face as trauma survivors. However, to recover, we must accept that we are 100% responsible for managing our healing and recovery.

## What Does Taking Full Responsibility For Our Trauma Healing Look Like?

### You must take responsibility for your emotional, physical & spiritual health

If you're in a negative place, you must be willing to take steps to move into a healthier place. This isn't to say you shouldn't feel painful feelings because this is an integral part of trauma healing and recovery.

This is about not allowing yourself to stay stuck in a negative emotional space or using being a trauma survivor as an excuse for being helpless and hopeless to get out of it. If you can't move into a healthier space emotionally or physically on your own, you must be willing to seek or accept outside help. This help can include reaching out to friends, coaches, doctors, therapists, or psychiatrists.

It can also include practicing mindfulness, and meditation, taking classes, and exploring different trauma-based healing practices or modalities.

### You must take responsibility for who & what you tolerate in your life

This involves setting or raising your standards for the types of people you allow in your life.  It also involves setting boundaries with people or behaviors that aren't in your best interest.

If you're engaging in a behavior or substance that's hurting you physically, emotionally or that's causing problems for your health, relationships, or work, taking responsibility looks like putting a plan in place to moderate or abstain from it and/or replacing it with a healthier coping mechanism.

If you aren't successful in doing so on your own, you're willing to reach out to a therapist, a Twelve-Step group, a recovery hospital, a harm-reduction program, or another support system designed to help you find healing and recovery.

The reason it's crucial to take 100% responsibility for the energy you bring or tolerate in your life is that you can't heal your trauma or improve your life if you're consistently surrounded by energy, people, or situations that stress you out, bring you down or re-traumatize you.

I've often found that when I get stuck, there are hidden areas where I haven't taken complete responsibility for my healing or well-being.

A good question to ask yourself to see if this may be the case for you is, *Where might I not be taking 100% responsibility for my healing, recovery, or fulfillment in my life?*

The good news is that you don't have to figure out how to do all this alone. In the following chapters, I will share all of the tools, programs, trauma therapies, and practices that have helped me achieve long-term recovery from anxiety, alcohol, drugs, food, weight, codependency, and childhood trauma.

## The Value In Knowing The Signs You're Recovering from C-PTSD

Knowing what life should look and feel like when you're on the right track toward healing your trauma is key to your success. Without clarity about what you're after, you risk spinning around in terminal ambiguity.

Below, trauma expert and psychotherapist Pete Walker has done a great job sharing the signs of recovering from C-PTSD. Reviewing the signs of recovery is an excellent way to determine the next step in your healing journey. It also feels great to see what you can look forward to as your healing progresses.

## Signs of Recovering from C-PTSD

- Effective recovery work leads to an ongoing reduction of emotional flashbacks. Over time, with enough practice, you become more proficient at managing triggered states. This, in turn, results in flashbacks occurring less often, less intensely, and less enduringly.

- Another key sign of recovering is that your critic begins to shrink and lose its dominance over your psyche. As it shrinks, your user-friendly ego has room to grow and to develop the kind of mindfulness that recognizes when the critic has taken over.

- This, in turn, allows you to progressively reject the critic's perfectionistic and drasticizing processes. More and more, you stop persecuting yourself for normal foibles. Additionally, you perseverate less in disappointment about other people's minor miscues.

- A further sign of recovering is a gradual increase in your ability to relax. With this comes an increasing ability to resist overreacting from a triggered position. This further allows you to use your fight, flight, freeze, and fawn instincts in healthy and non-self-destructive ways.

- This means you only fight back when under real attack, you only flee when the odds are insurmountable, you only freeze when you need to go into acute observation mode, and you only fawn when it is appropriate to be self-sacrificing.

- Deep-level recovery is also evidenced by you becoming gradually more relaxed in safe enough company. This, in turn, leads to an increased capacity to be more authentic and vulnerable in trustworthy relationships. With enough grace, this may then culminate in you acquiring an intimate, mutually supportive relationship where each of you can be there for the other through thick and thin.

- Advanced recovery also correlates with letting go of the salvation fantasy that you will never have another flashback. Giving up the salvation fantasy is another one of those two steps forward, one step backward processes. We typically have to wrestle with denial a great deal to increasingly accept the unfair reality that we will never be totally flashback free. Unless we do, however, we impair our ability to easily recognize and quickly respond to flashbacks from a position of self-compassion, self-soothing, and self-protection.

## Accepting Trauma Recovery Is an Ongoing Process Vs. There Being An End Point

As I dug deeper into understanding childhood trauma and what is required to heal, I learned it's not like curing an infection by taking antibiotics or recovering from an injury by going to physical therapy and then being done. It's more of an ongoing process where you gradually build a lifestyle focused on self-care, healing, and recovery.

Although it may be deeply disappointing to hear that healing trauma is an ongoing process vs. there being a specific cure or endpoint, it doesn't mean you'll have to suffer from trauma symptoms for the rest of your life. As a result of the steps I've taken to heal my trauma, the vast majority of my symptoms are very manageable, and many are entirely gone. Even though you'll need to manage your C-PTSD symptoms, you can lead a deeply fulfilling life if you're willing to do the work.

In a world of quick fixes and magic bullets, I believe it's helpful to get a realistic view of what the journey of healing childhood trauma entails. This is why setting realistic expectations for your healing journey is the most loving thing you can do for yourself.

## Healing Trauma Is Similar To Getting & Staying on Track With Physical Fitness

Healing C-PTSD is very similar to achieving and maintaining physical fitness. When starting a new exercise program, establishing a new routine is usually difficult at first. Over time, we build muscle and lose some weight, Our bodies get stronger, and our endurance increases.

We feel a new sense of well-being, have a clearer mind and enjoy having more energy. After a while, our fitness routine becomes a habit and part of the rhythm and routine of our day. In fact, when we aren't able to exercise, we crave it because it makes us feel so good.

The downside is that if we stop exercising altogether, we gradually lose the muscle and endurance we built, gain back the weight we lost and lose the sense of well-being, energy, and vitality it provided.

This same process holds true with trauma healing. We need to practice a trauma-healing mindset and lifestyle to build resilience and maintain our trauma healing and recovery. As long as we maintain trauma-healing practices, healthy relationships, and a healthy lifestyle over time, we can expect to experience a more connected, healthy, joyful, and fulfilling life.

The key here is to take small daily steps toward your recovery goals. Over time you'll build a healthy lifestyle on emotional, physical, and spiritual levels that will foster significant positive changes in your life. Therefore, it's entirely up to you by the choices you make, how much your life flows, how much you thrive, or how much you suffer from C-PTSD symptoms.

## How The Healing Path Is Different For All of Us

Today I see C-PTSD symptoms as a set of adaptations. They reflect how a survivor's brain, body, and mind adapted to survive in an environment filled with chronic toxic stress.

Healing C-PTSD involves identifying how we adapted to cope with the stress from our childhood adversity and finding healthier or more optimal ways to stay regulated and get our needs met. Accomplishing this is what it means to heal or manage C-PTSD.

Since we were all raised in different families, we all adapted differently to survive and will have different experiences during our healing journey. Some survivors' symptoms will decrease or completely disappear, while others may occur intermittently or persist indefinitely.

For treatment-resistant symptoms, what's worked for me is to keep on experimenting with different methods. Over time I've always found one that works. The key is to never give up. If you trust the process, you'll get there eventually. Just remember, constantly experiment and never give up.

CHAPTER 26

# BUILDING RESILIENCE IS CRITICAL IN HEALING TRAUMA

On the other side of a storm is the strength that comes from having navigated through it. Raise your sail and begin.

—Gregory S. Williams

When I first discovered I had C-PTSD, I noticed the term resilience was often referred to as something vital for survivors to build to prevent and heal trauma. At first, it seemed odd that resilience was such a critical component for a trauma survivor to possess.

Yet, it began to make sense once I understood what resilience means from a childhood trauma and nervous system perspective. In this context, resilience has more to do with the healthy regulation of the stress response or nervous system than a form of mental toughness.

A healthy stress-response system provides flexibility in its response to stress. This means you can become stressed without burning out or shutting down. In a global sense, building resilience improves one's ability to regulate the body, mind, emotions, and behaviors when under stress.

What is stress? By nature, humans are programmed to stay in balance. Stress is what we experience when we take on something that causes our body, brain, or mind to fall out of balance, which results in our feeling uncomfortable or distressed.

When the systems in our brain, body, and mind return to being balanced, the reward pathways in the brain fire and give us a feeling of relief or pleasure. Examples of this are being tired and feeling refreshed from getting a good night's sleep or feeling sad and being comforted by a friend. When our systems are in balance, we feel a sense of well-being, which is also known as being regulated; when they are out of balance, we feel distressed or uncomfortable, which is also known as being dysregulated.

## You Need Some Stress to Build Resiliency

Although building resilience is about handling stress more effectively, to build it, you actually need stress, at least in small increments. You can look at resilience like a muscle. If you don't work it and put pressure on it, the muscle won't grow. However, if you work a muscle too hard and put too much stress on it, you can tear or traumatize it.

In some families, kids are overprotected and robbed of the ability to endure the stress they need to build resilience. When they become adults, they're ill-prepared to face the stress of being an adult. In other families, kids aren't protected or are neglected or abused. This puts too much stress on them, which can result in trauma. When these kids grow up, they, too, are ill-prepared to handle all the stressors of being an adult.

There's a range of stress we need to shoot for when raising kids, as well as when we're building resilience as adults. I liken it to the Goldilocks principle: not too much, not too little, but just the right amount of stress works best. As you begin your resilience-building journey, you'll discover what stress level is right for you.

### Discovering I'd Inadvertently Been Building Resilience For Three Decades

Although I didn't know it at the time, a big part of my recovery in AA, my training to become a certified life coach, and the myriad of personal and spiritual-growth books I read and workshops I'd done over the years all involved resilience-building practices.

It wasn't until I began learning about childhood trauma that I saw that the resilience-building practices I found in the trauma literature were practically identical to the personal-growth work practices I'd been doing for years. The only difference was the resilience practices I'd cultivated in the past used phrases such as: building community, practicing mindfulness, self-care, building agency, and building competence, to name a few.

### Why Every Survivor Needs Resilience-Building Practices To Heal Their Trauma

Since one of the most disruptive symptoms of C-PTSD is a dysregulated stress-response system, and resilience-building practices are known to regulate and strengthen it, it only makes sense that building resilience should be an essential part of every survivor's trauma-healing journey.

## The Top Fifteen Resilience-Building Practices

The following resilience-building practices have been the most effective for improving my physical, emotional, mental, and relational trauma recovery:

### 1. Prioritize Building Healthy Relationships

Childhood trauma, at its core, is relational trauma. To fully heal, we must be open to approaching healing our relational wounds in a slow, safe, and healthy way. After being heavily steeped in healing C-PTSD for several years, I've come to realize that all my addictions were maladaptive attempts to develop the soothing, regulating effects that safe, supportive relationships were supposed to provide for me as a child.

Since the people who were supposed to be there for me to soothe and help keep me regulated were not available, I established substitute relationships, first with food and then with alcohol and marijuana. Over time, I found food and substances could never fully satisfy what I truly needed, which were safe, soothing, human connections.

Even though I'd been passionate about personal growth and evolution for several decades, I wasn't aware of how imperative close relationships were to my healing until I learned I'd been suffering from C-PTSD. It was so enlightening to learn that early humans would not survive without staying connected to their tribe. This helped to make sense of why we get anxious and depressed when we're not connected in close relationships. We're wired to be connected to other humans. We need relationships to regulate our emotions and nervous systems.

Trauma therapist Tian Dayton, Ph.D., touches on the importance of this topic in the below excerpt from her book *Neuropsychodrama in the Treatment of Relational Trauma*:

There is another kind of trauma that is a part of our inborn fear of aloneness. A fear that nature coded into us and reinforces with each and every interaction to ensure that we place the need for human connection above all others. When this profound, innate yearning for connectedness is continually frustrated, manipulated, or abused, we experience it as a violation to our core instincts.

This excerpt illustrates why experiencing a chronic lack of connection is so traumatizing for humans. Before I understood this, back in my early Twelve-Step recovery, I remember believing that if I yearned to be in a romantic relationship, it was somehow unhealthy or possibly a sign of love addiction or codependency. I now know that desiring intimate, interdependent connections with other human beings is not only a healthy way to operate but is an absolute requirement to be able to lead a happy, healthy life.

I also know that using food, drugs, alcohol, work, or other relational substitutes can't provide the regulation that human connection can. This is why I've found that one of the main tasks for those of us with childhood trauma histories is to find safe and healthy-enough humans we can gradually learn to connect with.

For many survivors, working with a trauma-informed therapist or coach is the first attempt to experience a safe, nurturing relationship with another person. Once we accomplish this task, we can gradually branch out to developing nurturing friendships and romantic relationships.

## How Early Programming Sets Us Up for Tolerating Unhealthy & Relationships

Two of the main factors determining whether we live a life we love, or one that we hate or tolerate are determined by who we spend our time with and what we spend our time doing. Since many trauma survivors have never experienced safe, supportive relationships, they may not realize that some of the people in their lives may be draining, hurting, or retraumatizing them. If they do realize this, they may not have the tools or know how to request what they need or how to stop engaging with them.

A big part of healing childhood trauma is relational recovery. This means learning how to forge safe, nurturing, healthy relationships. To accomplish this, we must take a look at who we're allowing into our lives and what we want and need for our relational recovery going forward.

I came to realize in my early codependency recovery that a big roadblock to my forming healthy, fulfilling relationships was due to certain beliefs that my mother and the Catholic Church had instilled in me regarding how I needed to be with people to be considered a good person. Thankfully, part of recovering from codependency required that I question the validity of these beliefs.

Once I identified and rooted out the beliefs that sabotaged me in my relationships and replaced them with healthier ones, my relationships began transforming. I'm so grateful that I took the time to do so because today, all of my relationships are mutually supportive and provide deep comfort and joy in my life.

## Beliefs We Must Embrace To Forge Mutually Supportive Relationships

1. I deserve to make my needs a top priority. When my cup is full, I can give from the overflow. This replaces the belief that putting myself first makes me selfish or bad.
2. I deserve to surround myself with people who calm me down, lift me up, enhance my health, and bring me joy. This replaces the belief that I should be there for people no matter how draining, abusive, negative, or triggering they are and that if I don't, I'll be judged as bad, selfish, or unkind.
3. No one is worth jeopardizing my physical, emotional, spiritual, or mental health over. This replaces the belief that I must be there for my friends or family no matter what, or I'll be considered disloyal, bad, uncaring, unkind, or selfish.
4. I'm not responsible for other adults' emotional, physical, or financial well-being. This replaces the belief that I'm responsible for helping people to manage their emotional, financial, spiritual, or health issues — Or I'm morally obligated to rescue, take care of, or fix them, or I'll judged as bad, uncaring, or selfish.

5. I have the right to change my mind. If I have made an agreement but realize it is not in my best interest to follow through with it, I will do my best to get out of it as responsibly as possible. This replaces the belief: Once I commit or agree to something, I can't back out of it, or I'll be considered untrustworthy, unethical, or a bad person.

## The Power of Releasing Duty & Obligation Beliefs

As you become more able to release these "duty and obligation" beliefs, you'll be able to approach your relationships from a place of genuine caring and a desire to help vs. to avoid the guilt and shame of duty and obligation.

And once this happens, all of the strings that used to be attached to you in your relationships fall away. You're then freed up to blossom into developing healthy, life-enhancing relationships that offer mutual healing, support, and connection.

## Getting Support To Forge Healthy Relationships

Since many of us were raised to feel responsible for other people's feelings and well-being, it can be extremely challenging to say no without feeling terrible guilt or shame at first. Also, once we do start saying no and setting boundaries with friends and family, we'll likely get a lot of pushback from those who've relied on using guilt and shame to manipulate us to get what they want.

If you're having difficulty setting boundaries or letting go of friends or family members who aren't healthy for you, I strongly recommend you seek support from a trauma-informed coach or therapist or an Al-Anon or Codependents Anonymous group.

## We Can't Heal Our Trauma If We Continue To Engage in Unhealthy Relationships

It's important to remember that what's good for you is also good for other people. If you continue to allow yourself to be used, shamed, blamed, drained, or abused, you simply can't heal your trauma and will continue to suffer from C-PTSD symptoms.

When you choose health-oriented, introspective friends and mates, you'll find it much easier to heal your trauma, maintain your emotional and physical health, and experience much more joy and fulfillment in your daily life!

Countless studies show we tend to mirror the habits and lifestyles of the five people we spend the most time with. Thus, if you want to know what your future will look like from an emotional, physical, financial, and lifestyle standpoint, take a look at the five people you spend the most time with. If you like what you see, congratulate yourself and keep nurturing these relationships. If you don't, it's time to get clear about your values and goals and find like-minded people on a similar path.

If you are financially dependent on your spouse or are unable to leave an abusive or unhealthy personal or professional relationship, you can start with baby steps by connecting with new, healthier people. See the appendix for listings of various online and in-person self-help groups. Visit several until you find a group you feel safe in and will attend consistently.

If you are in a violent or emotionally abusive relationship, please see the appendix to reach out to an appropriate domestic violence hotline. There is an abundance of support for victims of domestic violence (domestic violence includes emotional and physical abuse toward women, men, and children). You and your children deserve to live in a safe, nurturing home.

## How High Levels of Hope & Support Dramatically Improve Physical & Mental Health

It was stunning to see the graphs below proving that people with high support and hope experience 250-300% better physical and mental health.

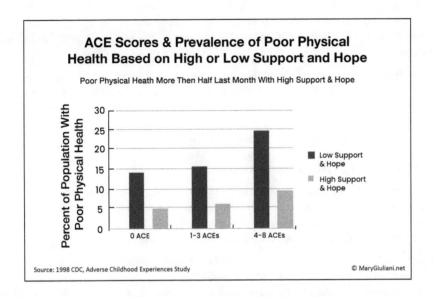

The above graph illustrates that the health of those with low levels of support and hope was 250% worse than those with high levels of support and hope.

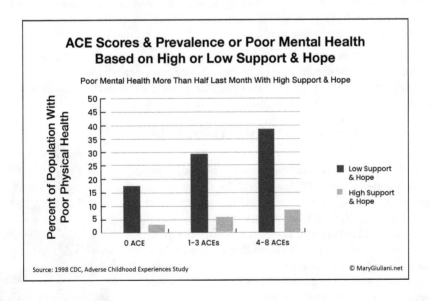

The above graph illustrates that the mental health of those with low levels of support and hope was 300% worse than the mental health of those with high levels of support and hope.

Both of these studies make it crystal clear that investing in building a solid support system is not only worth it but essential if you want to protect your mental and physical health.

## Join Like-Minded Groups or Communities

Some people find it safer to begin working on healing their ability to form healthy relationships in a group setting. This was certainly true for me in my early AA recovery. Becoming active in Twelve-Step and other self-help groups with like-minded people was key to getting the social support that helped me feel connected to others.

In fact, joining and being active in a local lesbian social group is one of the best decisions I've ever made because that's where I met my partner, Maria, and also where I've made many other close friends. The key to connecting through self-help or like-minded social groups is finding ones that meet weekly and committing to attend consistently. Consistent attendance is the only way to get to know the members, which will open the door to developing one-on-one relationships.

## Finding My Tribe: Joining PACEsconnection.com

I've found joining groups aligned with my purpose, personal goals, and professional aspirations has also been a great way to form relationships and connect with like-minded people. Finding groups that attract people committed to living their best lives and interested in evolving and making a difference for others is an excellent way to get and stay on track for your goals.

Once I learned that I'd been suffering from childhood trauma, I wanted to find like-minded survivors I could connect with who were also on a trauma-healing journey. I searched online and fortunately found PACEsconnection.com. PACEs is an acronym for Positive & Adverse Childhood Experiences. PACEsconnection.com is a social and professional network comprised of trauma-oriented practitioners, leaders, activists, and people from many sectors of society.

What's so wonderful about PACEsconnection.com is that its main objective is to bring together professionals from many different sectors to raise awareness about positive and adverse childhood experiences and to collaborate on preventing and healing childhood trauma.

One of the gifts of joining PACEsconnection.com has been the many colleagues and close friends I've made through it. Developing friendships with people who really understand what it's like to deal with the long shadow of childhood trauma is invaluable.

I've attended several childhood trauma conferences, movie screenings, and various social events with friends I've met from PACEsconnection.com. Also, my weekly accountability partners who have helped keep me on track with this book are also women I met through PACESconnection.com. This is the power of consistently engaging with a community of safe, like-minded people.

## Meeting Two of My Heroes: Dr. Vincent Felitti & Dr. Gabor Maté

In 2017 I heard through the PACEsconnection.com blog that Dr. Vincent Felitti, co-founder of the ACE Study, and Dr. Gabor Maté, author of *In the Realm of Hungry Ghosts: Close Encounters With Addiction,* were going to offer a joint session at an upcoming California Association of Marriage and Family Therapists (CAMFT) conference in my area. I was so excited to learn this since both men had made such a profound difference in my trauma-recovery journey. I immediately purchased a ticket and reached out to my local friends at PACEsconnection.com to see if they wanted to join me.

Fortunately, a colleague of mine had contacted Dr. Felitti before the conference and had scheduled to meet with him after his session to give him a signed copy of a book she'd recently published about

Dr. Vince Felitti, ACE Study Co-Founder, and I at a CAMFT conference

her trauma-healing journey. After his speaking session, my friend graciously introduced me to him and invited me to join them for lunch!

There I was, sitting right next to and chatting with Dr. Felitti. It was such an honor to be in the presence of someone so instrumental in uncovering the most significant revelation about the link between childhood adversity and later negative health and social outcomes. Also, at the end of Felitti's and Maté's talk, I was thrilled to be able to get a photo with both of these extraordinary men.

Having these experiences is a beautiful example of how connecting with like-minded people is a critical piece of healing trauma. After all, childhood trauma is relational trauma, so the more we learn how to connect with safe people who are also committed to healing their trauma, the better chance we'll have to heal and live our best lives.

## 2. Practice Self-Care

People who make the most progress over the long term with healing trauma are committed to a lifestyle focused on minimizing stress and maximizing self-care.

Since many survivors were not adequately cared for by their parents, many never learned to care for themselves. This accounts for why self-care is such a common struggle for survivors and why we must learn how to care for ourselves to be able to foster resilience and heal our trauma.

- **Eat healthy, hydrate, and get enough sleep:** Promoting positive lifestyle factors—such as healthy eating, ample sleep, and hydration—can strengthen your body to adapt to stress and reduce the toll of anxiety and depression. I've dedicated an entire chapter to what I have done to incorporate healthy eating in my life in Chapter 33, "Food Addiction and Weight-Loss Recovery Options for Survivors."

- **Move your body:** When I got into recovery, I began doing easy bike rides every weekend, and my sober friends and I would grab lunch somewhere afterward. I found that moving my body and connecting with like-minded friends in nature was the highlight of my week.

  I slowly built my endurance to where we did longer and longer rides. Out of my weekly commitment to riding my bike, I not only lost weight; I also improved my emotional and physical health and developed several close relationships. I also developed a love for bicycling and still ride today. For more information on incorporating healthy exercise into your life, see Chapter 33, "Food Addiction and Weight-Loss Recovery Options for Survivors."

- **Practice mindfulness:** Practicing mindfulness has been one of the most powerful tools I've used to get and stay regulated. It's one of the best skills you can develop to calm down your nervous system, which helps build resilience and shifts you out of stressful or ruminating thoughts. As a result of my mindfulness practice, I feel much more peaceful in my day-to-day life.

In *Healing The Fragmented Selves of Trauma Survivors: Overcoming Internal Self-Alienation,* trauma expert and psychotherapist Janina Fisher writes about the value of practicing mindfulness in healing trauma.

> Mindfulness has an important role to play in the treatment of trauma because of its effects on the brain and body. Mindfulness practices counteract trauma-related cortical inhibition, regulate autonomic activation, and allow us to have a relationship of interest and curiosity toward our feelings, thoughts, and body responses.
>
> Mindfulness is an act of hospitality, a way of learning to treat ourselves with kindness and care that slowly begins to percolate into the deepest recesses of our being while gradually offering us the possibility of relating to others in the same manner....

- **Journaling:** There's something about putting pen to paper that opens up a portal deep within that has helped me understand how to handle difficult emotions or other upsetting situations. Just knowing I can pick up a pen and a pad of paper is calming in and of itself because I know it will help shift me out of my pain and give me the clarity I need to find a resolution.

- **Get support to handle addictions or self-destructive habits:** Addiction is extremely common for survivors. If you struggle with addiction, please know you're not alone. Using alcohol, drugs, food, or other self-destructive behaviors is an attempt to soothe the emotional pain resulting from a chronically dysregulated brain, body, and mind due to childhood trauma. The problem with engaging in a drug or alcohol addiction is it makes it impossible to heal your trauma. It sets you up to be continually retraumatized due to the brain, mind, and body becoming hijacked by the addiction. This is why it's crucial to find an addiction recovery or harm-reduction program while simultaneously getting the support you need to heal your trauma. To access resources for addiction recovery, see Chapter 32, "Alcohol and Drug Addiction Recovery Options for Survivors."

- **Get support to handle mental health issues:** The ACE Study proved that people with high ACE scores are much more likely to suffer from anxiety, depression, or other mental health issues. When mental health issues aren't managed, they can wreak havoc in survivors' lives and undermine resilience. This is why being willing to get the support necessary to handle mental health issues is critical in building resilience and healing trauma. See the appendix for mental health resources.

- **Remove or minimize stress:** Just as people with diabetes must reduce or eliminate their sugar intake to stay healthy, people with C-PTSD must minimize the stress in their lives. Since C-PTSD is about having a highly sensitive and reactive stress-response system, making decisions on a personal and professional level to keep your stress levels to a minimum is vital for healing trauma. Managing stress is also critical for preventing stress-related illnesses, substance relapses, or addictive behaviors. Removing or minimizing stress also includes refraining from or minimizing watching or listening to media or news that fuels fear, shame, outrage, depression, or contempt.

## 3. Build A Sense of Agency

Since a sense of powerlessness is part and parcel of childhood trauma, building a sense of agency is critical to healing trauma and building resilience. Agency is the opposite of helplessness. Developing a sense of agency builds confidence and the capacity to take purposeful, effective action.

You know you have choices when you have agency. You speak up for what matters to you. You seek meaning and act with purpose to achieve the conditions you desire in your life versus responding passively to circumstances. Since many survivors were shamed or punished for asserting themselves and asking for what they needed, speaking up can be extremely difficult.

**Becoming proficient in the following four competencies is crucial to building a sense of agency:**

### a) Set & Hold Your Boundaries

Learning to set and hold healthy boundaries is critical in maintaining a sense of agency. When we have weak boundaries, we inadvertently allow others to take over our time, space, energy, and moods. This contributes to feelings of helplessness instead of being in charge of your life. I often joke that one of the greatest gifts my mother gave me was the opportunity to earn my Ph.D. in boundary setting!

### b) Raise Your Standards

Ensuring your standards are set or raised to a level that facilitates meeting your needs is essential to experience a sense of agency. When you don't set or maintain adequate standards, you settle for less-than-fulfilling relationships, careers, and health. Taking baby steps to raise my standards has been a critical strategy for building a sense of agency.

### c) Be Proactive

A way to be proactive is to ask yourself, "What actions can I take to solve this problem?" If the problem seems too big to tackle, break it down into manageable pieces. If you still feel stuck, reach out for help. I've found that Google and YouTube are fantastic resources for getting ideas for solving all kinds of issues.

### d) Set & Move Toward Your Goals

Develop realistic goals and take regular action. Even when you take baby steps and make what seems like insignificant progress, each win empowers and encourages you to continue. Over time, your cumulative wins turn into significant progress. Instead of focusing on tasks that seem unachievable, ask yourself, "What's one thing I can accomplish today that helps me move in the direction I want to go?" Then make sure you do at least that one thing.

## 4. Get Okay With Disappointing People

We can't be everything to everyone, and if we try, we end up depleted, angry, anxious, or depressed. To build resilience, you must develop the ability to say no to people when it's not in your best interest to say yes. If guilt or shame prevents you from disappointing people, make seeking help from a trauma-informed coach or therapist your first priority to overcoming it.

I once had a coach who gave me the assignment of disappointing at least three people a week. This assignment was not meant to be mean-spirited. Instead, it helped me say no to requests when I normally would have said yes.

At first, I cringed at doing this exercise because on some level, I knew it would bring up major guilt and shame. This goes back to my mom telling me that saying no meant I was selfish and bad. It also brought up the part of me that felt responsible for someone's sadness or disappointment when I said no.

I'm so grateful to this coach because this exercise profoundly changed my life! Just being willing to be uncomfortable with knowing some people would be disappointed with my no and saying it anyway helped me see that I can say no and still be loved and connected with people. Over time it got easier and easier. Today it's no big deal to say no, even when I know it will disappoint someone. Also, if someone in my life can't respect my need to say no, I know they aren't the kind of person I want in my life anyway.

## 5. Don't Take Failure Personally

All humans are imperfect and will fail. In fact, we must be willing to fail to succeed. Failing is part of the journey to success. It's completely normal and should be expected.

However, if we see one failure as proof that our entire self is a failure, we experience shame.

We must learn to separate failing in one area of life or failing at one goal from believing that our entire self is a failure. Getting support from a trauma-informed coach or therapist is essential if you're struggling with guilt, shame, or the fear of failure. I also recommend reading and doing the exercises in chapter 29, "Letting Go of Guilt and Shame."

## 6. Gain Competencies

Gaining competencies is about acquiring the skills necessary to achieve your goals in particular areas. Becoming competent naturally fosters a sense of self-efficacy, which fosters resilience.

In my late twenties, I felt trapped in my job as a medical insurance biller because I didn't have a college degree or any other marketable skills. In desperation to get out of my soul-sucking job, I asked my girlfriend (who I lived with) if she would financially support me while I took care of meals, errands, laundry, shopping, and household chores. Thank goodness she said no.

Being unable to depend on my girlfriend for income created the financial tension necessary to motivate me to find work more aligned with who I'd become.   In doing so, I developed the sales, marketing, and business skills I would need to launch my first business. At the time, having to stretch and risk failure by changing jobs and learning new skills was extremely uncomfortable for me. Yet doing so was a critical developmental step because I gained the invaluable experience of knowing I could take care of myself by learning a new skill in order to become competent in a new career. The experience of gaining competence has given me the confidence to pursue and achieve many personal and professional goals.

## 7. Build Reserves of Money, Time, and Relationships

One of the greatest lessons I learned from the *Personal Foundation* course by Thomas Leonard (who was considered the father of the life coaching movement) was the necessity of building reserves in my life.

I learned that without adequate reserves of money, time, and relationships, I would be relegated to living in survival mode, which is a very constricted, miserable way to live.

Scarcity and fear-based thoughts naturally decrease when you've built enough money, time, and relationship reserves.  This opens up the space for authenticity and creativity to flourish, setting the stage for creating a fulfilling life.

Understanding this principle was a key reason that, in 2002, I decided to pursue online marketing and advertising sales versus continuing as an entrepreneur after I recovered from my relapse with alcohol. I knew I needed to build back my financial reserves before I considered launching another business. Also, since my compensation in advertising sales was performance-based instead of hourly, I could get my work done in half the time, which helped me maintain reserves of free time.

I quickly learned that having adequate reserves provides an abundance of choices that aren't otherwise available. Having the ability to leave a soul-sucking job or an unfulfilling or abusive relationship is often impossible without having the necessary reserves in place.

When making decisions on a personal or professional level, I always ask myself if the decision will help or hinder my money, time, or relationship reserves. In fact, the very reason I was able to take time off to write this book is because of the reserves of time, money, and relationships I've been committed to building and maintaining over the years.

## 8. Embrace Healthy Thoughts

- **Question your thoughts:** Identify areas of irrational thinking, such as a tendency to catastrophize difficulties, and ask yourself, "Do I know for a fact that my thoughts regarding this issue are true?" Often I say to myself either, "I need more information" or "What am I making up about this?" This helps me calm down because I'm acknowledging that until I know the facts, I really am making stuff up.

  I've also found that bringing levity to a fearful thought by saying to myself, "Mary, stop going to makeupshit.com"is really helpful in shifting myself out of a fearful state in a fun way.  The reality is that unless I have the facts, I really am making shit up! Until I have more information, it's in my best interest to stop terrorizing myself with fear-based, arbitrary thoughts. Once I can get some distance from these made-up thoughts, I automatically calm down.

- **Accept Change:** Accept that change is a part of life. It's important to face that certain goals or ideals may no longer be attainable due to various circumstances. Accepting what you can't change can help you focus on what you can. AA's Serenity Prayer, *God grant me the serenity to accept the things I cannot change, the courage to change the things I can, and the wisdom to know the difference* captures this principle. If you're uncomfortable with the word *God*, you can simply leave it out or use whatever term you're comfortable with while reciting this prayer.

- **Maintain a hopeful outlook:** It's hard to be positive when life isn't going your way or when you're in a triggered fear-based trauma reaction. I learned through the polyvagal theory that when I'm triggered and in a dysregulated state, my brain can't help but serve up fearful thoughts. Once I understood this, I realized I can't always trust my perceptions to be accurate.

  As long as there's no evidence that I'm in danger or some terrible thing really is going to happen, I've found it helpful to handle these negative thoughts by saying to myself, "Mary, you're experiencing a neuronal glitch." This helps me stay in a place of non-resistance while at the same time not taking my fearful thoughts seriously. I then focus on what steps I can take to get regulated.

- **Access the wisdom you've gained from overcoming past obstacles:** By looking back at who or what was helpful in previous times of hardship or distress, you may discover how to respond more effectively to your current situation. Remind yourself of where you've found strength from previous difficulties and recall how you were able to overcome or get through them. Also, ask yourself what you've learned from those experiences and apply the wisdom you've gained to overcome the current challenge.

- **Practice Acceptance:** I first learned about practicing acceptance in AA. An excerpt from page 417 of AA's Big *Book* (the main text of the AA program) was often read at the beginning of meetings.

  > Acceptance is the answer to all my problems today. When I am disturbed, it is because I find some person, place, thing, or situation—some fact of my life—unacceptable to me, and I can find no serenity until I accept that person, place, thing, or situation as being exactly the way it is supposed to be at this moment. Nothing, absolutely nothing, happens in God's world by mistake. Until I could accept my alcoholism, I could not stay sober; unless I accept life completely on life's terms, I cannot be happy. I need to concentrate not so much on what needs to be changed in the world as on what needs to be changed in me and my attitudes.

  Whenever I had difficulty with something in my early recovery, I would remind myself that *acceptance was the answer to all my problems today.* After hearing the acceptance excerpt recited in AA meetings for years, I got to know it by heart and would use it as a mantra when I was struggling with something. Practicing acceptance alone has saved me from so much needless suffering.

  Practicing acceptance doesn't mean we should bury our heads in the sand if we can take action or work on healing something distressing us. I still take action and do my healing work, but I can do so while doing my best to stay unattached to the outcome.

- **Look at challenges as opportunities for healing and self-discovery:** Remind yourself how you've grown due to previous struggles. This can help reframe a current challenge not as something that's happening *to* you but as something that's happening *for* you.

  I've also found it helpful to ask myself, "In what ways can I grow from this struggle?" This helps me shift from feeling disappointed and sad to feeling hopeful for the growth the experience will offer.

  The great thing about honing my skills as an author is I'm able to look at everything that happens in my life—the good, bad and ugly—as potential content for this or another book. I also look at it as a possible topic for speaking engagements or as hard-earned wisdom I can use to overcome future difficulties or share with my partner, friends, clients, and followers.

## 9. Embrace Your Authenticity & Find Your Purpose

Experiencing a sense of meaning and purpose in life is a natural human need. When you're not honoring your authentic self and living your purpose, it feels like life is passing you by. Without being clear about who you are and your purpose, life feels empty and meaningless, which is an extremely painful place to be.

Having a purpose sets a framework and focus for your life. Finding a way to make doing what you love part of your career or vocation can help fulfill the sense of meaning and purpose we naturally need as humans. It also fosters self-worth, enables you to connect with like-minded people, and provides a sense of satisfaction knowing you're helping others. This is why every aspect of living your purpose helps build resilience.

Those who lack purpose or meaning are vulnerable to depression, which drives the need for relief and sets the stage for using substances or other self-defeating behaviors to cope.

When we don't discover who we are and what we value and align it with our unique purpose, our lives become like leaves in the wind, blown about by outside forces rather than directed by who we are and what we most want to contribute to the world. This makes us vulnerable to being swayed by the tides of family, culture, friends, or employers.

When I got on my personal growth path, I did a lot of work identifying goals that would naturally pull me forward. I used to ask myself whether a new goal was a game worth playing. Posing this question helped me discover what goals best honored my core values. Identifying what you love is about tapping into your authentic self.

What I've found is that it wasn't until I let go of my shame about my addiction and obesity history that my purpose revealed itself to me. Therefore if you're struggling to get clear on your purpose, just keep the focus on healing your trauma, and eventually, your purpose will be revealed to you.

## 10. Reach Out For Help

Many of us couldn't depend on our family members while growing up, so it's common for survivors to be fiercely independent and resist needing help from anyone. Getting help when you need it is crucial in building resilience and healing from childhood trauma. It's natural to need help. Nobody recovers alone.

Part of trauma recovery is learning to trust people in gradual, safe ways. For me, seeking outside help has been a critical component of healing my trauma, getting sober, maintaining a healthy weight, and forming healthy relationships. In fact, every aspect of my recovery has involved reaching out for help.

Reaching out starts with baby steps. If you're willing to stretch outside your comfort zone, you'll be amazed at how many wonderful people are waiting to help you. In the appendix, I list dozens of groups, websites, podcasts, and books that have helped me build resilience and create a life I love.

## 11. Be Willing To Stretch Outside Your Comfort Zone To Heal Your Trauma

Although learning about C-PTSD is a critical first step on the trauma-healing journey, to experience true healing, we must have what is known as "corrective experiences." A corrective experience occurs as a result of a survivor stretching outside their comfort zone by operating differently than they normally would.

**Examples of corrective experiences:**

- You ask for your needs to be met when you usually wouldn't, then experience getting them met without being shamed, overlooked, or ignored.
- If you do get shamed, overlooked, or ignored, you stand up for yourself and ask for what you need and get it.
- If you still don't get your needs met due to someone not being willing or able to do so, you find someone else who can.
- You share an opposing opinion when you normally wouldn't feel safe doing so and are met with

respect. Or you use healthy anger to call someone out who is disrespectful toward you.

- You ask someone to stop doing something that bothers you when you normally wouldn't, and you're met with understanding and respect instead of invalidation, shame, or ridicule.
- You say no to someone knowing they'll likely be disappointed.

These are the types of corrective experiences that provide a visceral sensation in your body and an emotional experience necessary to heal trauma. Just having a cognitive understanding of how healing trauma works isn't enough. It must translate into how you show up in your relationship with yourself and others.

Whenever I show up in a healthier or more constructive way with myself and others, I give myself the gift of a corrective experience. Also, intentionally asserting my needs, defending or protecting myself when I normally wouldn't, is another way to give myself a corrective experience.

Interpersonal relationships offer the perfect opportunity to practice giving yourself corrective experiences. Since we were wounded in relationships, we also must heal in relationships. Initially, practicing corrective experiences will be uncomfortable because they're counter to how you've operated in the past. Practicing corrective experiences provides the neural exercises that your brain and body need to heal your trauma. By staying committed to doing so in your relationships, over time, you'll experience a whole new sense of connection with yourself and others.

What's essential to remember before engaging with someone with the intention of having a corrective experience is that you choose safe people or environments so that you don't become overwhelmed or get retraumatized. If you're not comfortable practicing with a friend or partner, working with a therapist or a trauma-informed coach can provide the safe space necessary for this healing experience.

## 12. Tell Your Trauma Story

Another fascinating fact I learned in researching childhood trauma is how beneficial it is to your health to share your trauma story. After the initial 17,000 Kaiser Permanente members answered the ten ACE Study questions and discussed how each ACE had impacted them with their doctor, Kaiser Permanente saw a 35% reduction in their doctor office visits and an 11% reduction in their emergency room visits the following year.

This speaks to how having a trusted, empathetic person to tell your trauma story to is very therapeutic for your emotional and physical health.

In another example of this phenomenon, Dr. Christiane Northrup stated during a summit on building resilience, "If you've been victimized, you need to have that validated. Most of my medical practice was witnessing wounds. When the wound is witnessed, the person can heal."

Once again, this demonstrates the healing power of sharing your story. If you're uncomfortable or are not ready to share your trauma story, you don't have to share it with another person. But for the sake of your mental and physical health, acknowledging it to yourself by writing about it in a journal or diary can still be very therapeutic.

- **Find people to share your story with:** Twelve-Step groups and communities were safe places for me to share my story. Groups such as Adult Children of Alcoholics (ACOA), Codependents Anonymous (CoDA), Al-Anon, Alcoholics Anonymous (AA), Narcotics Anonymous (NA), and Overeaters Anonymous (OA) were all safe places for me to share my story.

  It's important to visit a few Twelve-Step groups and go for coffee or a meal with members afterward to see which ones are the best fit for you. There are also sponsors in each group who work with members who are safe to share your story with. The first step is showing up at a meeting.

- **How to make it safe to share your story:** Before you tell your story, it's essential to set yourself up for a safe experience. I recommend telling your chosen confidant in advance that you would like to share something really vulnerable and asking if they are open to listening to you. Then ask them if they are willing to listen with compassion and refrain from feedback. If they're unwilling or seem to hesitate at your requests for safety, I'd move on to someone who is.

## 13. Talk About Your Feelings

No one ever talked to me about the stress of witnessing my mother's rage and alcoholism and how she terrorized our family for over a decade during my childhood. This is an example of how we get traumatized not only by witnessing actual events but also by not being able to talk about them afterward.

These bottled-up emotions contributed to my need to find relief. Since I couldn't turn to my family for understanding and support, I developed substitute relationships with food, alcohol, and marijuana.

Over the years, I've found I always feel better after sharing with my partner, a trusted friend, or my therapist about my trauma or any type of difficulty I'm going through. I've learned time and time again that I must talk about what's going on with me with a safe person to make sense of it and resolve it. Just thinking about it or putting it out of my mind doesn't work.

When survivors don't talk about difficult emotions, the trauma energy stays alive in the body and mind and can wreak havoc on the nervous system. This primes us for physical and mental health issues and addictions. Also, to experience true intimacy with another person, we must be willing to share our vulnerable selves.

### Hiding My Vulnerability Came with a Price

In my early recovery from alcohol and drugs, I shared only the positive things going on in my life at my AA meetings. I didn't realize the reason I wasn't sharing my pain and setbacks was because of the deep shame I had about revealing them. Back then, I equated accomplishments with self-worth and emotional pain or setbacks with failure or weakness. I feared if people knew about my struggles, they'd judge me and not want to be my friend.

It wasn't until I returned to AA after my relapse twelve years later that I began sharing the good, bad, and ugly of what was going on in my life. As a result, I made many more friends in the program and received much more support. That was one of the best lessons and gifts I got in my second round of recovery.

Pete Walker's quote *Profound loneliness is the price we pay when we only reveal the good things that are happening in our lives* beautifully captures the price I paid when I wasn't willing to be vulnerable about my pain. When I first stepped outside my comfort zone to share my vulnerable self, the key was picking safe people and groups. I'm so grateful since I no longer suffer the loneliness I did when I felt the need to hide the less-than-shiny parts of myself.

We need at least one person to share our deepest thoughts and feelings with to maintain our emotional health. If you don't have a close friend, spouse, or family member to share your feelings with, reach out to a trauma-informed therapist, coach, or practitioner for support. Feeling seen, heard, and supported is key to building resilience, healing trauma, and living a happy, healthy life. See the appendix for resources on finding safe support.

## 14. Practice Somatic Mindfulness

Once I learned body emotions were ubiquitous among trauma survivors, I began making a conscious effort to be more mindful when I had pain or discomfort in my body to discern what my body was trying to tell me. Listening in to my body's sensations made me realize how disconnected I had been from it.

Before learning I had trauma, I was unaware of the tension in my body. If I did notice it, I rarely connected it to stress or difficult emotions related to circumstances I was facing at the time. And I definitely wasn't aware that tension or health-related symptoms could be due to a past trauma getting triggered.

Learning that survivors automatically and unconsciously shut down their body sensations for self-protection helped me understand how body emotions work. After becoming more aware of my body and understanding that physical symptoms may indicate repressed emotions, I recalled some symptoms I frequently had when I sang in front of audiences. About an hour before I was to go on stage, if you'd asked me if I was nervous, I would have said I felt fine. But my body was telling me a different story. I frequently felt bloated and had stomach cramps or sometimes even diarrhea. It's so apparent now that these symptoms were body emotions. Even though I was not conscious of being nervous, my body expressed my anxiety through these physical symptoms.

Understanding how common body emotions are for survivors opened the door for me to embrace a somatic mindfulness practice. The nice thing about somatic mindfulness is how easy it is to do. I simply scan my entire body and feel into even its slightest sensations. I also started a gentle stretch yoga class to strengthen my somatic mindfulness practice. The nice thing about yoga is that it automatically includes deep breathing as part of the practice. Over time I noticed more and more sensations in my body. It felt so good to get back into my body. Over time my somatic mindfulness practice became an automatic way of being, to where I didn't even need to consciously do it anymore because it was running all the time.

Now that I understand the connection between my emotions, physical symptoms, and trauma triggers, I automatically assume that I'm having a body emotion when my body acts up. I can often tie it into something that would typically be stressful, even if I don't feel stressed. This allows me to process it. Sometimes just noticing my bodily sensations and dialoguing with them to see if they are related to a past trauma getting triggered is enough to identify and release the pain or discomfort. Other times it's helpful to stretch, do yoga and breathwork, journal, or talk to my partner or a safe friend.

Sometimes I'm unable to connect a body issue with current stress or previous trauma. But just understanding the connection between my body, brain, and mind makes me feel more connected to my whole self. As a result of gaining this awareness and implementing a somatic mindfulness practice, I have fewer body emotions. And I'm also able to be much more present, which in and of itself feels wonderful.

## 15. Focus On Your Strengths

Since feeling powerless is part and parcel of childhood trauma, learning to focus on your accomplishments and the strengths you've developed to achieve them is a wonderful way to shift into knowing that you have what it takes to achieve your goals.

One of the rituals I've performed at the end of every year since becoming a Master Certified Coach twenty-five years ago is making a list of all my accomplishments for the year and identifying the strengths I accessed to achieve them.

Listing our accomplishments and strengths proves that we have the competency and power we need to create what we want in our lives. This is why compiling a list of our accomplishments and strengths feels so amazing. When we don't review or acknowledge our accomplishments and strengths, instead of getting to feel the sense of healthy pride, agency, and fulfillment we were after in pursuing them, they fade away and become distant memories.

When our *fulfillment tank* remains empty, we continually spin around, attempting to fill it with the next accomplishment, not realizing we have a hole in our tank. Once we plug the hole by acknowledging our accomplishments and strengths, we'll experience much more fulfillment since we'll be reminded of how competent we are and what a contribution we make to the world.

To utilize this exercise when healing C-PTSD, we first take a look at what challenges we faced as a child and what strengths we developed to survive our childhoods (e.g., getting through school, learning to ride a bike or a sport, dealing with a parent or caregiver who was dysfunctional, abusive, neglectful, and/or who struggled with addiction or mental illness, etc.) List anything that was difficult for you as a child and how you managed to cope or get through it.

Some of the strengths I identified that got me through my childhood were being acutely aware of people's feelings and being positive, resourceful, innovative, and independent. I have relied on all of these strengths throughout my personal and professional life.

Then we take a look at what we are most proud of accomplishing in our adulthood and identify what strengths it took to accomplish them. When we tally up which strengths show up most frequently from both our childhood and adulthood, we've identified our top strengths. If one strength stands out over the others, it may even be our superpower!

The strengths I've identified that have helped me accomplish the things I'm most proud of as an adult are self-awareness, commitment, perseverance, resourcefulness, enthusiasm, and innovation.

Want to know what your top strengths are? Complete the below *Identifying Your Strengths Worksheet*.

# IDENTIFYING YOUR STRENGTHS WORKSHEET

**Directions:**

1. List three strengths it took to get through or survive your childhood (e.g., getting through school, learning a sport, dealing with a parent, caregiver, sibling, bully, or other person who was dysfunctional, abusive, neglectful, and/or who struggled with addiction or mental illness, etc.)

2. List five accomplishments you're proud of as an adult and the strengths it took to achieve them.

3. Count how many times each strength is listed in your childhood and adulthood. The strengths listed most often are your top strengths. And the strength listed most often is likely your superpower. List your top strength and superpower below.

4. Take a few minutes to acknowledge the strengths you developed to survive your childhood. Also, take a few minutes to acknowledge the accomplishments you've listed and the strengths it took to achieve them as an adult. Consider sharing them with a safe friend or spouse.

5. List how you can tap into your top strengths in your day-to-day life.

**Childhood  Challenges/Accomplishments**          **Strengths It Took To Achieve Them**

1. _____          _____

2. _____          _____

3. _____          _____


**Adult Accomplishments You Are Most Proud Of**          **Strengths It Took To Achieve Them**

1. _____          _____

2. _____          _____

3. _____          _____

4. _____          _____

5. _____          _____

# YOUR TOP STRENGTHS

**What Four Strengths Are Listed Most Often From Your Childhood and Adulthood?**

1. _____

2. _____

3. _____

4. _____

# YOUR SUPERPOWER

**Would You Consider One of Your Top Strengths Your Superpower?  If So, What Is It?**

_____

# ACKNOWLEDGE YOUR ACCOMPLISHMENTS & STRENGTHS

Give yourself a few minutes to stop and take in your accomplishments.  Allow yourself to feel proud of yourself for overcoming the obstacles you did to achieve these feats.  Also, take the time to acknowledge and feel proud of the strengths you developed to achieve them.

1. How does it feel to acknowledge your accomplishments and strengths?

_____

2. How often will you acknowledge yourself for your accomplishments and strengths?

_____

3. Who will you share your accomplishments and strengths with?

_____

4. How can you tap into your top strengths in your day-to-day life?

_____

_____

_____

# CHAPTER 27

———————

# REDEFINING RELATIONSHIPS TO MEET YOUR NEEDS

It's the quality of our relationships that determine the quality of our lives.

—Esther Perel

## What Do You Need for Healthy, Fulfilling Relationships?

Since childhood trauma is relational trauma, close relationships tend to trigger physiological and psychological stress responses, making it uncomfortable and stressful for survivors to maintain close relationships. Since being able to develop and maintain safe relationships is critical for a survivor's recovery, it begs the question, How do we connect with people when we're bombarded with triggers when we attempt to do so?

The first step in healing relational trauma is becoming aware of what your triggers are and how to know when you've become triggered. This is why mindfulness and somatic mindfulness practices are critical for your recovery.

An excellent way to learn how it feels to be triggered is to be extra mindful the next time someone you know you're uncomfortable being around will be at an event or when a certain topic gets brought up with your spouse or other family members. Get curious about the sensations you feel in your body, the thoughts you're thinking about, and the behavior you tend to engage in when you're around this person or when this topic is brought up. What this process accomplishes is making the implicit explicit, which is what's necessary to heal trauma.

For example, when someone new comes into my life, and there's a potential for a close friendship, my triggered state begins with my ruminating about the person's emotional health and if there's a potential for them to shame or drain me. This trigger is from my shaming and draining relationship with my mom. I may also experience anxiety in my body and thoughts about how to handle our initial interactions, which can trigger a craving to numb or calm myself down with sweets or carbs. I also may have rigid, perfectionistic standards of who I allow into my life. I'm aware that this serves as an avoidance strategy for self-protection.

236

Now that I'm aware of my relational trauma history and know what it feels like to be triggered, I'm able to acknowledge when I'm experiencing a trigger. I remind myself that the state I'm in is an emotional flashback from my childhood, this person is not my mother, and even if this potential friend has similar traits that she had, I'm an adult now and can protect myself. I also remind myself that nobody is perfect and that I can trust myself to choose good enough friends.

My first priority is making sure I pick safe people to become friends with. Finding groups dedicated to healing relational trauma has been the best place for me to do so. When I first got into healing my trauma and wanted to find like-minded people I could connect with in my area, I Googled childhood trauma groups. That's how I found PACEsconnection.com, a huge network of professionals all over the United States who are all about healing and preventing childhood trauma.

As a result of my involvement in PACEsconnection.com, I met dozens of people online and in person and made many safe friends who are also passionate about healing childhood trauma.

Codependents Anonymous (CoDA) is another excellent support group of safe people. The nice thing about CoDA meetings is you can slowly get to know people without pressure to develop one-on-one relationships. Over time and with consistent attendance, friendships grow organically from these types of groups.

For some survivors who have experienced severe abuse and neglect, connecting with other humans can be so overwhelming that, for a time, it may just not be possible to form close, personal relationships. In this case, bonding with a dog or cat can be very therapeutic for a survivor. Experiencing a nurturing connection with a pet can be a great stepping-stone before expanding into developing relationships with either a therapist or coach or through making new friends.

## What Do You Desire in a Relationship?

Before you embark on improving existing or developing new relationships, it's essential to clarify the relationship standards you need to set to give you the best chance of engaging in positive, healthy relationships.

Since survivors were traumatized in close relationships, when we don't consciously set or raise our standards for the people we allow in our life, we will default to choosing relationships that mirror what we grew up with.

## How I Stopped Picking Partners I Wasn't Attracted To

Before I got into recovery, while in my twenties, my self-esteem was so low that I never thought to ask myself what I wanted or needed in a relationship. Back then, if a woman was attracted to me, was fun to be with, and drank and partied like I did, that was enough for me to be with her. Being attracted to her wasn't something I required. Given I was so overweight, drank so heavily, and felt so unattractive, I didn't think I deserved to make attraction a must-have with the women I dated.

After I got sober and lost 140lbs through Overeaters Anonymous and found myself still choosing women I wasn't attracted to, I realized this dysfunctional pattern had to be serving another purpose other than my not feeling worthy of someone I was attracted to due to my appearance.

After doing some introspective work to uncover what this pattern was about, I discovered that picking partners with whom I felt an emotional connection but not an attraction kept me safe from being vulnerable since I couldn't fall in love with them. This pattern caused a lot of pain and heartache throughout my twenties and early thirties.

Thankfully, through my personal healing journey, I learned I needed to commit to setting a new standard to only date women to whom I had both an emotional connection and an attraction. As a result of raising my dating standards, I have only been with women I've been attracted to for the past thirty years and have enjoyed several deeply fulfilling long-term relationships.

## Choosing Between Being Authentic or Protecting Your Attachment Relationship

Dr. Gabor Maté is the first author I've found to address the common conflict humans have between honoring their authenticity vs. giving it up to protect their attachment relationships. In the excerpt below in his book *The Myth of Normal: Trauma, Illness & Healing in a Toxic Culture,* he writes about how when children are not seen and accepted for who they are, or that certain parts of them are acceptable and others are not, a split begins to form in their sense of self. And if this internal split is not addressed and healed, it can negatively affect them and their relationships for their entire lives.

> The statement *Good children don't yell,* spoken with annoyance, carries an unintended but most effective threat. *Angry children don't get loved.* Being nice (read: burying one's anger) working to be acceptable to the parent may become a child's way of survival. Or a child may internalize the idea that *I'm lovable only when I'm doing things well,* setting herself up for a life of perfectionism and rigid role identification cut off from the vulnerable part of herself that needs to know that there's room to fail, or just be unspectacularly ordinary and still get the love she needs.
>
> Although both needs (attachment and authenticity) are essential, there is a pecking order. In the first phase of life, attachment unfailingly tops the bill...If the choice is between—hiding my feelings even from myself and getting the basic care I need—and being myself and going without, I'm going to pick that first option every single time. Thus, our real selves are leveraged bit by bit in a tragic transaction where we secure our physical or emotional survival by relinquishing who we are and how we feel.
>
> The fact that we don't consciously choose such coping mechanisms makes them all the more tenacious. We cannot will them away when they no longer serve us precisely because we have no memory of them not being there. There is no notion of ourselves without them. Like wallpaper, they blend into the background...
>
> As these patterns get wired into our nervous system, the perceived need to be what the world demands becomes entangled with our sense of who we are and how to seek love. Inauthenticity is thereafter misidentified with survival because the two were synonymous during the formative years, or at least seemed so to our young selves...
>
> For most of us, it may require a crisis of some kind before we question the veracity and solidity of the self-concept we act from before it even occurs to us that it might conceal something truer about us...The onset of inauthenticity may not be a choice, but with awareness and self-compassion, authenticity can be.

One of the crises' that forced me to confront choosing my attachment relationship over my authenticity happened after I'd done significant work on healing shame and guilt. Instead of deferring to my partner's opinion about my being the problem in the relationship, I stood up for myself. I became willing to share opinions and feelings I knew she wouldn't agree with or may be upset by. I knew I was risking losing the attachment to my partner by doing so, but I had reached a point in my growth where it was more painful to be inauthentic than it was to hold onto a relationship where I couldn't be my authentic self.

What taught me to abandon my authentic self to protect my attachment relationship? When I was a little girl, I was taught I was responsible for my mom's feelings. This is why I had to put her feelings and opinions above my own to be loved. If I didn't, I was chided as being a selfish, bad daughter. As Dr. Gabor Maté states above, the choice to stay safe by protecting my attachment to my mom vs. being true to myself wasn't a choice at all; it was an automatic survival instinct that every child is programmed to make.

This is how automatically putting my partner's feelings above my own to be loved got programmed as a survival mechanism in my body, brain, and mind, and why it kept showing up in my romantic relationships. Sadly, many people never reach the level of pain where they are forced to wake up to how they're abandoning their authentic selves due to a childhood survival instinct that's no longer needed and that is actually counterproductive for adults. Although we don't need to hit bottom to squarely face what may be a mild river of misery running through our lives, experience has taught me that whatever I don't confront gets bigger.

The pain we experience by abandoning our authentic selves must find a way to express itself. Whether it be through addiction, illness, depression, anxiety, or unfulfilling or abusive relationships. One way or another, the drive to honor our authentic selves will keep clamoring to get its way. My philosophy is that I'd rather confront it early than wait for the crisis to show up.

Although I hope that none of these crises come to pass for you or for those you love, if they do, when we look back, they often were our greatest teachers and marked major turning points in our lives. When we reframe a crisis as happening *for us* vs. *to us* and heed its lesson, we can apply our hard-earned wisdom to other areas of our life and make it a gift that keeps on giving.

## Assessing Your Satisfaction In Your Relationships

The first step in creating healthy relationships is to take a look at your current and past close relationship choices. If you don't currently have any or haven't had many close friends, you're not alone. It's very common for trauma survivors to have few, if any, close friends. This is a well-documented symptom of unhealed childhood trauma.

This doesn't mean there's something wrong with you. It simply means you're suffering from a common symptom of relational trauma. Instead of feeling bad about yourself, it's a call for self-compassion. It's important to know that it's not your fault and there is a solution. Acknowledge yourself for taking the first step toward healing by reading this book.

Below is an exercise to assess your satisfaction level with your current and past close friendships or romantic relationships. According to psychiatrist Paul Dobransky, four specific criteria must be present to experience a healthy, fulfilling friendship.

Although Dobransky doesn't mention that these four criteria apply to romantic relationships, I've found that they have for me. For this reason, I suggest you include both past or current romantic relationships and friendships when doing this exercise.

Using Dobransky's four criteria to assess where your relationships have succeeded or failed is extremely helpful in giving you a bird's-eye view of the dynamics you tend to attract in relationships. Using this tool has made me much more conscious of connecting with people in healthier and more fulfilling ways.

## The Four Criteria for Fulfilling Relationships:

1. **Consistent Contact** – Both parties must connect on a regular, consistent basis.

2. **Mutual Investment** – Both parties must be close to being equally invested in the relationship.

3. **Shared Vulnerability** – Both parties must share vulnerable parts of themselves.

4. **Positive Emotions** – The relationship must generate mostly positive emotions for each party.

Dobransky states, "When a friendship fails, one or more of these four criteria is missing. When a friendship lasts, it is durable, happy, and organically blossoming; all four of these are well maintained."

The next step is to assess how well you're doing or have done regarding whether your current or past friendships or romantic relationships contain or have contained these four elements.

# CREATING FULFILLING
# RELATIONSHIPS WORKSHEET

**Directions:** List the five friends or romantic partners you currently or used to spend the most time with. Enter one point for each of the four. traits listed across the top row that this relationship fulfills or fulfilled. Add up the total points for each person (4 max.) and enter it under the "Total Points" column.

For any relationship that has 3 or less points enter an action you will take under the "Actions To Take" column to improve this relationship (only if you are interested in nurturing it.)

An example of an action you can take to improve your relationship with a friend you enjoy but would like to connect with more consistently is asking them if they'd be willing to schedule a weekly phone or lunch date.

| Name-current or past close relationship | Consistently see or talk one or more times per week | Both people are equally invested | Vulnerability shared by both parties | Generates more positive than negative emotions | Total points | Actions to take to increase score, i.e. improve the relationship |
|---|---|---|---|---|---|---|
| | | | | | | |
| | | | | | | |
| | | | | | | |
| | | | | | | |
| | | | | | | |

It's common for those of us with C-PTSD to attract or tolerate relationships with people with only one or two of the above attributes. All this means is you are showing a common symptom of C-PTSD, which is experiencing difficulty with close relationships.

To improve a relationship, it's essential to see if you are, or are not experiencing the kind of satisfaction you desire in them and, in each case, determine what's causing it.

If you're satisfied with your friendships and/or romantic relationships, congratulate yourself and keep doing what you're doing. But if you're not, this exercise can help you get proactive about nurturing the four elements in your existing relationships and seeking out these elements in future ones.

This exercise can also help you decide if the people that score a two or lower are people you want to spend your time with. Time is finite; therefore, when you keep spending time with people you don't enjoy, you block people who could meet your relationship needs from entering your life.

## How This Process Reveals Your Relationship Patterns

This exercise can quickly reveal why some of your relationships are deeply satisfying, others have been less than fulfilling, and why some have ended. This can help you identify your relationship pattern vulnerabilities and help you to be more mindful of your existing relationship dynamics and choices.

When I reviewed my list of former relationships, a few patterns emerged. I noticed the most common missing elements were a lack of mutuality and a lack of positivity. Interestingly, this was the exact dynamic I had with my mother.

Now that I can see how I tend to be drawn to or tolerate patterns in relationships that mirror the relational dynamic I had with her, I can either steer clear of them or make requests or set boundaries to see if doing so will make the relationships I'm in more satisfying.

I can also look at where I need to do some healing work around how I contribute to these kinds of relationship dynamics or where I may need to do some additional work around healing family-of-origin issues.

## How Tolerating Negative or Toxic Relationships Can Make Us Sick

Over the years, I've found that the quality of my close relationships is the single most powerful influence that makes up the quality of my life and health. But it wasn't until I read *Social Intelligence: The New Science of Human Relationships* by Daniel Goleman, I discovered that there is scientific evidence citing that the quality of our relationships affects the quality of our health.

In the excerpt below, Goleman cites that science now tracks how our health is impacted by the company we keep.

> Perhaps most astonishing, science now tracks connections between the most stressful relationships and the operation of specific genes that regulate the immune system. To a surprising extent, then, our relationships mold not just our experience but our biology. Nourishing relationships have a beneficial impact on our health, while toxic ones can act like slow poison in our bodies.

This excerpt reveals how our choices about who we allow into our lives will, for better or worse, affect our health. This is a reminder to think twice about who you let into your life since it can literally mean the difference between staying healthy or setting yourself up for illness and suffering.

## Raising Standards and Setting Boundaries

Some of the best advice I've ever received from a life coach I worked with was, "If your life is filled with chaos, unfulfilling relationships, or unfulfilled dreams, you need to raise your standards and set your boundaries."

Chaos and lack of fulfillment are classic symptoms of a lack of healthy boundaries or difficulty raising or setting the standards of what you settle for. Raising your standards can look like raising the bar of the types of people you allow into your life. Setting boundaries can mean telling someone you're not okay with how they treat you.

When you take care of yourself by raising your standards and setting boundaries, after some initial resetting time, you'll notice that all the energy you had allowed to drain you gets freed up so you can live your best life with your chosen tribe.

Many survivors were punished or shamed when they set boundaries or asked for their needs to be met, which makes it extremely uncomfortable and triggering to do so as an adult.zv

Setting boundaries and asking for my needs to be met used to be a huge shame trigger for me. However, once I was able to heal my shame and guilt, I was also able to set healthy boundaries and ask to get my needs met.

Attending CoDA meetings was instrumental in helping me develop the ability to set boundaries with family members, bosses, and friends. Now I can do so without feeling guilt or shame. Although setting boundaries and raising standards can be extremely uncomfortable at first, I discovered that I could make the process much easier if I reframed it.

A great reframe that worked wonders in my early codependency recovery that psychotherapist Melody Beattie wrote about in her book *Codependent No More* is it's a good sign when you feel guilty after setting a boundary since you know you're on track with healing your codependency.

Over time and with a lot of practice, I've gotten so good at asking for what I need and setting healthy boundaries that people intuitively sense what they can and can't get away with. Once I reached this level, I noticed I didn't need to set so many boundaries since the energy I embody does it for me.

## Setting Boundaries

By setting boundaries, you're telling people they can't use or abuse you, make you responsible for their feelings, or take what you have on a physical, time, financial, emotional, material, or social level.

The goal of setting healthy boundaries isn't to build walls around yourself. The purpose is to gain security and preserve your sense of self so you are safe enough to have close relationships without losing yourself, being smothered, or being imposed upon.

The cost of not setting healthy boundaries means you leave yourself open to being used, abused, manipulated, stolen from, and disrespected. This, in turn, can make you feel resentful, anxious, or depressed. It also creates a lot of drama and toxic stress, which is the last thing you need as a survivor.

Setting boundaries can be challenging for adult survivors since they often attract what they grew up with; dysfunctional relationships that use guilt, shame, and manipulation instead of healthy forms of communication. This is where the work of setting boundaries and raising standards needs to begin.

We must be willing to be uncomfortable by saying no and disappointing others while knowing we're not bad or selfish for doing so. We also need to be ready to let go of people who won't respect our boundaries. This is why creating a new support system of healthy friends is critical during this process. I go over this in more detail in Chapter 13, "Codependency: An Attempt to Stay Safe in a Crazy Family."

## Raising or Setting Standards

Raising your standards isn't about having high or low standards. It's about knowing where your standards currently are, then setting them at a level that allows you to get your needs met. Standards can be raised in many different areas. These include romantic partners, friends, behaviors, attitudes, the kind of vocation or career you pursue, the types of clients you're willing to work with, and the income you expect to receive from your work.

Personal standards should be based on your core values. Setting personal standards requires you to get clear about what's important to you and be willing to take a stand for it. Staying committed to sticking to your standards literally determines the quality of your life.

Those who struggle with perfectionism need to lower their standards. Since perfection is an illusion and a defense against shame, finding a "good enough" standard in your work, relationships, or other life area goals is crucial to create a life you love.

The cost of not setting and sticking to your standards is substantial. Nobody wants to be lying on their deathbed with the horrible feeling that they sold out and betrayed what they wanted to experience in this one short life. This is why identifying and setting your standards is a crucial piece of the puzzle to creating a rich and rewarding life. The below exercise is designed to help you assess what life areas and relationships need attention and what steps you can take to set boundaries or reset your standards.

# TRANSFORM YOUR LIFE BY SETTING BOUNDARIES & RAISING STANDARDS WORKSHEET

**Directions:** List the people or areas in your life that cause undue stress or are not meeting your needs. State the desired outcome you would prefer for each relationship or life area. State the boundary and the standard you need to set to achieve each outcome and the date when you'll take specific action steps to achieve your goals.

The people you list can include personal and professional relationships. The main areas of life can include romantic relationships, family, friends, work, money, physical environment, fun and recreation, emotional health/spirituality, and mental, physical, and behavioral health.

| Relationship or life area you'd like to improve | Desired outcome | Boundary to set | Standard to set | Action to take & date you will take it by |
|---|---|---|---|---|
| | | | | |
| | | | | |
| | | | | |
| | | | | |
| | | | | |

**I've Had To Say "No" To A Lot of People To Enjoy The Life I Have Today**

Sometimes when I think of how lucky and grateful I am to have such a fulfilling romantic relationship, supportive, safe friends, and to finally be doing the work I love, I have to remind myself that luck has little to do with it. I'm not saying I've not experienced good fortune because I have.

However, had I not invested in my personal growth and healing to the degree I have, there is no way I would be experiencing the life I have today. The quality of my life and relationships is a direct reflection of the work I've done on myself over the years. The truth is I've had to step out of my comfort zone and say "no" to a lot of people to enjoy the life I have today. This is not to say being mean-spirited is necessary to live a life you love. Actually, it's quite the opposite. Being true to yourself will likely disappoint some people. But it also means you'll attract like-minded people to join you on your journey and inspire others to be true to themselves.

I don't know about you, but I'd much rather disappoint a few people to be able to live my truth with my chosen tribe and inspire others to live a life they love.

The *Transform Your Life By Setting Boundaries & Raising Standards Worksheet* has been one of the most effective processes I've used to improve the quality of my life and relationships for over twenty years now. This is why I'm here to say if you're committed to improving your life, completing this, along with the remaining exercises in this book, will help you get there.

# CHAPTER 28

---

# SHRINKING THE CRITIC

If I am not good to myself, how can I expect anyone else to be good to me?

—Maya Angelou

While listening to the chapters *Shrinking the Inner Critic* and *Shrinking the Outer Critic* in *Complex PTSD: From Surviving To Thriving*, I stumbled upon an entirely new understanding of the term "inner critic." The first difference I noticed was author Pete Walker's definition of the critic. He states that there is not only an inner critic but also an outer critic. The second difference was learning they were both fueled by childhood trauma. Before this discovery, I was only aware of the concept of an inner critic and had assumed it was driven by low self-esteem or shame. In the below excerpt, Walker describes the nature of the inner and outer critics.

## Origin of the C-PTSD Critic

A flashback-inducing critic is typically spawned in a danger-ridden childhood home. This is true whether the danger comes from the passive abandonment of neglect or the active abandonment of abuse. When parents do not provide safe enough bonding and positive feedback, the child flounders in anxiety and fear. Many children appear to be hard-wired to adapt to their endangering abandonment with perfectionism.

A traumatized child becomes desperate to relieve the anxiety and depression of abandonment. The critic-driven child can only think about the ways she is too much or not enough. The child's unfolding sense of self (the healthy ego) finds no room to develop. Her identity virtually becomes the critic.

In this process, the critic becomes increasingly virulent and eventually switches from the parents' internalized voice: "You're a bad boy/girl" to the first person: "I'm a bad boy/girl" Over time, self-goading increasingly deteriorates: "I'm such a loser... I'm so pathetic... bad... ugly...worthless...stupid...defective."

In my work with survivors, I am continually struck by how often the inner critic triggers them into overwhelming emotional flashbacks. The C-PTSD-derived inner critic weds our fear of abandonment with the entwined serpents of perfectionism and endangerment, which is the process of constantly projecting danger onto safe enough situations.

## Endangerment Attacks

As I heard Walker mention the term *endangerment attacks*, my ears perked up. He clarified that the difference between perfectionism and endangerment attacks is that the former is engaged when you attack yourself. The latter is engaged when you fear someone will attack you.

I was aware of how I used to chronically ruminate about my life, business, or job falling apart, which I now see as an endangerment attack. But I never understood that it was driven by the C-PTSD inner critic. It felt so good to finally understand where all this endangerment energy had come from.

## The Fourteen Inner Critic Attacks

In the below excerpt from *Complex PTSD: From Surviving to Thriving*, Walker outlines the fourteen most common C-PTSD-fueled inner critic attacks.

1.  Perfectionism
2.  All-or-none and black-and-white thinking
3.  Self-hate, self-disgust, and toxic shame
4.  Micromanagement, worrying, obsessing, looping, over-futurizing
5.  Unfair devaluing, comparisons to others or to your most perfect moments
6.  Guilt
7.  Shoulding
8.  Over-productivity, workaholism, busyholism
9.  Harsh judgment of self and others, name-calling

### Endangerment Attacks

10. Drasticizing, catastrophizing, hypochondriasizing
11. Negative focus
12. Time urgency
13. Disabling performance anxiety
14. Perseverating about being attacked

When I first reviewed this list, I recognized that I'd suffered from every single one of them at one time or another. Although I was grateful to have worked through resolving most of them over the years, I noticed a deep sadness come over me.

Before learning that inner and outer critic attacks were caused by childhood trauma, I blamed and ridiculed myself for causing them. A deep sadness arose when I thought about all the years of peace and joy squandered due to being plagued with a toxic, incessant critic and having suffered even more by mistakenly blaming myself for causing it.

## How to Tame the Inner Critic

When we're unaware of the nature of the inner and outer critics and unconsciously believe and engage with them, we keep them alive. Therefore, the first step in shrinking the inner critic is to notice it. It's a mindfulness practice of watching what your thoughts say to you and then challenging them with new thoughts.

I had no idea how hard I'd been on myself until I embraced a self-compassion practice in my forties. Just giving myself permission to be self-compassionate revealed how much my critic wanted to jump in and assert itself. It would try to justify its harsh judgment by saying, *If I'm not hard on you, how can you expect to grow or reach your goals?*

What worked best at taming my inner critic was experimenting with several thought-correction responses until I found ones that worked. With repetition and time, my responses to the critic became like mantras, to where eventually, they no longer tortured me.

## Overcoming Endangerment Thoughts

Before I understood the concept that when triggered into a fight, or flight state, the brain automatically generates fearful thoughts even if there's no rational evidence of any danger, I would spin around ruminating for hours or even days, attempting to stop my disturbing thoughts.

Now when I have an irrational endangerment thought that I can't seem to get rid of, I say to myself, "Mary, you're having a neuronal glitch." This allows me to recognize the thought while not resisting it or taking it seriously because I know it's untrue programming that my brain is running. Just having this understanding and not taking my thoughts so seriously has been extremely helpful in getting my fear-based thoughts to decrease and eventually subside.

## The Outer Critic

Learning that C-PTSD also has an outer critic was a major aha moment for me. The below excerpt from *Complex PTSD: From Surviving To Thriving* summarizes how the outer critic impacts relationships.

### The Outer Critic - The Enemy of Relationships

In C-PTSD, the critic can have two aspects: inner critic and outer critic. The inner critic is the part of your mind that views you as flawed and unworthy. The outer critic is the part that views everyone else as flawed and unworthy. When the outer critic is running your mind, people appear to be too awful and too dangerous to trust.

The outer critic is the counterpart of the self-esteem-destroying inner critic. It uses the same programs of perfectionism and endangerment against others that your inner critic uses against yourself.

When we regress into the outer critic, we obsess about the unworthiness (imperfection) and treacherousness (dangerousness) of others. Unconsciously, we do this to avoid emotional investment in relationships.

The outer critic developed in reaction to parents who were too dangerous to trust. The outer critic helped us to be hyperaware of the subtlest signal that our parents were deteriorating into their most dangerous behaviors. Over time the outer critic grew to believe that anyone and everyone would inevitably turn out to be as untrustworthy as our parents.

Now in situations where we no longer need it, the outer critic alienates us from others. It attacks others and scares them away, or it builds fortresses of isolation whose walls are laundry lists of exaggerated shortcomings. In an awful irony, the critic attempts to protect us from abandonment by scaring us further into it. If we are ever to discover the comfort of soothing connection with others, the critics' dictatorship of the mind must be broken. The outer critic's arsenal of intimacy-spoiling dynamics must be consciously identified and gradually deactivated.

---

## Seeing My Outer Critic in My Dating Profile

Learning about the outer critic reminded me of a time when I was single and looking to start dating. I was living with my friend Sue, who was also single. Since we both wanted to start dating, we decided to post our profiles on several online dating sites. Before doing so, we asked each other for feedback on the profiles we'd come up with.

When Sue read mine, she laughed out loud. Not knowing whether to be amused or offended by her response, I asked, "What's so funny about it?"

She replied, "Mary, you have twenty bullet points of who and what a woman must be for you to date her. Don't you think that's a bit much? If I saw your profile, I'd run! My concern is that this kind of profile will scare women away."

At first, I thought, *So what if I'm discerning. How will I get the qualities I want in a relationship unless I put them in my profile?* I decided to post the profile anyway. After several weeks and zero responses, it was obvious Sue was right. Once I changed my profile to include just a few must-haves, I began getting dates.

After learning that perfectionism drives the outer critic, I understood what compelled me to write that dating profile. Although it was helpful to understand what was behind my perfectionistic expectations, it also made me sad to see how I'd unknowingly pushed away the very connection and closeness that I'd longed for.

## Using Mindfulness & Grief Work to Shrink the Inner & Outer Critics

Walker continues in the below excerpt with how to shrink the inner and outer critics.

> Reducing outer critic activity requires a great deal of mindfulness. Mindfulness, once again, is the process of becoming intricately aware of everything that is going on inside us, especially thoughts, images, feelings, and sensations. In terms of outer critic work, it is essential that we become more mindful of both the cognitive and emotional content of our thoughts.
>
> This is the same as in inner critic work, where the two key fronts of critic shrinking are cognitive and emotional. Cognitive work in both cases involves the demolition and rebuilding processes of thought stopping and thought substitution, respectively.
>
> And emotional work in both instances is grief work. It is removing the critic's fuel supply—the unexpressed childhood anger and the un-cried tears of a lifetime of abandonment.

It made sense that practicing mindfulness, thought stopping, and thought substitution would be necessary to shrink the inner and outer critics.

What caught me off guard was learning that grief work was also necessary to shrink the emotional aspects of the inner and outer critic.

I've found that whenever I learn that more grief work is necessary to heal my trauma, I feel immediate resistance. I've come to realize it's because it pisses me off that I have to put even more energy into healing issues that were never my fault to begin with.

Yet I also know if I want to be free from my C-PTSD symptoms, it's in my best interest to feel my anger which is part of doing grief work. So, I angrily add it to my "to be grieved list" and soldier on.

# CHAPTER 29

---

# LETTING GO OF GUILT & SHAME

Shame is the lie that someone told you about yourself.

—Anaïs Nin

I completely immersed myself in healing shame and guilt for several years before I learned I was suffering from C-PTSD. I read dozens of books, joined therapist-led groups, and did several online courses. The healing I experienced was profound and life changing.

In chapter 8, "Emotional Liberation: Healing Shame & Guilt," I share what it was like when I first discovered Dr. Brené Brown's work about shame and the insights and transformation I experienced as I learned how to resolve it. If you haven't read this chapter, I highly recommend you do so since it will give you a deeper understanding of the nature of shame and guilt, and you'll also get to hear the story of one of the most liberating experiences of my life.

Through my deep dive into learning about healing shame and guilt, I discovered the first step involves resolving any lingering guilt you may have. The reason guilt must be handled before healing shame is that if you have unresolved guilt, you can't help but feel unforgivable. And when you feel unforgivable, you feel shame. Once we have forgiven ourselves, we are then ready to take on healing shame.

## Letting Go Of Guilt

Before I understood the nature of guilt, I had a very tenuous relationship with it. Sometimes I was able to let go of my guilt over something I'd done, and sometimes I wasn't.

Being raised Catholic and by a mother who was quick to blame and shame me is where my relationship with guilt began. When you're raised to believe normal human needs are immoral or sinful or that you're responsible for other people's feelings and overall well-being, you're set up to take on an enormous amount of guilt.

Since children raised in dysfunctional families aren't mature enough to understand that the ongoing river of pain they and their family members are experiencing isn't their fault, they often blame themselves and feel guilty for causing it.

Unresolved guilt has consequences. It weighs on us. It often drives dysfunctional relationships and self-destructive behaviors. Once I understood the nature of guilt, what fuels it, and how to resolve it, my entire life transformed.

## The Purpose of Guilt

We're supposed to feel guilty when we act outside our values. In this light, guilt is a built-in warning signal that we're off track. It's there to help us get back on track by honoring our values. Once we get back on track, stop the behavior, and make any necessary amends, we can forgive ourselves and heed the lesson to not do it again.

Guilt becomes a problem when we don't learn from what it's trying to communicate, which is to stop the behavior and find a more ethical or healthy way to meet our needs. If we stop the behavior we feel guilty about but continue to beat ourselves up for it, we shift from feeling guilty to feeling unforgivable.

When we feel unforgivable, we feel shame about who we are. Shame isn't helpful. In fact, it's toxic and causes many emotional, spiritual, and behavioral problems.

## Determining Authentic vs. Inauthentic Guilt

If I'm feeling guilty, I first need to determine if my guilt is over something I hold as a value. If I feel guilt over something my spouse, family of origin, friend, church, or society thinks I should value when, in truth, I don't, then I am experiencing inauthentic guilt.

If I determine that an act I've committed upsets someone, but it isn't a violation of my true values, then no forgiveness is needed because my personal values weren't violated.

However, I do need to address the person who's upset with me since we obviously have had a misunderstanding. I need to tell them that I didn't realize we weren't on the same page regarding values and share with them that I don't hold the same value as they do regarding the issue at hand. Assuming it's not a deal-breaker, I can ask if we can agree to disagree on it or work it out for the future. If it is a deal-breaker, we may need to part ways.

# Self-Forgiveness

One of the most liberating experiences of my life was learning how to forgive myself. Out of the many books I've read on the topic, I found the below definition and concepts shared in *Forgive for Good: A Proven Prescription for Health and Happiness* by Self-Forgiveness Project Founder and psychologist Dr. Frederic Luskin to be the most helpful.

### Definition of Self-Forgiveness

- Choosing to give up earned resentment toward yourself
- Earned resentment is defined as reasons to be angry with yourself or others

### The Nature of Self-Forgiveness

- Self-forgiveness doesn't mean you have to forget what happened or that what you did was okay. We mustn't forget where acting outside of our values or self-destructive behaviors has taken us. By doing so, we can "think the behavior through" if we get tempted to do it again and be better prepared to resist doing it.
- We don't need other people's forgiveness to forgive ourselves. We need only our own forgiveness to be forgiven. We also don't need anyone else's approval to forgive ourselves.

### The Essence of Self-Forgiveness

- Recognizing that to be human is to be imperfect; hence, everyone will hurt themselves or others at some point during their lives.
- When we can learn from what our misdeeds are there to teach us, we can avoid repeating them and can forgive our imperfect selves.
- I no longer need to feel like a bad person for what I did.
- I no longer need to pay for what I did.
- I hold the authority to decide if I am forgiven or not.
- I can choose a self-forgiveness process that resonates with me

### How Forgiving Yourself Helps Others

- Self-forgiveness frees you up to bring a positive, creative energy that enhances and elevates people vs. a negative, destructive, shame-based energy that hurts those around you.
- When you forgive yourself, you can forgive others, which allows you to spread more kindness, compassion, and goodwill into the world.

### How Not Forgiving Yourself Hurts Everyone

- By not forgiving yourself, you hurt yourself and others by perpetuating shame, which leads to relationship and health problems, depression, anxiety, and addictions.
- Not forgiving yourself teaches others, including your children, to not forgive themselves, which leads to shame which causes a host of negative health, behavioral, and relationship outcomes.

## The Criteria for Self-Forgiveness

Self-forgiveness is only warranted if whatever behavior you're feeling guilty about has stopped, you've made any necessary amends, and you're committed to staying stopped. See the appendix or chapters on recovering from substance or behavioral addictions for support to stop addictive or compulsive behaviors you feel guilty over.

## Why Self-Forgiveness Is Necessary to Avoid Shame

When you fail to forgive yourself, instead of feeling like you did something wrong or bad, the feeling shifts to feeling unforgivable. Feeling unforgivable is the essence of feeling like a bad person and feeling like a bad person brings on shame. Since shame is never helpful and is known to drive relationship difficulties, and self-defeating behaviors, it's essential to have a self-forgiveness process in place and be committed to using it.

## The Power of Self-Forgiveness

Learning about the nature of guilt and completing the following *Self-Forgiveness Worksheet* have been the most effective steps I've taken to let go of some long-held guilt.

As I have shared earlier in this chapter and in previous chapters, releasing guilt has been one of the most emotionally liberating experiences of my life. Therefore, if you are carrying any unresolved guilt, I wholeheartedly recommend giving yourself and your family the gift of self-forgiveness by completing the following *Self-Forgiveness Worksheet*.

# SELF-FORGIVENESS WORKSHEET

1. **List three or more things you've done you feel guilt over or beat yourself up about.**

   If you're uncomfortable disclosing these items, use initials, or a symbol only you would be able to decipher.

   _____

   _____

   _____

2. **Write about or talk to a safe person regarding how you feel about the specific acts you feel guilt over.**

   It's important to get in touch with how you feel about each behavior or act you feel guilt over before forgiving yourself. Writing about how you feel about your guilt is an excellent way to do so. Talking with a trusted therapist, coach, or non-judgmental friend or spouse can also be helpful.

3. **Forgive yourself by reciting the below self-forgiveness declarations.**

**Directions:** Recite the following self-forgiveness declarations out loud while being mindful of your emotions and sensations in your body. Make a separate declaration for each act you you've listed.

- For how I have hurt _____, for _____I now offer myself forgiveness.
- For how I have hurt myself by _____ I now offer myself forgiveness.
- I now choose to let go of my guilt and forgive myself.
- I'm aware that if I forgo forgiving myself, I hurt everyone; therefore, as long as I've learned from my mistake, am no longer engaging in the behavior, and have made any amends I believe are necessary, it is for everyone's benefit that I forgive myself.
- For the highest good of all concerned, I now choose to forgive myself.

This process is designed to help you identify where you've hurt yourself or others, feel the guilt and sadness, learn the lesson the guilt is meant to teach you, and complete the process by forgiving yourself so you can move on to living a life you love and being a productive member of your family and society.

This process should be done with the empathy and compassion you would have if you were doing it for a young child. Be sure to be mindful of any shame that comes up and use this process to release it as another act you've hurt yourself with.

Once you are finished stating out loud that you've forgiven yourself for a specific act or behavior, check in with your body and mind to discern whether you feel truly forgiven. If you don't feel any different or just slightly different about your guilt, it's an opportunity to dig deeper into what's going on.

It took several rounds of listening to or reading the books I had on self-compassion and self-forgiveness and reciting the above forgiveness declarations for me to feel that I'd forgiven myself. Therefore, don't give up after one or two tries; it may take many repetitions for you to reprogram your brain, body, and mind to feel completely forgiven. Given how liberating and life-changing releasing guilt can be, it truly is worth all the time you put into this exercise.

## My Experience After Doing the Self-Forgiveness Process

When I first recited my self-forgiveness declarations, I didn't feel much relief from my guilt, and I wondered if this "self-forgiveness thing" would work for me.

After doing some digging, I realized my indoctrination into the beliefs of the Catholic Church had been blocking my ability to feel okay with giving myself the authority for self-forgiveness.

Looking back, between the ages of four to seventeen, I was taught that only a priest could forgive me for my sins. The church wouldn't grant us the authority for self-forgiveness because we were seen as morally corrupt due to being born with original sin. This was how the church justified that only a priest or God had the moral capacity to forgive people for their sins.

Once I saw this unconscious belief for what it was (toxic and untrue) and irradicated it, I was able to forgive myself. However, it did take several rounds of reciting the self-forgiveness declarations to feel that I had forgiven myself on a visceral and emotional level to where I knew it had really "taken."

## How Using A Self-Forgiveness Process Liberated Me

Going through the self-forgiveness process was nothing short of a miracle in helping me release some major guilt that I'd been carrying for decades. I felt not only emotionally lighter but physically lighter as well! I had no idea how guilt had been weighing me down until I did this process.

This experience made me realize that life is too short to squander our aliveness and potential by continually punishing ourselves with unnecessary guilt. If I've learned anything on this journey, it's that everyone has or will do things that will hurt themselves or others. This is part and parcel of the human condition. Learning from these experiences is how we attain wisdom.

Another gift of resolving guilt is that it opens the door to the next critical step on the healing journey: letting go of shame.

# Letting Go Of Shame

> Where there's shame, there's trauma, and where there's trauma, there's shame.
>
> —Dr. Peter Levine, Trauma Expert & Somatic Experiencing Founder

## Understanding Shame

Interestingly, it wasn't until I learned I had trauma that I gleaned an even deeper understanding of why shame was so deeply entrenched in my body and mind and so difficult to let go of.

Shame's purpose is to keep us safe. In the hunter-gatherer days, it protected us from being shunned from our tribe or clan since being shunned literally meant death. In today's world, and in particular, with childhood trauma, shame's purpose is to protect a survivor from becoming angry at their primary caregiver since it could cause a volatile confrontation with them and jeopardize the attachment relationship. So instead, survivors direct their anger and judgment toward themselves. Shame is also protective in how it makes us contract, withdraw, and disconnect from others. This is what makes shame a survival response.

Shame is not just an extremely painful emotion; it's a highly distressing nervous system state. And as Stephen Porges (who discovered the Polyvagal Theory) has written about, our state drives our thoughts. Therefore, when we're in a shame state, we can't help but tell ourselves scary and convincing stories about how broken and unlovable we are, even though it's not true. But if we aren't aware of how shame works and that it's highjacked our nervous system and perception of ourselves, we'll be absolutely convinced that we are as broken and unworthy as shame tells us we are.

Shame also attempts to sabotage our efforts to eradicate it by convincing us that whatever we try will never work, so why even bother. And to make matters worse, we then have shame about feeling so highjacked by our shame since, deep down, we believe our perceived brokenness is our own fault!

Another reason shame is so common for survivors is that their brain's shame circuits become highly sensitized. This is due to how often shame circuits fire in survivors' brains and how early it occurs during brain development. As a result, it takes much less for survivors to get triggered into a shame storm than for non-traumatized kids, and it takes longer for survivors to find their way back to regulation.

## Self-Acceptance: The Anecdote To Toxic Shame

Many of us believed blaming and shaming ourselves would motivate us to become better sons or daughters so we could get the love we needed. The truth is you can't shame or belittle yourself into being good enough or worthy of love and belonging. This is where cultivating self-compassion and self-acceptance comes in.

While studying healing shame, I was surprised to learn that self-acceptance is one of the main keys to resolving it. When I first discovered this, it seemed too simple. I remember thinking, *How could self-acceptance resolve such an entrenched toxic belief about oneself?* But as I continued to learn more about self-acceptance and shame, I realized accepting ourselves is much bigger than a simple shift in beliefs or an attitude adjustment.

It's not the simple act of accepting oneself that heals shame. It's what opens up in your life as a result of self-acceptance. When we accept our whole self, warts and all, we can shift from building self-esteem—which typically involves endless striving to prove our worthiness and is contingent on outside accomplishments and others' approval—to building a life following our heart and core values, which is where true fulfillment lies.

## The Key To Healing Shame Is To Cultivate Self-Acceptance vs. Self-Esteem

Many people think if they just feel good enough about themselves, failing won't make them feel shame. However, since feeling good enough about oneself (aka self-esteem) is a global evaluation of the self based on a subjective construct that isn't real and can't be measured, it's literally unattainable.

I define self-acceptance as accepting my whole self "as is." Whereas self-esteem is the nebulous goal of *feeling good enough.* How "good" do I need to feel about myself to feel "good enough?" Obviously, it's impossible to measure what feeling "good enough" is. This is what makes pursuing self-esteem so elusive.

### Self-Acceptance Feels Like

- I'm perfectly imperfect, and I accept myself "as-is"
- I am who I am, and I love myself, warts and all

### Self-Acceptance Fosters

- A sense of authenticity
- A sense of true satisfaction with yourself and your life
- A sense of meaning and fulfillment

## The Goal Is To Seek Fulfillment, Not Self Esteem

Life satisfaction is impossible without self-acceptance because without accepting yourself as is, you'll get caught up chasing elusive self-esteem goals. Pursuing self-esteem goals can't truly satisfy you because they don't address what can bring true fulfillment. True fulfillment is achieved by attaining value-based goals for specific areas of your life, such as your relationships, health, career, finances, or spirituality.

To experience fulfillment, we must focus on how well we're doing with specific behaviors or goals and work on improving them. When we improve specific areas of our life, we automatically experience fulfillment. The best way to judge how you're doing in a global sense is to focus on whether your behaviors or goals serve you and support your values.

## Why Self-Acceptance Is a Wiser Goal Than Self-Esteem

When you focus on improving your life from a specific life area perspective, you can decide what behaviors best align with your values for the goal for that life area. When you assess how you're doing in a particular area of your life versus your whole self, it's much easier to look at what's working and what could use some improvement because your whole self isn't on the line.

## Benefits of Cultivating Self-Acceptance vs. Self-Esteem

- You let go of being attached to what people think of you since you have your own approval
- You're willing to take more risks and be vulnerable and are less attached to the outcomes
- You're able to handle criticism and judgment from others more easily
- You no longer need to impress or compare yourself with others
- You have healthier friendships and intimate relationships
- It's easier to accept your limitations and imperfections
- You handle conflict more effectively
- You're able to forgive yourself
- Your curiosity increases
- You're more optimistic

## Why Using Shame and Self-Criticism as Motivation Isn't Helpful

Many people think being hard on themselves is an effective way to stay motivated to achieve their goals. However, research shows that self-compassion and self-acceptance are better motivators in achieving goals.

Prior to doing my shame work, I'd been pretty hard on myself. I thought using a tough-love approach would keep me motivated and in line. I feared that if I was kind and compassionate with myself, I'd become a slacker and wouldn't achieve my goals. But when I look back, it never worked.

I've since learned that you can't shame or belittle yourself or anyone else into reaching a goal or stopping unwanted behavior. It wasn't until I was able to access self-compassion, self-forgiveness, and self-acceptance that I was able to heal the shame and guilt that had been holding me back from reaching my personal and professional goals.

## How Self-Compassion Fosters Self-Acceptance

Interestingly, I'd been practicing self-compassion for a few years before I took on healing shame. It came in handy since I would come to learn it's a key component of cultivating self-acceptance. According to self-compassion expert Dr. Kristen Neff, the three components of self-compassion include:

### 1. Self-Kindness

- Being understanding rather than judging yourself harshly
- Providing yourself with support and self-care
- Transforming suffering into an opportunity for kindness and connectedness

## 2. Common Humanity

- Recognizing you are part of a larger human experience rather than being alone in your pain
- Knowing you're not perfect and life isn't perfect

## 3. Mindfulness

- Acceptance and nonjudgment of your experience

### Four Components of Mindfulness

1. Paying attention to experience in the present moment
2. Relating to experience without judgment or resistance
3. Relating to experience with the desire to alleviate suffering
4. Recognizing that you have a choice about what you can change, which is how you relate to the present moment with either compassion or harsh judgment

## Responding to Myself During a Relapse With Self-Compassion Instead of Contempt

Before relapsing with medical marijuana, I'd completed about four years of intense self-compassion, self-forgiveness, and self-acceptance work. This new level of self-compassion and self-acceptance gave me the presence of mind to pause and respond to myself in a completely different way with my marijuana relapse than I did during a prior relapse with alcohol.

When I relapsed with alcohol, I felt intense shame, regret, and contempt toward myself for being weak, a loser, and for not working a good-enough Twelve-Step program. But when I relapsed with marijuana, I had the presence of mind to respond differently.

Instead of going into a shame spiral and hating myself for relapsing, within a few seconds after taking my first hit of marijuana, I said to myself, *Wait a minute. Let's bring in some HUGE compassion here,* as tears welled up and I grieved losing my sobriety yet again. I then walked over to my bed and allowed myself to collapse into it and just cry. With tears streaming down my face, I placed both palms gently over my heart and said, *I love you. I know you're in a lot of pain, sweetheart.*

Just acknowledging my pain and having compassion for myself gave me an immediate sense of relief. I then got up from my bed and walked over to my bathroom mirror. While looking directly into my eyes, I said, *I'll always be here for you no matter what, whether you relapse or not. We'll get through this together, sweetie. We'll figure it out.*

For the first time in my life, I felt an exquisite feeling of unconditional love and compassion wash over me. I felt understood and cared for. I also trusted that I was going to be okay. It was as if a huge burden was lifted from me because I knew I would love myself no matter what and whether I was sober or not.

Until then, I hadn't realized how much contempt I had for myself when I relapsed before. I also expected others to follow suit with the same judgment and contempt toward me. I realize now that I felt it was a healthy form of tough love to emotionally abandon myself when I relapsed. In my book, relapse is the worst thing a person with an addiction can do. Relapse was the ultimate failure because, in my eyes, it was my own fault.

I now see relapse as a barometer indicating that extremely high levels of unbearable emotional pain are present. A person in relapse is simply attempting to find a solution to end the pain. This is why I love Dr. Gabor Maté's statement: "Don't ask why the addiction. Ask why the pain." In essence, this is what I did for myself by consciously bringing in this huge dose of compassion and understanding for my pain and having unconditional love for myself.

As a result of practicing self-compassion and reaching out for different types of support, I was able to quit smoking marijuana and have been in recovery ever since.

# 14 STEPS TO RESOLVING SHAME

1. The first step to combat shame is recognizing it's both an emotional and a nervous system state. And since our state drives our thoughts, when we're in a shame state, we can't help but feel terrible about who we are, and since it's such a visceral state, it's extremely convincing. Therefore, when in a shame state, be sure to remind yourself you're in a temporary physical and emotional state that's running a negative narrative that's not true.

2. Healing shame involves cultivating kindness and compassion for your suffering. The goal is to provide the level of compassion, kindness, and care you would if you were trying to soothe a child in distress. Being curious about your physical sensations and thoughts is also helpful in finding your way back to regulation.

3. When in a shame state, attempt to shift from being irritated or judgmental of yourself to care about the fact that you are suffering. Stay as mindful as possible and feel into your physical and emotional sensations and reassure yourself that it's temporary and will be over soon.

4. Since shame develops in the context of relationships, part of your healing work must be done within relationships. Find safe people or groups you can share on a vulnerable level with for your healing journey. 12-step groups such as Codependents Anonymous and therapist-led healing shame support groups have been very helpful for me during my healing journey. See the appendix for resources.

5. Reach out to a safe friend, spouse, or trauma-informed coach who understands you are working on healing shame and guilt and has agreed to provide empathy and compassion for you.

6. Consciously bringing to mind a person you felt soothed by can help you shift out of a shame state and into a more regulated state.

7. If you have unresolved guilt, you more than likely have shame over feeling unforgivable. Therefore, it's important to use the self-forgiveness process to resolve any lingering guilt.

8. If you are engaging in any behavior that you continually feel guilt or shame about and are having difficulty stopping, it is imperative to get the support you need to stop since continuing will keep feeding your guilt and shame. Once you have stopped and are committed to staying stopped, you can move on to the self-forgiveness process for these issues. See chapters 32 and 33 and the appendix for resources for food, weight, and addiction recovery options for survivors.

9. Develop a daily self-compassion and self-acceptance practice. Find self-acceptance affirmations in books or online to reprogram your brain and mind to become more self-compassionate and self-accepting.

10. Complete listening to or reading this book and complete all of the exercises in it. Listen to or read other recommended books below on healing shame and guilt and do the exercises in them.

11. Reframe past situations that caused you to feel guilt or shame with kindness and compassion for yourself and other parties involved until you feel shifted and more peaceful with the memory.

12. If there are people in your life who shame or blame you or who use subtle put-down jokes, set boundaries with them to stop. If they don't respect your boundaries, stop spending time with them. Leave groups and organizations that foster shame, guilt, coercion, or manipulation. See a trauma-based therapist or coach for support if you are struggling with handling these types of people or groups.

13. Create a mantra that resonates with you and captures the essence of how you would like to feel about yourself when you have let go of shame by embracing self-acceptance. An example of a popular self-acceptance mantra that I love is Popeye's: *I am who I am.*

14. If you are struggling with achieving self-compassion, self-forgiveness, and self-acceptance on your own, reach out to a trauma-informed therapist or coach who specializes in healing shame, guilt, and C-PTSD for support.

# HEALING SHAME WORKSHEET

1. Steps I will take to cultivate self-compassion and self-acceptance

2. Steps I will take to find at least one safe person or group to share my shame with

3. Steps I will take to become aware when I'm in a shame state.(e.g. mindfulness or somatic mindfulness)

4. Who will I bring to mind that I have felt soothed by to help me shift out of a shame state? This can be anyone alive, deceased, or those in the spirit realm

5. Steps I will take to reduce, eliminate or accept specific behaviors I feel shame or guilt over

6. What mantra do I resonate with that captures how I want to feel when I've achieved self-acceptance?

7. What requests or changes do I need to make with people or groups who shame or guilt me?

## Cultivating Shame Resilience

Even if you've let go of a significant amount of shame, it's normal for it to come up from time to time. The tools you're learning will help you release toxic levels of shame and will also help you become more shame resilient. This means you'll experience shame less often and move through it more quickly when you do.

You're literally rewiring your brain's shame circuits when you practice self-compassion and self-acceptance in the face of shame. Since what fires together wires together, over time, you'll notice your brain's shame circuits firing much less frequently.

Releasing shame by cultivating self-acceptance is one of the greatest gifts of the trauma-healing journey. Like anything worth working for, achieving true self-acceptance is a long-term process. By staying committed to your self-acceptance practices, you'll gradually become more peaceful and connected and feel a sense of harmony with life. You'll also notice that you are less and less attached to the good opinion of others. It's a truly beautiful experience and worth all the time and energy you put into it.

## Favorite Books On Letting Go of Guilt & Shame

The first step in letting go of guilt and shame is to learn about its nature and how to resolve it. The books listed below have been especially helpful for me in healing my shame and guilt. Additional titles can be found in the appendix under the category: Healing Shame & Guilt.

- I Thought It Was Just Me (but it isn't): Making the Journey from "What Will People Think?" to "I Am Enough," Brené Brown, PhD, LMSW
- Self-Compassion: The Proven Power of Being Kind to Yourself, Kristin Neff, PhD
- Forgive for Good: A Proven Prescription for Health and Happiness, Frederic Luskin, PhD
- Radical Self-Forgiveness: The Direct Path to True Self Acceptance, Colin Tipping
- Radical Acceptance: Embracing Your Life With The Heart of A Buddha, Tara Brach, PhD

# CHAPTER 30

---

# USING NEUROFEEDBACK TO REGULATE THE BRAIN, BODY, MIND & BEHAVIOR

Evidence with neurofeedback suggests that trauma-informed treatment should also be brain-informed treatment—and not just to know that the brain is an issue, but to work with it directly.

—Sebern Fisher, MA, BCN

The first time I heard the term Neurofeedback was in *Part Five: Paths To Recovery* while listening to *The Body Keeps the Score*. Once I heard Van der Kolk state it was one of the most effective ways to train a traumatized brain and nervous system to operate in a more regulated way, I knew I wanted to learn more.

While listening to the chapter on Neurofeedback, Van der Kolk references a book titled *Neurofeedback in the Treatment of Developmental Trauma: Calming the Fear-Driven Brain* by trauma psychotherapist and neurofeedback practitioner Sebern Fisher. After hearing him discuss the remarkable results Fisher had gotten for survivors by combining neurofeedback with psychotherapy, I knew I wanted to read Fisher's book.

Within the first few chapters of *Neurofeedback in the Treatment of Developmental Trauma*, I was riveted by the many case studies Fisher presented that demonstrated how it had radically transformed many of her young patients' lives when no other therapies, including her own talk therapy, had worked. I was also struck by how much I related to many of the signs, symptoms, and feelings Fisher said were common among survivors.

Fisher worked with children and adolescents in residential care facilities who were hopelessly stuck in debilitating anxiety, depression, and dissociative states. Most of them were heavily medicated and had received psychotherapy from Fisher for years. Nothing had made much of a difference until she started providing Neurofeedback along with psychotherapy.

Between Van der Kolk's endorsement of its efficacy in regulating survivors' brains, Fisher's amazing stories of the results she had obtained, and knowing I'd never used a brain-based therapy to heal the neurological aspects of my C-PTSD, I knew I wanted to give Neurofeedback a try.

## What Is Neurofeedback?

Neurofeedback is a treatment used to train the brain to reach a new frequency setpoint. It's based on harnessing the phenomena known as neuroplasticity, which is how the brain creates new pathways and connections as needed throughout life. It's been found that people who suffer from C-PTSD, PTSD, anxiety, depression, and ADHD have different brain wave frequencies from those who experience a healthy sense of well-being.

Neurofeedback employs the principle of operant conditioning. Operant conditioning is a learning method that uses rewards and unpleasant feedback to change behavior. The behavior Neurofeedback targets are brain frequencies. Since brain frequencies determine moods, thoughts, cravings, behavior, memory access, and bodily functions, training them to operate more optimally can significantly change a person's life.

Neurofeedback is a noninvasive treatment that tracks brain frequencies through electrodes placed on the subject's scalp. The electrodes are connected to a laptop that runs a neurofeedback software program. The subject then watches visual feedback and listens to music that responds to their brain frequencies in real time.

When an optimal brain frequency state is reached, the subject receives pleasant audio and visual feedback, which acts as a reward to nudge the brain to stay in that optimal frequency state. But when the brain fails to stay in an optimal frequency state, the visual feedback becomes dark, making it difficult to see, and the audio feedback becomes faint or shuts off, making it difficult to hear. This is considered unpleasant feedback to the brain and motivates it to shift back into a more regulated, optimal state.

The goal of repeated neurofeedback sessions is to provide enough repetition to train the subject's brain to reach a new optimal frequency setpoint, producing a lasting effect on the subject's mood, behavior, and overall well-being. Once the new optimal frequency setpoint is reached, brain frequencies stay more regulated, leading to better emotional, behavioral, nervous system, and overall bodily regulation.

Neurofeedback is also referred to as brain training or brain-wave training. You can look at Neurofeedback as a tool that fine-tunes the brain, which fine-tunes the body and mind and helps regulate behavior.

One of the most common issues for trauma survivors is having a brain stuck in hyperarousal, which causes anxiety and the subsequent need to soothe the anxiety through substances, food, or other destructive behaviors. Finding a way to calm down my nervous system to reduce my C-PTSD symptoms was what made the idea of using Neurofeedback so appealing.

## Working With A Neurofeedback Practitioner or Buying Your Own Equipment?

I debated whether to work with a local neurofeedback practitioner or purchase my own neurofeedback system and learn how to train my own brain at home. While researching local neurofeedback practitioners, I was disheartened to discover that none mentioned using it to help those with childhood trauma symptoms. I found that most of the local neurofeedback practitioners were using it to either help children with ADHD focus better in school or help athletes improve their ability to compete.

After hearing Fisher state that it can take one to two hundred sessions to get sustainable results for C-PTSD and learning the average fee per session was over $100, I decided it made more sense to buy my own system and learn how to train my own brain at home.

Although the neurofeedback field isn't regulated, I was surprised at how difficult it was to find a company that would sell neurofeedback equipment to me since I'm not a licensed therapist or doctor. Finally, after researching and checking out reviews, I found Brain-Trainer.com. I had a lengthy conversation with them about what type of system and equipment I needed.

I decided to purchase my system through them since they had excellent reviews, their pricing was competitive, and they included all the equipment, information, and supplies I needed, along with four hours of phone mentoring and videos to assist me in learning how to train my brain at home.

## Learning To Use Neurofeedback To Train Your Own Brain

It's important to understand that there's a steep learning curve to becoming proficient at training your own brain with a home-based neurofeedback system.

You must be dedicated to learning the neuroscience and neurofeedback concepts and the requisite terminology. You also must become proficient at using and troubleshooting the equipment, supplies, and software; and interpreting live neurofeedback data.

Even though I'm quite comfortable with technology, computers, and brain science, it still took me a good three to four months of intense study and practice to become proficient at using my neurofeedback system.

## How Neurofeedback Helped Me Finally Quit Smoking Marijuana

A few years before I learned I had trauma; I'd struggled for several years with a significant chronic pain condition known as complex regional pain syndrome-CRPS. After trying but not getting results with traditional nerve pain medication, I began using medical marijuana. Although it helped with my pain, I found that I wanted to use it even when I wasn't in pain. Over time, my use began interfering with my life. Although I'd attempted to quit several times, once an overwhelming craving to smoke hit, I couldn't seem to resist it and ended up relapsing.

I'd heard of several double-blind studies showing how Neurofeedback had been extremely effective at helping people with alcohol and drug addictions get and stay sober. This gave me enormous hope that I could finally stop smoking marijuana for good.

I started training my brain three times per week in one-hour sessions. My hope was that it would help regulate my nervous system enough so the cravings to smoke marijuana would weaken and finally end.

After a week of three one-hour sessions, I noticed my cravings to smoke decrease. Then within a few more weeks, the strength of my cravings decreased even more, and I was able to significantly decrease my use. Within a month, the cravings were practically gone, and I was able to stop completely with relative ease. I continued my brain training for another year and a half to make sure the brain changes stuck and to work on other issues.

This was a significant breakthrough because I'd been trying to quit through therapy and Twelve-Step groups for several years. Experiencing such a dramatic decrease in cravings, quitting with relative ease, and staying stopped proved that my dysregulated brain was a significant factor behind my marijuana addiction. Once my brain became more regulated, I no longer needed to find a way to calm it down; hence my cravings evaporated, and I could quit with relative ease.

This is not to say that neurofeedback alone could have helped me quit; however, it was the final piece of the puzzle that pushed me over into finally being able to quit and stay stopped.

## Why Neurofeedback Alone Wouldn't Have Helped Me Quit Using Marijuana

Since many survivors (including myself) frequently latch onto one healing approach, technology, philosophy, or practitioner as the "be all end all" salvation fantasy that will save them, I want to make sure that I'm not presenting Neurofeedback in this way.

Neurofeedback wasn't the only trauma-based therapy or practice I used during the period when I quit using marijuana. It was one part of a multiprong approach I used to heal my trauma and get sober.

I was also working on healing my relational trauma through seeing a trauma-oriented psychotherapist, going to Marijuana Anonymous Twelve-Step meetings, practicing traditional and somatic mindfulness, doing yoga, connecting with like-minded survivors, attending various trauma-based webinars, and reading many books on healing trauma.

Neurofeedback just happened to be the final piece of the puzzle that was necessary, combined with everything else that I was doing, that provided the tipping point to help me finally quit. This is why I firmly believe Neurofeedback alone wouldn't have been enough for me to achieve long-term recovery with marijuana.

Since childhood trauma impacts a survivor's brain, mind, stress-response system, and body, as well as how they engage in relationships, each of these areas needs to be addressed when choosing which therapies and practices to include in healing trauma and getting sober.

Sebern Fisher addresses this issue in her book, *Neurofeedback in the Treatment of Developmental Trauma: Calming the Fear-Driven Brain.*

> Neurofeedback alone will help patients learn to regulate their affect (emotions). Also, for patients with severely dysregulated brains, learning to regulate their affect through Neurofeedback is necessary in order for psychotherapy to even happen.
>
> The reason psychotherapy is necessary in conjunction with Neurofeedback is it teaches patients how to relate and over time, helps them integrate the significant changes they're experiencing in their sense of self. With both Neurofeedback and psychotherapy in place, patients learn the most important of life's lessons-that relationship is the only harbor.

## Additional Ways Neurofeedback Helped Improve My Life

Over about a year and a half, I logged approximately one hundred and seventy-five one-hour sessions of Neurofeedback. I typically did two to three one-hour sessions per week.

After several months of brain training, I noticed it was easier to fall and stay asleep, and I was more relaxed and at ease in social settings. I was also less impulsive with food. After a year and a half of brain training, due to my brain reaching a more optimal setpoint, I was able to decrease my antidepressant dosage.

Needless to say, I'm very happy with the results I've seen in each of these areas after combining Neurofeedback, psychotherapy, Twelve-Step recovery groups, and various other trauma-informed body, brain, and mind therapies and practices.

I list in detail the many trauma-informed therapies and practices that I have used and that are recommended by experts in the field of healing trauma and addiction in Chapter 35, "Trauma Healing Practices and Recovery Menu."

## Finding A Neurofeedback Practitioner Who Specializes In C-PTSD

If you're considering working with a neurofeedback practitioner, you should know that the results you get will be directly related to the practitioner's skill level. I also strongly recommend you only work with practitioners who have gotten excellent results with neurofeedback for trauma survivors and who are also psychotherapists who specialize in C-PTSD.

Dr. Bessel van der Kolk's organization, The Trauma Research Foundation (TRF), offers a vetted practitioner directory that lists practitioners who have completed their TRF Traumatic Stress Studies Certificate Program or their TRF Neurofeedback Certificate Program. See the appendix for TRF neurofeedback practitioner listings.

# CHAPTER 31

---

# GRIEVING THE LOSSES OF C-PTSD

Time does not heal wounds without acknowledgment of what has happened. You need to clarify your feelings and express in detail what you have lost and how much you care about what you have lost.

—Peter Leach and Zeva Singer

Grieving disappointment and loss has always been difficult for me. When you're raised in a family where it seems to lurk around every corner, the need to numb or shut down painful feelings was a necessary strategy to protect me from the emotional pain I had no capacity to deal with.

My mother grieved disappointment and loss by getting drunk, crying, or raging at my dad. She also compulsively searched for anyone willing to listen to her woes. When all else failed, she would fall into a deep depression.

My dad numbed his grief with food and expressed anger and contempt through sarcasm and disparaging remarks. He also found solace in his grief by turning to his mistress.

Looking at how my parents modeled grieving helped me understand why I struggled to navigate it in my own life. Since I was never taught how to grieve in healthy ways, I coped with grief as my parents did; by using food and mind-altering substances.

When your brain, body, and mind have been wired to automatically shut down emotional pain by ingesting food, caffeine, alcohol, or drugs, and you've been doing it for decades, becoming open to dealing with grief and loss in healthier ways can be a bit dicey at first, to say the least.

Reading trauma therapist Pete Walker's book, *The Tao of Fully Feeling: Harvesting Forgiveness Out of Blame,* helped me wrap my head around why I struggled with grief and loss. It also taught me specific steps I could take to grieve. The below excerpt from *The Tao of Fully Feeling* illustrates how critically important grieving childhood losses is for healing trauma.

> Grieving is the age-old healthy human process of expressing sadness and anger about hurt and loss. It is the psyche's natural way of releasing the natural pain caused by the loss of someone or something we value. Grieving is as necessary to emotional health as urinating and defecating are to physical health. Grieving removes the emotional hurt and pain from the psyche as the physiological functions of elimination remove chemical toxins from the body.

Grieving plays an essential role in reclaiming the capacity to fully feel. An individual's emotional trauma recovery is, in fact, reflected in the degree in which she reclaims and regularly welcomes grieving as the ongoing life-enhancing process that it is.

Grieving, like nothing else, extricates us from our webs of tension and distraction. We can let go of unhealthy allegiances to old family rules that do not allow us to acknowledge the pain of our childhoods. We no longer need to squander our vitality imprisoning our memories in guarding against the escape of our pain.

## Noticing How Uncomfortable and Resistant Grief Work Has Been for Me

Understanding through Walker's work that the degree of recovery I experience from my C-PTSD symptoms is directly related to how willing I am to fully grieve my childhood losses has been a mixed bag for me.

While writing this chapter, I noticed a growing discomfort arise in me. Writing about the importance of grieving meant I couldn't escape the fact that if I was going to walk my talk and get relief from my C-PTSD symptoms, I would need to feel the pain of my childhood losses.

My first impulse was to minimize my losses by telling myself, "Maybe I don't need to do much grief work since I've likely grieved the majority of the pain from my childhood through the healing work I had done before I learned I had trauma."

Yet when I got honest with myself, I had to admit that I didn't even know about the many losses I'd sustained until I learned how pervasive childhood trauma's impact had been throughout my life.

While processing my grief, I realized that my resistance to grieving loss began as a way to survive as a child. On some level, I knew I wasn't equipped to handle the overwhelming sadness of the chronic day-in, day-out losses I faced. I adapted by numbing through eating or reframing losses in a more positive, Pollyannaish light as a way to hold on to some semblance of sanity.

At thirteen, I attempted to deal with my grief by stopping myself from crying when my mom was on another drunken rage attack toward my dad. Since crying hadn't helped stop my pain before, I thought I wouldn't feel as much pain if I stopped myself from crying.

Once I turned sixteen, I added alcohol, marijuana, and cigarettes to the mix of the strategies I used to deal with my grief. Although these strategies saved my sanity as a child and through my teenage years, they became life-threatening liabilities as an adult.

## Being Willing to Feel the Pain to Give up the Suffering

As I took in what I was learning about the importance of grieving my childhood losses, it became clear that if I didn't allow myself to grieve, I would stay stuck with my C-PTSD symptoms indefinitely. That was when I became willing to feel the pain of my grief to give up the suffering of my C-PTSD symptoms.

It helped to remind me that being open to acknowledging and feeling the pain of my losses doesn't mean the pain will last forever, as it did when I was a child. I'm in the driver's seat now and can choose how fast or slow I take my grieving process.

It also helped to acknowledge that as an adult, I have healthy resources to protect and soothe me that I didn't have as a child. These include my own internalized, nurturing inner parent who is always there for me. I also have the support of my safe, compassionate partner, Maria, and several close friends who are also on a trauma-healing and recovery path. If necessary, I can reach out to a trauma-informed therapist or coach. Having an abundance of healthy resources at my disposal has made all the difference in my ability to forgo using food or caffeine to cope with grieving my losses.

## The Cost Of Denied Grief & Premature Forgiveness

Another insight I had about my difficulty with grief was hearing Pete Walker share how upset he was by how often he sees clients who've been expected by their therapist to prematurely forgive others vs. grieve their losses and the price they pay by doing so in his book *The Tao of Fully Feeling*.

I witness too many therapists pathologizing their clients for not choosing to get over the past. My skin crawls when I hear putdowns like: "Stop feeling sorry for yourself. Stop crying over spilled milk. Stop bellyaching over something you can't change."

How can professionals declare the past irrelevant? The past is not even the past. For so many people, it is alive and dictating their present. All too often, they are tortured by self-attacking mindsets which concretized in childhood

Yet therapists and New Age evangelists everywhere are pushing *Forgiveness* as the latest panacea... Survivors everywhere are shamed out of healthy emotional upset about unspeakable parental behavior. Many are pushed to forgive parents who are still abusing them!

Interestingly, when I recalled hearing different therapists and spiritual teachers I'd worked with speak of the importance of letting go of past anger, hurt, or sadness through forgiveness, I never thought they were asking me to bypass my grief. At the time, I assumed choosing forgiveness was a healthy, positive way to heal, grow and move forward in my life.

Yet Walker's writing on this subject helped remind me that just because a therapist or a spiritual teacher believes forgiveness is the best choice for me to heal and grow doesn't automatically make it so. Once I understood that to experience the maximum relief from C-PTSD symptoms, I needed to fully grieve the losses of my childhood. I became fully willing to face the grief monster.

Trauma psychotherapist Tian Dayton, Ph.D., speaks about the necessity of grieving in the below excerpt from her May 29, 2017, article in huffpost.com, "Denied Grief: When the Heart Hurts in Silence."

This is a kind of pain that people don't want to speak of because they fear if they do, they will lose their courage to move on; it feels negative and threatening. But locked within this unspoken grief is our joy waiting to get loose, our faith in love's ability to repair and renew itself.

In my experience, people spend years and decades avoiding the feelings that may take only moments to feel. It is the fear of feeling that comes to have a twisted life of its own whilst feeling it is really quite the straightest path.

When I first read this article, it struck me how tragic it is that so many of us aren't taught how to grieve our losses in healthy ways simply because our parents never taught us how to do so, which is more than likely due to their parents not teaching them.

The good news is it's never too late to grieve the losses from our childhoods. I am so grateful to the many authors I've mentioned throughout this book who have taught me the value of grieving our childhood losses and what steps we can take to do so.

## How I Started Processing My Grief

The first step was to take an honest and in-depth look at what I lost due to the adversity and trauma I experienced as a child. I also needed to reflect on how trauma had created losses for me as an adult.

As I began contemplating my losses, I once again felt really uncomfortable. After taking a moment to check in with what was going on with me, I realized it was due to the decades of Law of Attraction work I'd done before working on healing my trauma.

One of the central teachings of the Law of Attraction is to do whatever is necessary to shift yourself into a "feel good" state. Given grief work is the antithesis of what feels good; needless to say, it was a huge stretch.

To get the ball rolling, I gently said to myself, *Sweetie, you can start by just writing a basic bullet list of your losses. Just take baby steps at your own pace.* So, I sat down at my computer, opened up Word, and made my list.

Below is the list of what I've lost to childhood trauma. In previous chapters, I elaborate on the feelings that came up for me when I covered some of these losses. Below this list, I go into more detail about some of the losses I haven't discussed in previous chapters.

The list below represents a mixture of losses I experienced during childhood. It also includes the losses I became aware of since learning about the long-term impact childhood trauma has had on my brain, body, mind, behavior, and relationships.

Since I had done three decades of healing work (which included some grief work) before discovering I had trauma, most of the losses I experienced in childhood have been grieved. As for the losses I've recently become aware of since I learned I had C-PTSD, I am in various stages of healing.

## What I Lost to Childhood Trauma

- Missing out on having a mother who could self-regulate and attune with me resulting in my having difficulty with regulating my emotions and nervous system.
- Not feeling safe, seen, known, guided, and protected by my parents.
- Missing out on experiencing a relatively happy, connected family and carefree childhood and all the happy memories that go with it.
- Difficulty forming healthy long-term friendships and romantic relationships.
- A lack of feeling safe and secure in the world due to not having a family I could count on or feel safe with.
- Missing out on having a fully functional brain, nervous system, and mind that automatically regulates impulses, emotions, behaviors, and attention.
- The loss of physical and financial well-being due to being run by a highjacked brain that drove addictions to alcohol, marijuana, cigarettes, and food for many years.
- The loss of dignity, self-respect, self-esteem, and peace of mind due to suffering from chronic toxic shame about being severely obese and believing I was weak and a failure for not being able to control my eating, drinking, smoking, or weight.
- Rarely feeling at peace for several decades due to suffering from anxiety, ruminating thoughts, fears, guilt, shame, and an unrelenting inner and outer critic.
- Difficulty feeling safe socializing with people.
- A compromised ability to be embodied and fully feel and express the full range of emotions.
- A compromised ability to freely celebrate my sexuality due to being shamed by my family, church, and culture for being a lesbian.
- The loss of having a healthy relationship with food and my body.
- The loss of experiencing a sense of meaning and purpose in my work due to disabling emotional flashbacks.
- Squandering decades of time, money, and energy attempting to undo all the damage I suffered from being brought up by emotionally immature parents who modeled toxic relationship dynamics and self-destructive coping behaviors.
- Years of missed opportunities to build a stable, fulfilling life due to dozens of mental health clinicians missing I'd been suffering from C-PTSD and failing to provide me with trauma-based therapies to heal sooner.

## Lost Potential & Opportunities

Learning I had untreated trauma brought to light that for the previous thirty years, the many psychotherapists and psychiatrists I had seen had failed to identify that the root cause of my struggle with anxiety, depression, addictions, and close relationships was untreated childhood trauma.

Had I been told ten, twenty, or thirty years ago that the reason I struggled with all of these issues was due to childhood trauma and been offered trauma-based therapies, the entire trajectory of my life would have changed.

Being diagnosed correctly and receiving trauma-based therapies could have relieved me of decades of unnecessary suffering and could have given me opportunities to build an entirely different life. Instead, I was left to suffer without knowing the root cause of these seemingly intractable problems.

As the entire picture of how trauma had impacted my life became clearer and clearer, I took in the gravity of how massive these losses were.

First, it felt like I'd been ripped off from getting to have a happy childhood and a loving family by being raised by insanely dysfunctional parents. Then it felt like I got ripped off again due to the dozens of therapists and psychiatrists missing that I was suffering from trauma and their failing to provide the treatment I needed to heal the root cause of my symptoms.

It was heartbreaking to think about who and what I could have become as a person, a partner, and a professional if my brain, body, and mind had been fully functional instead of hijacked by trauma. Where would I be today had I not been traumatized and subsequently consumed with managing one crisis after another with addictions, obesity, shame, guilt, anxiety, and difficult relationships?

By sharing the grief of my lost potential, I have no doubt there will be those who attempt to try to get me to sugarcoat it by saying things like, "You wouldn't be where you are and writing this book and helping others heal if you hadn't been traumatized."

Sugarcoating is an excellent strategy to sidestep pain when in a pinch. But if you are about the business of resolving your C-PTSD symptoms, the only way out is through. To heal, I must face the truth of what I lost. This requires looking at and feeling the pain of what my potential could have been if I hadn't had to deal with the limitations that trauma put on me.

## How Unhealed Trauma Keeps Survivors Stuck Surviving But Never Thriving

Looking back on my life through a trauma-informed lens, it makes sense that it would be difficult to get into a creative flow with career goals or develop deep, connected relationships. Living with unhealed trauma keeps you in a chronic state of survival. Because my nervous system was so unstable, I was always looking for ways to regulate my brain, body, and mind through whatever snack, caffeinated beverage, substance, activity, or personal-growth book I could get my hands on. After contemplating how much energy it takes a survivor just to get through the day, I thought, *No wonder I overused food, substances, and caffeine*. With unhealed trauma, just making it through the day is a major accomplishment.

I felt a deep sadness for my lost potential as I contemplated how much of it was squandered due to just trying to manage the symptoms of childhood trauma instead of focusing on living my best life.

If I'd been raised by healthy parents, I likely would have had healthy self-esteem, natural energy, and a brain, body, and mind that automatically self-regulated. This would have freed me up from constantly attempting to manually regulate my energy through food and substances.

Being raised by healthy parents would have also allowed me to go through the normal developmental stages of childhood and early adulthood instead of having it stalled by out-of-control addictions, severe obesity, and dysfunctional family dynamics.

I likely would have had the emotional and financial support from my family and the self-esteem and drive to go to college. This would have enabled me to start my career as a young woman instead of slogging through a decade of life-threatening addictions to alcohol, drugs, and food while living paycheck to paycheck at a soul-sucking job. I would have also been able to contribute on a much higher level and make a more significant impact on improving humanity.

Without having to navigate the minefields of relational trauma, I would have been able to attract and maintain healthy relationships much earlier in my life. I would also have the ability to deal with conflict and repair ruptures as they came up and enjoy the love and support of my parents and siblings, long-term friendships, and romantic relationships.

As a trauma survivor, there's no way I could have manifested this kind of life because my brain, body, and mind were too dysregulated to operate on the level that this kind of life required.

Frankly, it feels like it has taken thirty years of healing and recovery just to get to the starting line where non-traumatized people begin.

So how do I reconcile these feelings about what could have been?

I must grieve. I must allow myself to witness and validate the sadness I feel for my lost potential and for all the lost opportunities that will never come to fruition for me.

## Profound Loss That Hasn't Been Mourned

I was deeply moved while reading the excerpt below from *Understanding and Treating Chronic Shame: A Relational/Neurobiological Approach,* where Patricia DeYoung shares a trauma therapist's view on how frequently survivors unconsciously sidestep feeling their childhood losses.

> Their deep early losses will not be made up for them. As we listen to their repetitive stories of impossible longing and striving met by disappointment, we can keep our impatience in check by remembering that this is their core story, even deeper than their story of shame; profound loss that has not been mourned. Then we may be able—slowly, gently—to weave with them a narrative of compassion for their longing, striving, disappointed self.

Reading this passage touched a deep level of sadness in me for the many losses I suffered but hadn't completely mourned. It also stirred the sadness I have for the countless survivors all over the world who also have losses they've yet to mourn.

It speaks to how frequently survivors get caught up in endless longing and striving for one thing or another as an unconscious attempt to make good on early childhood losses.

Yet, the only way to achieve a sense of completion with these longings is to mourn the original loss by feeling the unfelt pain and disappointment.

This passage reminded me of an experience I had several years ago while doing inner-child work. At the time, I'd discovered that my inner child was having difficulty letting go of the hope that one day an ideal wise mother or father figure would show up to nurture, guide, and protect her in the way she'd longed for.

I learned I needed to become a nurturing, wise, protective mother and father figure for myself. To accept that I had to become my own nurturing parent, I first had to let go of my inner child's longing to be saved by a nurturing parent figure outside of myself.

To grieve this loss, I had to accept the fact that my parents had never been there for me and never would be. I then needed to get honest about how I felt about this.

It wasn't until I experienced the deep sadness, anger, and loss from being emotionally abandoned by my parents that I could embrace becoming the nurturing, wise parent for my inner child. That was when I could let go of the salvation fantasy that some teacher or strong parental figure was coming to save me.

This experience helped me realize that when we sidestep the grieving process by chasing what we can never catch—such as a substitute for a parent or family who will finally be there for us, we do so at our own peril.

Unresolved grief can run roughshod through our lives, keeping us endlessly spinning while chasing the latest salvation fantasy. It also keeps us stuck in unfulfilling work, unhealthy relationships, and other pursuits that continually disappoint us and squander the precious time we have left in this one short life.

When I looked at the price I've paid—and the price I'll continue to pay—by not grieving my childhood losses, I could finally see that grieving my losses is, in truth, the easier, softer way.

## How to Grieve Your Losses

Trauma therapist Tian Dayton's book *The Soulful Journey of Recovery: A Guide to Healing from a Traumatic Past for ACAs, Codependents, or Those with Adverse Childhood Experiences* helped me see how we don't offer the space, structure, or rituals for grieving losses from childhood trauma or addiction like we do with grieving the death of a family member.

> Funerals are incredibly helpful at honoring the death and the life of the person we have lost. They offer us structure through which to legitimize our loss and to grieve. To actually feel the pain we're in. But there are no ceremonies for a child who loses a parent slowly to the disease of addiction.
>
> Or the traumatized individual who lost a connection with themselves. There are simply no rituals for these. No black armbands to let the world know we are hurting. No casseroles are dropped off to keep us fed until we can get on our feet again. And no one honors the addict who only sort of died. Or for us for losing them by inches or noticing the part of us that died a little bit too.
>
> Besides, we would need two eulogies, one the classic going over of his life, his strengths, contributions, and those he left behind who will mourn him. That one is very important and healing. But there's a shadow eulogy that never gets said because it happens long before the real death. "This man is dying while he is living, and he's taking a part of us along with him."

This excerpt speaks to how common it is for survivors to unknowingly sidestep grieving their childhood losses since there is no space or ritual in our culture to do so.

Sadly, when we repress or resist grieving the pain from our childhoods, we not only block the painful feelings. We also lose access to the full range of emotions, such as joy, connection, and love. So, if we want to experience all that life has to offer, we must bite the bullet and grieve our losses.

## How to Process Your Grief

After reviewing my losses and how many years I struggled with addiction, weight, anxiety, relationships, work, and all the misdiagnoses, I felt a mixture of anger, sadness, and overwhelm. This left me feeling unclear about where to even start processing my grief.

The below excerpt from Gay Hendrick's book *Learning to Love Yourself: A Guide to Becoming Centered* helped me gain some perspective on grieving.

> All we need to do is acknowledge our sadness. Perhaps if we still think if we become willing to feel, we must go around sad the rest of our lives. When people truly open themselves to a particular feeling, even deep grief or rage, the expression of that feeling only lasts a few minutes.
>
> Further, they always feel good afterward. People tell me they feel cleansed, whole, light. I have never seen anyone not feel better after being willing to feel something they had been holding back.

After reading the first sentence of this excerpt, "All we need do is acknowledge our sadness." I thought, *Okay, I can do that.* And I immediately felt relieved. It also helped reading further into the excerpt to know that my pain will only last a few minutes.

## The Four Grieving Practices

According to Pete Walker in his book *Complex PTSD: From Surviving to Thriving,* there are four different practices we can use to grieve:

1. Verbal ventilating
2. Angering
3. Crying
4. Feeling

Walker states that specific types of grieving help us heal and resolve trauma in specific ways, such as:

- Verbal ventilation heals abandonment and resolves emotional flashbacks
- Angering diminishes fear and shame
- Feeling can heal digestive problems
- Crying can resolve fear, shame, and self-abandonment

## Verbal Ventilation

Verbal ventilation is verbally processing or talking about grief. I've always been an external processor, so talking about my feelings with a safe person comes naturally to me and is extremely regulating. The key I've found is finding a safe person and setting ground rules so I can share my feelings without worrying about them giving advice or inappropriate feedback.

Journaling is another method I've used to verbally ventilate on paper. Something about writing brings out feelings I didn't even know I had. It's like priming the pump. I've also found that asking myself questions while I journal, such as, *What does this bring up?* And *What about this makes me mad?* These are great ways to excavate feelings and clarify what's next.

Writing this book has been extremely helpful in processing the grief of my childhood losses. Since it's designed to be a teaching memoir, it has required me to lay out my losses and look at what I've done to grieve them. Seeing all of my losses together for the first time brought up a new level of grief when I took in the sheer volume of what I'd lost. This illustrates how writing down or speaking to another person about what you've lost to trauma can be a powerful way to excavate and grieve your losses.

## Feelings

Over the years, I've noticed that feelings act like independent entities. In some ways, they remind me of little children. They must be allowed to express themselves and be heard with understanding and compassion to feel validated so they can calm down. But like with small children, when their feelings aren't heard, the resulting frustration, anger, and sadness builds up until they cry, shut down, or throw a tantrum. But since it's not acceptable for adults to express their feelings so openly, they choose more acceptable ways to express themselves. These can include passive-aggressive behavior in relationships or using food or substances to numb their pain. Depression and anxiety are often the symptoms of unexpressed feelings.

To prevent the various ways unexpressed emotions cause more pain than they were initially attempting to avoid, we must find a way to allow our feelings to be expressed if we want them to resolve and heal. Just like little children, all they need to calm down is for us to allow them to be heard while we hold the space of compassion and empathy for them while they express themselves.

I've found that sharing my feelings or struggles with a safe spouse, friend, therapist, or coach can prime deeper emotions to arise. Once I feel a painful emotion bubbling up, the key for me is to consciously stop myself from pushing it down and focus on allowing it to come up in a gradual, safe way. Watching movies that touch on themes of grief can also help me get in touch with my own grief and can be very therapeutic.

## Crying

Crying is another cathartic way to discharge grief and loss. Although I don't often cry, when I feel a good cry bubbling up, I stay mindful of allowing it to come up and out versus pushing it down. After a good cry, I love the tremendous sense of relief I feel. I've also found that talking to a safe friend or my partner, Maria, about something vulnerable or painful can create the space for tears to come up.

## Angering

I never knew that expressing anger about injustice is a way to process grief until I read Walker's book *The Tao of Fully Feeling*. But once I understood it, it made total sense.

When I first realized that as someone with an ACE score of six, my risk of developing addictions to alcohol, drugs, and cigarettes, becoming severely obese, and developing depression and anxiety was between 200 and 700% higher than someone who has an ACE score of zero, I was shocked.

And given all of these outcomes have come to pass for me, it became crystal clear how much damage and suffering childhood trauma had created throughout my life. When I reflected on the fact that I was still struggling to recover from the effects of this trauma fifty years later, I didn't know what to feel.

On one level, I was totally pissed off at my parents for the hell they put me through and the long shadow of hurt and suffering it has caused throughout my life. On another, I felt sad that it even had to happen. It's a weird space to be in since I know my parents were operating on autopilot from their own trauma. Yet, I also know they were ultimately responsible for taking care of me as their child and failed miserably. In this light, I know my anger is completely justified and is actually necessary for me to process my grief.

One of the most important things I've learned in all of this is how important it is to give ourselves permission to acknowledge and fully feel our anger and sadness about what happened to us. If I've learned anything about healing childhood trauma, it's when we repress or minimize our feelings about what happened to us that we'll inadvertently block our healing and keep our C-PTSD symptoms alive.

## Expressing Healthy Anger is Vital for a Survivor's Healing

Expressing anger is not only about authentic self-expression but also about self-protection. When we express our anger in a healthy way, we're sending a clear signal to ourselves and to the universe that we won't tolerate abuse or neglect from anyone ever again. We know we have our own backs, and just knowing that is a huge corrective experience and is extremely regulating for a survivor.

As a child, I didn't feel safe knowing that my parents would stand up for or protect me from what was happening at home or school, so knowing as an adult that I can depend on myself for protection is a wonderful healing experience.

## My Journey Through Grief

Although the concept of getting in touch with and processing difficult feelings may sound simple, if you're anything like me and have spent a lifetime pushing down or numbing painful emotions, it's not easy and definitely takes some work.

Once I realized that my knee-jerk reaction to painful feelings was to block them with food or caffeine and was a trauma response wired into my nervous system, I had more compassion for myself. This is why learning to allow feelings to be felt takes understanding, self-compassion, commitment, and perseverance. With the right support, it's possible to allow yourself to feel difficult emotions instead of immediately numbing them with whatever your numbing behavior of choice is.

Learning how critical grieving is to healing trauma and the specific ways I can access and resolve my grief has been extremely helpful. Had I not discovered how critical it was to grieve my childhood losses, I likely would have skipped right past it as I had for the better part of my life.

One major insight I've had about grieving is that everyone grieves differently. Just because your grieving doesn't look like someone else's doesn't mean you're doing it wrong, you're cold, or you somehow don't care. It actually doesn't mean anything other than everyone has their own way of grieving.

I've also learned that grieving the losses from my childhood trauma is a process. It doesn't have a clear beginning, middle, and end. Giving myself this space to grieve at my own pace and in my own way has been extremely helpful and liberating.

## Getting Support To Grieve The Losses of C-PTSD

Since grieving the losses of C-PTSD can bring up some intense emotions, and healing trauma requires special trauma-based therapies, I recommend seeking out a trauma-trained psychotherapist who works on a brain, body, and mind level to help you process your grief.

See chapter 35, "The Trauma Healing Practices & Recovery Menu," under body, brain, and mind based psychotherapy for exploring different types of trauma therapies. The appendix also lists several directories for trauma-based psychotherapists.

# CHAPTER 32

---

# ALCOHOL & DRUG ADDICTION RECOVERY OPTIONS FOR SURVIVORS

The goal here is to create a situation you no longer have to escape or a life you don't have to numb. The achievement of sobriety is not the point; it's a by-product of the work. The work is the point. Addiction is the hook that gets you in the door, and quitting is the catalyst to heal deeper wounds.

—Holly Whitaker

My journey of recovery from alcohol and drugs began in 1986. Below I share the various methods and types of support that have worked for my ongoing recovery over the past thirty-five years. I do want to mention that people who struggle with behavioral addictions vs. substances such as work, sex, spending, gambling, video games, or people pleasing often suffer and cause their families to suffer just as much as those addicted to alcohol, drugs, or food.

If behavioral addictions are impacting you or a loved one, you can still utilize the information in this chapter by replacing the word alcohol and drugs with whatever behavioral addiction you or your loved one is dealing with.

If you haven't struggled with alcohol, drugs, food, weight, or other behavioral addictions, I believe this chapter can still provide great value for you. In it, I provide a unique trauma-informed perspective of what loved ones who struggle with trauma and addiction are dealing with and what options are available for their recovery.

Using a trauma-informed perspective when approaching a survivor struggling with addiction can make a huge difference in helping them feel safe, seen, and understood. This is critical in helping them become more open to embarking on a healing and recovery path.

Additionally, if you are struggling to cope with a friend or family member's alcohol, drug, food, or other behavioral addiction, I highly recommend attending online or in-person Al-Anon or Codependents Anonymous meetings. Both groups are designed to provide healthy ways to cope with the pain and stress of dealing with a loved one engaging in self-destructive behavior. A list of support groups for friends and family members of those suffering from addiction can be found in the appendix.

## Recovery Approaches Must Include Healing C-PTSD & Treating Addiction as A Chronic Brain Disease

Although I've written extensively about addiction being an attempt to relieve the pain and dysregulation of childhood trauma, it's also important to recognize that heavy, prolonged use of drugs or alcohol changes the brain. Once enough brain changes have taken place, addiction takes hold and acts as a chronic brain disease.

Once a person becomes addicted to alcohol or drugs, trauma survivors must understand and accept that they now have two illnesses to contend with, C-PTSD and the chronic brain disease of addiction. This is why survivors must focus on recovering from and managing both illnesses.

## Being In Recovery From Substances Is Critical to Healing Childhood Trauma

When in the throes of serious substance or other behavioral addictions, the addiction takes on a life of its own and becomes a new source of trauma. Therefore, you can't heal your trauma when practicing a serious substance or behavioral addiction.

The first step to healing complex PTSD for those struggling with a serious substance or behavioral addiction is to achieve stability with the addiction. Achieving stability for some life-threatening addictions may require a hospital setting. However, for many (like me), 12-step or other recovery programs may offer enough support for survivors to achieve stability with their addiction.

Once stability with addiction is achieved, it's essential to include both addiction recovery and trauma healing practices and therapies in a survivor's healing and recovery journey.

## Alcoholics Anonymous

Alcoholics Anonymous (AA) and various other Twelve-Step programs are the main recovery programs that helped me initially get and stay sober. It took a few starts and stops and a few months of attending AA meetings before I was able to put over twelve years of continuous sobriety together. I'll be forever grateful to the people in AA and the Twelve Steps for being there for me when I needed them the most.

I was an avid AA member for about five of my initial twelve-and-a-half years of recovery that began in 1987. I returned for about two years in 2002 after a relapse.

In my early recovery, I worked the Steps, was a secretary and spoke at meetings, worked with a sponsor, developed several close sober friendships, and fully participated in my recovery.

Alcoholics Anonymous provided the foundational pieces that were necessary for me to build long-term recovery. This included a framework to follow through the 12 steps, sponsorship and a local and worldwide community of sober members that supported me while I went through the ups and downs of my early sobriety.

The flexibility of AAs: *Take what you like and leave the rest;* philosophy really appealed to me. Knowing it was okay to work my program in whichever way I wanted helped me stick around the rooms of AA. If you're willing to attend regular meetings, get a sponsor, and work the Steps, you'll build a solid foundation that will give you the best chance of getting and staying in long-term recovery.

As with any support group, it's essential to find one that resonates with you. Finding gay and lesbian meetings where I could feel safe sharing who I was in the 1980s was a lifesaver for me. See the appendix for dozens of different 12-step and non-12-step recovery meetings.

Once you find a meeting you resonate with, be sure to attend each week and go for coffee or a meal afterward. Out of doing so, friendships naturally blossom, and you'll be on your way to building a community of sober friends.

## Realizing AA Was a Form of Limbic System Therapy for Me

Learning about trauma's impact on a survivor's limbic system (the emotional part of the brain) reminded me of something I noticed about AA in my early recovery.

When I first started attending AA, I remember sharing at meetings that there had to be some kind of magic in the rooms of AA. In my mind, what else could account for my being able to quit drinking? For the previous decade, I'd never been able to quit for even one day until I went to AA.

Once I understood the neurobiology of nervous-system regulation for people with childhood trauma, I was able to put together what lay behind AA's seemingly magical ability to help even what was considered hopeless alcoholics get and stay sober.

By attending gay and lesbian AA meetings on a regular basis, I was unknowingly regulating my nervous system by forging safe, sober relationships in a community I felt I belonged in. The more regulated I felt the fewer cravings I had to drink. By attending AA meetings and establishing a safe network of close sober girlfriends, I permanently changed what I turned to for relief.

By staying sober, going to meetings, and working the steps, my limbic system rewired to turn to healthy relationships and to the principles and fellowship of AA instead of alcohol and drugs to stay regulated

Interestingly AA provided the kindness, nurture, and attunement I had longed for but wasn't able to get growing up with my parents.  So, in a full circle kind of moment, AA played a major role in helping me feel safe enough to turn to relationships instead of substances to stay regulated, which is what healing relational trauma is all about.

## The People You Hang Out with Matter

Another big lesson I learned in my early recovery is how important it is to be discerning about the people you spend time with since they'll directly influence your sobriety. Choosing friends who were also in recovery or those who didn't drink was key to my staying sober. Doing so also helped me learn to use new, healthier outlets to have fun or cope with stress. It also helped me realize I could have just as much fun and often even more fun hanging out with my sober friends as I did with my old party buddies.

People in recovery also hold an extremely sacred space for your sobriety. It's treated as a matter of life and death because it is. People who don't understand addiction may encourage you to try to moderate your drinking or using because they don't realize you can't.  In a weak moment, you may take them up on their idea to moderate and find yourself in a terrible relapse.

Although AA was the foundation of my initial sobriety, I found that I needed more to meet my personal and spiritual growth needs after a few years. This was when I began exploring other psychological and spiritually oriented philosophies. See the appendix for a list of the books and authors that have been the most helpful for me on my recovery journey.

After I stopped going to regular Twelve-Step meetings, I continued my recovery journey by attending various self-help and therapy groups.  I've also found great value in seeking individual psychotherapy and working with several life coaches as well.

## Choosing A Psychotherapist Who Specializes In C-PTSD & Addiction Recovery

Over the past three decades, I have worked with over a dozen psychotherapists and several psychiatrists to overcome my struggle with alcohol, marijuana, food, weight, and relationship issues.  Now that I am aware that untreated childhood trauma had been the root cause of all of these struggles, and not one of my therapists or psychiatrists had caught on to this fact, I would be extremely cautious about who you choose to work with in the mental health field for your addiction issues.

Although I have significantly benefited from talk therapy for issues unrelated to addiction and C-PTSD, in my experience, the majority of mental health practitioners are not trained to recognize, diagnose or properly treat childhood trauma and addiction. This is why choosing a therapist specializing in treating C-PTSD and addiction is crucial for your recovery.

## How *Parts Work* Psychotherapy Treats The Root Cause of Addiction

In *Healing The Fragmented Selves of Trauma Survivors,* trauma expert Dr. Janina Fisher reveals the mechanism that drives self-destructive behavior and offers a trauma-informed brain, body, and mind oriented therapy to heal.

> Self-destructive behavior stems from a perfect storm of variables. First, a trigger evokes trauma-related implicit memory. Second, the implicit memory's association with danger activates the emergency stress response system —inducing a sympathetic nervous system reaction and shutting down the pre-frontal cortex —impairing the individual's judgment and disempowering the normal life self.
>
> Now *parts* with different defensive responses have free reign to act on their survival instincts leading to some action intended to bring relief. Whether it is binging and purging, cutting, suicide attempts, addictive behavior, or restricting food.
>
> For a short time, perhaps only minutes, clients report a temporary feeling of control or well-being that reinforces the connection between the aversive feelings, dysregulated arousal, and an immediate need for an action that will bring relief.
>
> Because often there is little felt connection between the apparently benign or mildly distressing trigger— the hurt and sadness or shame of *child parts* and the impulsive behavior of *fight or flight parts* — even the client does not understand his or her behavior, except as a statement about the actions taken—*I want to kill myself.* Stabilization of high-risk behavior requires addressing the *part's* part—a step not included even in newer cutting-edge treatments.

When Fisher states the "part's" part needs to be addressed to successfully treat addiction and trauma, she is referring to a type of therapy known as *parts work.* *Parts work* is a trauma-informed, mind-body-oriented type of psychotherapy based on the concept that survivors learn to disconnect from the painful, traumatized *parts* of themselves to cope with the overwhelming emotional pain of being raised by dysfunctional, abusive, or neglectful parents. These "fragmented" or cut-off parts of survivors are addressed and healed by doing *parts work.*

We all have different parts operating within us. An example is when we hear someone say, *"A part of me feels like going to the party, and another part feels like staying home and being a couch potato."* For non-traumatized folks, the different parts of the self are typically benign. However, when a survivor's traumatized *part* gets triggered, it can wreak havoc in their life.

Compartmentalizing traumatized *parts* allows a survivor to function with what Fisher refers to as the "going on with normal life self." This is the *part* that takes care of everyday tasks, such as work, school, family, finances, and household chores. It also allows survivors to go through the normal developmental stages of childhood and stay attached to their dysfunctional or abusive caretakers One of the goals of *parts work* is to identify and get to know all of our parts. Another goal is to develop a loving, compassionate relationship with each part. Ultimately, *parts work* is designed to help us resolve the conflicts between our *parts,* which in turn helps us heal our trauma.

Trauma psychotherapist Dr. Arielle Schwartz discusses the role of *parts work* therapy in healing C-PTSD in the below excerpt from her website drarielleschwartz.com.

In truth, most people have *parts*...and this doesn't mean that you have multiple personalities. Rather, it is a sign that you are human and have your share of hurts and wounds that need attention...

*Parts work* therapy attends to the conflicts between *parts* that, when left unresolved, can sabotage your efforts toward healing. For example, within therapy, there are times when you might be attempting to work through a difficult or traumatic memory. Even though you are ready to heal, there might be a *part* of you that interferes with the process in an attempt to protect you from vulnerable feelings that feel threatening to your sense of self.,

Successful treatment of childhood trauma or Complex PTSD requires the ability to work with *parts* and ego states. Within *parts* work therapy, you achieve trauma resolution by recognizing disowned *parts* and giving these *parts* a voice. The goal is to help you develop an embodied sense of self that can compassionately hold your emotions, vulnerable sensations, and young *parts* of self.

Several types of psychotherapy use the *parts work* model. The most common one I have seen in the C-PTSD field is IFS-Internal Family Systems, created by Richard Schwartz, Ph.D.

### For Severe, Treatment-Resistant Addictions or Other Self-Destructive Behaviors

For those suffering from severe, life-threatening treatment-resistant addiction, who are suicidal, or who are suffering from other types of self-destructive behavior, finding a therapist or treatment facility certified in *Trauma-Informed Stabilization Treatment TIST* might be helpful for you. See the appendix for the TIST directory's website.

### What I've Done to Get and Stay Clean and Sober For the Past 35 Years

- **Attending AA/NA /MA/CoDA/ACOA Twelve-Step meetings:** I regularly attended meetings in the early years of my recovery. I built a solid foundation of recovery in AA by working the Steps with a sponsor. I returned to AA, NA, and MA to get sober after a relapse.

- **Staying surrounded by close sober friends and a sober community, I felt safe in.** In my early recovery, all my close friends were sober or didn't drink or do drugs.

- **Psychotherapy and life coaching support:** I've benefited greatly by working with several psychotherapists and life coaches.

- **Relationship discernment:** To stay sober and free from overeating, I must be very discerning in my personal and professional relationship choices. Since childhood trauma is relational trauma, I've found that when I engage in unhealthy relationships or relationships with heavy drinkers or drug users, I risk developing cravings to drink or use which can put me at risk for relapse.

- **Knowing & respecting my limitations:** I learned the hard way that I can't be in a romantic relationship with someone who drinks or uses drugs.

- **Stress awareness and reduction:** Since I'm aware that my sobriety and recovery with food are highly vulnerable to excess stress, I keep my personal and professional choices aligned with keeping my stress levels to a minimum.

- **Medications:** I've been taking antidepressants for twenty-five years for generalized anxiety disorder and dysthymia. Also, using Antabuse and AA got me back into recovery after a relapse. I used a nicotine patch to quit smoking after one year of continuous sobriety.

- **Commitment to a healthy lifestyle:** Moderate daily exercise and a healthy food plan with weekly treat days have been key to maintaining my physical and emotional recovery.

- **Neurofeedback:** Helped calm down and regulate my nervous system. This helped reduce my cravings which helped me stop smoking marijuana

- **Mindfulness/somatic mindfulness practice:** Staying mindful of my thoughts and sensations in my body throughout the day has been an excellent way for me to stay regulated.

- **Yoga:** Gentle stretch yoga classes are an excellent way to stay regulated and incorporate breathwork at the same time.

- **Massage:** I get occasional massages and use a back knobber massage tool and a percussion massager to help relieve tension in my body.

- **Breathwork:** I use deep breathing techniques to calm my nervous system.

- **Commitment to maintaining my emotional health:** I enjoy deep conversations with my spouse and close friends. I limit the time I spend watching the news or other media that dysregulates my nervous system. I also journal and read or listen to books to support my emotional health.

- **Staying committed to my personal & professional growth & evolution:** Reading, watching, or listening to various books and media on healing C-PTSD, relational trauma, and addiction recovery has played a big part in my healing and recovery. See the appendix for the types of media that have been the most helpful for my recovery.

## The Realignment of Desire Is Key for Long-Term Recovery

One area that has been critical for my long-term recovery has been realigning my relationship with desire. To pursue long-term fulfillment, I found that I needed to develop a more empowering personal narrative about who I am and what I'm capable of. This is where embracing my personal growth early in my recovery was a crucial step in realigning my desires for long-term fulfillment.

By enrolling in the Coaches Training Institute in the early nineties to become a certified life coach, I learned what goals would naturally pull me forward. I love embracing a lifestyle of achieving life-enhancing goals because it makes me proud of who I am and how I'm making a difference for others.

## Understanding & Dealing with Relapse

Although the goal in Twelve-Step groups and the majority of recovery programs with substances is abstinence, many people will face a relapse at some point (although not all).

In fact, according to the *Journal of the American Medical Association,* "among individuals with substance abuse disorders who get treatment, 40 to 60 percent will relapse within one year." Also, the National Institute on Drug Abuse states, "the chronic nature of the disease means that relapsing to drug abuse at some point is not only possible but likely."

By stating relapse is likely among people with addictions, I'm not saying a person is doomed to chronically relapse and suffer active addiction for the rest of their life. I'm also not saying it's okay to relapse or give a pass to those in recovery to give up their sobriety.

The truth is relapse is a huge deal. In fact, many who relapse never make it back. I've had friends who died due to relapsing. I've sat in countless Twelve-Step meetings and heard the tragic announcement that another member of our Twelve-Step fellowship had gone out and died due to relapsing.

My goal in discussing relapse is to educate those unfamiliar with the nature of addiction. Recovery can be messy. It's not always a perfect "once, and you're done" kind of process. It's important to discuss relapse as a possible part of recovery because the more we understand the nature of what we're dealing with, the better prepared we are to manage and prevent it.

## How Relapse Has Been Part of My Story

Although I first walked through the doors of AA in 1986, it took me several tries and a few months in AA before I was able to maintain continuous sobriety. Also, for the first year in AA, I continued smoking marijuana and cigarettes because I knew there was no way I could give up alcohol, marijuana, and cigarettes in one fell swoop. This is why I state that my initial sobriety started in 1987 instead of 1986.

As far as my food addiction goes—from when I was five until I got sober at twenty-seven, I chronically relapsed with food and weight. A few years after I got sober, I joined OA. Over the course of two years, I lost 140 pounds. But over the years, my weight continued to creep up. And once I hit some major life stressors, my food addiction took off, and I regained the remainder of my weight. It wasn't until I had weight-loss surgery at 42 that I was able to rein in my compulsive eating, lose 160 pounds, and keep it off for good.

Although I've had one relapse with alcohol and one with marijuana, I'm thrilled that I've stayed clean and sober for thirty of the past thirty-five years, which is more than 80% of the time. I'm also thrilled that I've stayed in recovery with my food and weight and have maintained my weight loss for twenty years.

I believe a big part of recovering from my relapses and staying in long-term recovery with substances, food, and weight has been my willingness to reach out for support inside and outside the Twelve-Step recovery world.

With my relapse with alcohol, getting a prescription for Antabuse and going back to AA was key in getting sober again. With food and my weight, it was having gastric bypass surgery, working on healing the brain, body, mind, and relational aspects of complex PTSD, and following a healthy food, exercise, and self-care plan. With my relapse with marijuana, it was using neurofeedback, psychotherapy, Twelve-Step meetings, and various trauma-oriented therapies and practices that helped me achieve long-term recovery.

My story is an example of how your recovery doesn't need to be perfect for you to go on to experience the gifts of long-term recovery. The key is to learn from what works and what doesn't, then make the necessary changes or get the support you need to course-correct, so you don't set yourself up for another relapse.

## Similarity of Relapse Rates Between Common Chronic Illnesses & Drug Addiction

It was mind-boggling when I first reviewed the below graph from JAMA-The Journal of the American Medical Association illustrating how relapse rates for people with substance use disorders are similar to relapse rates for other well-understood chronic medical illnesses—such as diabetes, and asthma with physiological and behavioral components.

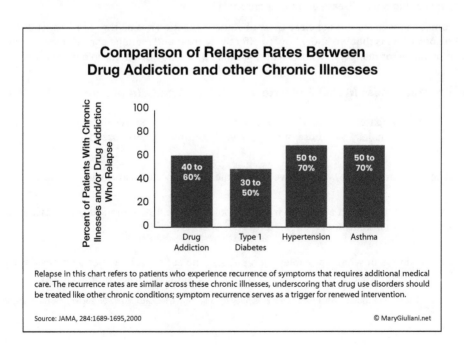

**Comparison of Relapse Rates Between Drug Addiction and other Chronic Illnesses**

Relapse in this chart refers to patients who experience recurrence of symptoms that requires additional medical care. The recurrence rates are similar across these chronic illnesses, underscoring that drug use disorders should be treated like other chronic conditions; symptom recurrence serves as a trigger for renewed intervention.

Source: JAMA, 284:1689-1695,2000                    © MaryGiuliani.net

## Relapse Does Not Mean Treatment Has Failed

Just like when people with diabetes relapse, the only thing a relapse indicates for a person recovering from addiction is that treatment needs to be adjusted or another treatment should be tried. We can then stop viewing a relapse with addiction as a personal failure. Instead, we'll see it like any other chronic illness that experiences a setback. We can then usher in a whole new narrative about the nature of addiction and, most importantly, how to treat it as the chronic health condition it is.

## Similarities Between Managing Heart Disease & Substance Use Disorders

| Drug Abuse | Cardiovascular Disease |
|---|---|
| Stay active in healthy activities: education, sports, arts, education | Engage in healthy eating and exercise |
| Know your family history | Know your family history |
| Reduce stress and develop positive coping strategies | Reduce stress and develop positive coping strategies |
| Get treatment when needed and adhere to the regimen | Get treatment when needed and adhere to the regimen |
| Source: National Institute on Drug Abuse-NIH | Monitor your cholesterol and blood pressure © MaryGiuliani.net |

## Reclassifying & Treating Addiction as a Chronic Illness

I was stunned when I saw the graph from JAMA illustrating how the relapse rates for chronic illnesses such as diabetes, hypertension, and asthma are strikingly similar to drug addiction.

I was equally stunned when I saw the NIH illustrate that managing drug addiction is practically identical to managing heart disease and other chronic illnesses.

These comparisons make it quite clear that substance addiction has all the characteristics of a chronic illness. The good news is that we know how to effectively treat and manage chronic illness. For decades, we've been doing so for diabetes, heart disease, asthma, and many other chronic illnesses.

## Using A Chronic Illness Model For Aftercare Dramatically Improves Sobriety Outcomes

The study below compares the sobriety outcomes for those who received continued care based on a chronic illness model* vs. those who received continuing care based on the current model.

Researchers found that of those who received a chronic illness modeled aftercare program:

> 69% vs. 19% remained abstinent from alcohol or drugs 4 to 9 months after discharge from residential treatment

This is just one example of what's possible when people who suffer from addiction receive the care they need from a treatment provider who views and treats their addiction as a chronic illness.

*Source: Mark D Godley, Susan H Godley, Michael L Dennis, Rodney R Funk, Lora L Passetti 12/20/06 Society for the Study of Addiction

### Why Reclassifying & Treating Addiction as a Chronic Illness Saves Lives

Another major benefit of treating addiction as a chronic illness is that it takes the perfectionistic, shameful moral judgment away from those struggling with it. Since stigma is why 93% of people who struggle with addiction don't seek treatment, reclassifying addiction as a chronic illness could save countless lives who would have otherwise been too ashamed to get help.

We don't treat diabetics, asthmatics, or heart disease patients like they have an acute illness and no longer need follow-up care after they have been discharged from the hospital. Suggesting this to any of their doctors would get you laughed out of their office since they know their patients suffer from chronic illnesses that need ongoing care to be managed effectively.

To save lives and improve the long-term care of people suffering from addiction, we must also respond to its chronic nature. Imagine how many lives could be saved or turned around and how much trauma and suffering could be averted by providing people who suffer from the chronic disease of addiction the ongoing care they need.

Given there are 20 million people (1 in 8) in the U.S. suffering from the chronic brain disease of addiction, if we could increase the recovery rate by just 1% due to addiction being reclassified and treated as a chronic illness, it would help an additional 20,000 people turn their lives around.

## How Medication-Assisted Therapy (MAT) Can Save Lives

I initially thought that MAT was used exclusively to manage opiate addiction. I have learned since that any medication that can help with addiction issues is considered MAT. I had no idea that MAT had played a key role in helping me not only quit smoking but quit drinking as well. It wasn't until I began doing research for this book that I learned that the form of MAT I used to quit smoking was the nicotine patch, and to quit drinking, I used Antabuse.

Although MAT is still considered controversial in some circles, I believe a primary key to gaining more acceptance of its efficacy and use for addiction recovery is education.

The bottom line is that medication-assisted therapy (MAT) is proven to reduce cravings, help patients stay in treatment, prevent relapse and overdoses, and ultimately save lives.

### How Medications Help Treat Addiction

Different types of medications may be useful for various stages of treatment.

- **To help a patient stop abusing.** Some medications block the brain from delivering the "feel good" or euphoric effects of the drug.

- **To help a patient stay in treatment.** Some medications help the brain gradually adapt to the absence of the abused drug. These medications slowly stave off cravings and have a calming effect on body systems. They can help patients focus on counseling and other psychotherapies related to their treatment.

- **To prevent relapse.** Science has taught us that stress, cues linked to the using experience (such as people, places, things, and moods), and exposure to the abused substance are the most common triggers for relapse.

### Medications Used to Treat Substance Addictions

- **Tobacco addiction:** Nicotine replacement therapies (available as a patch, inhaler, or gum, such as bupropion and varenicline)

- **Opioid addiction:** Methadone, buprenorphine, naltrexone

- **Alcohol and drug addiction:** Naltrexone Antabuse, acamprosate

Antabuse was pivotal in my getting sober after trying but failing on my own with AA to recover from a relapse. In all honesty, Antabuse may have even saved my life. Once I began using it and combined it with going to AA, I was finally able to stop drinking. It has been twenty years since that relapse, and I'm so grateful I haven't found it necessary to pick up a drink since.

Before using Antabuse, I spun around for two and a half years, going in and out of relapse every few weeks. My cravings were so strong that it felt like I was possessed by an energy that compelled me to drink whether I wanted to or not.

It was a living hell that I wouldn't wish on anyone. This is why I wholeheartedly believe that MAT should be available to help anyone struggling with addiction.

Learning how childhood trauma changes the brain, sensitizes the stress-response system, and, as a result, sets up so many survivors for addiction is another reason I'm so passionate about advocating for MAT for survivors.

I know firsthand that willpower is no match for a triggered survivor with impulse-control deficits. This is why so many survivors (including myself) need MAT's support along with a recovery program to get and stay sober.

Sadly, when we think we need the strength to overcome our cravings on our own or be considered weak, flawed, or not really sober, we set ourselves up for long-term suffering to stay stuck in the living hell of active addiction.

Tragically, countless people all over the world who have tried to stop self-destructive behaviors on their own and failed have either died or are living the nightmare of active addiction. Since addiction doesn't live in a vacuum, these people are traumatizing their children, spouses, and those around them. Unhealed trauma and active addiction also keep the cycle of generational trauma and addiction being passed down to the next generation.

My recovery is an example that it doesn't have to be this way. We have medications that can stop active alcoholism and opiate addictions. We have dozens of recovery programs to help people recover and rebuild their lives. We have surgeries that can reverse severe obesity and type two diabetes. And we have therapies and practices that can help heal the root cause of all these issues: complex PTSD.

# Using Harm Reduction for Alcohol, Drug & Food Addiction & Severe Obesity

Using a harm-reduction approach to manage addiction used to be a loaded topic for me until I needed it, and it worked. The below excerpt from the 4-22-19 article *How Harm Reduction Is Saving Lives* by Adi Jaffe, Ph.D., in Psychology Today, defines harm reduction and how it saves lives.

> Research shows that harm reduction is minimizing risk and keeping people alive.... Why is harm reduction important for recovery?
>
> There are MANY roads that lead to addiction - Adverse Childhood Experiences, environmental factors, biology, etc., and there are also many roads to recovery. No one arrives at addiction in the exact same way, which is why a one-size-fits-all approach doesn't work and why I advocate for more individualized paths to recovery.
>
> But what happens when society doesn't support any path to recovery besides the abstinence-only approach?
>
> Let's look at the facts. Drug overdose death rates in the U.S. are 3.5 times higher on average when compared to 17 other Western Countries. What does this tell us? People with drug addictions are dying, and you can't help someone recover who's dead. So, we need to do more to help people access treatment and feel confident in how they are treated.

We wouldn't criminalize a Diabetes patient for eating a doughnut, so why do we chastise those who choose medically assisted recovery options even though they've been proven to help?

It's time we stop viewing addiction as a personal failure or moral wrongdoing and instead treat those struggling with addiction or mental health issues with the compassion they deserve. Life is hard enough as it is, but it's especially harder for those who have had traumatic upbringings or who may be genetically predisposed.

Data from the U.S. and around the world suggest that treating problematic drug use as a health issue instead of a criminal one is a more successful model for keeping communities healthy and safe.

## My Journey with Harm Reduction

Harm reduction's primary goal is to reduce harm and save lives, whether or not a person achieves abstinence from substances. I'm happy to share that I've successfully used either a MAT-medication-assisted therapy or a harm-reduction method for my alcohol, marijuana, tobacco, and food addictions and my struggle with severe obesity. Harm reduction not only reduced the harm addiction had caused in my life but was also a critical step in helping me get completely sober.

## Willpower Alone Has Never Been Enough to Rein in My Addictions

While writing this chapter, I had a major aha moment as I started listing how harm reduction and medicated assisted therapy-MAT have helped me recover from addiction. I realized that I couldn't have gotten into recovery with any of my addictions without MAT or a harm-reduction method.

With alcohol and cigarettes, I used MAT (Antabuse and the nicotine patch). I used gastric bypass weight-loss surgery as a harm reduction approach to reduce the harm of severe obesity. With marijuana, I hired a harm-reduction counselor to help me reduce my use before being able to fully quit.

If I'd bought into the idea that I had to lick my addictions on my own or be considered weak or a failure, I would have never gotten sober or been able to reach and maintain a healthy weight. If I'd kept attempting to rely on my willpower alone, my life would be a total train wreck.

Even though in 2016, the U.S. Surgeon General declared that addiction is a chronic brain disease, 50% of people in the U.S. still believe addiction is a choice. This means half of our population believes that all people, regardless of their history of trauma, have the same ability to moderate or quit a substance they are struggling with.

Tragically, this false, deadly narrative results in millions of people believing they should have the inner strength to make the choice to cut down or quit, and when they continually fail, they're too ashamed to seek treatment since they've been taught to believe it's their own fault.  This results in countless numbers of people needlessly losing their lives to addiction every year.

The truth is the vast majority of the population is unaware that if you're a childhood trauma survivor, your brain is sensitized to stress, making you much more likely to be primed for addiction. Therefore, willpower alone will likely not be enough for survivors to overcome addiction.

In some cases, survivors' brains, bodies, and minds have been so ravaged by trauma and addiction that they simply don't have the innate capacity to moderate or quit, no matter what kind of support they receive. This isn't the survivor's fault.

If we want to reduce the harm of addiction, we must look at it and provide treatment as we do for any other chronic illness. We need to start by educating the general public that addiction isn't the addicted person's fault, just like diabetes isn't a diabetic's fault. People suffering from addiction deserve compassionate care and support while attempting to manage their illness to the best of their ability, just like anyone else suffering from a chronic illness does.

The bottom line is that harm reduction programs are a compassionate option that saves lives and reduces suffering. It not only reduces suffering for people with addictions but also for people close to them. And like it was for me, it can also be a stepping-stone toward abstinence.

Choosing abstinence or a harm-reduction approach for addiction is a personal choice and something you should discuss with your doctor, family, and mental health counselor. See the appendix for various books, support groups, and other media for support with addiction recovery.

**Trauma Healing Resources For Support In Recovering From Alcohol, Drug, or Behavioral Addictions**

Please see Chapter 35, "Trauma Healing Practices & Recovery Menu." This menu includes 36 specifically designed practices and therapies to help heal C-PTSD by calming down your nervous system, which will help decrease your need to self-medicate with alcohol, drugs, or other self-destructive behaviors. It will also help you find nourishment in healthy, sustainable alternatives. You can also find groups, organizations, books, and other media related to trauma and recovery in the appendix.

# CHAPTER 33

# FOOD ADDICTION & WEIGHT LOSS RECOVERY OPTIONS FOR SURVIVORS

### The Power of Never Giving Up

No matter how long you've struggled and failed, no matter your size, genetics, health issues, or age, I want you to know there is hope to overcome your struggle with food, weight, and your body. I can say this with absolute conviction because I struggled with food, my body, severe obesity, and all the pain and shame that went with it for almost four decades.

In this chapter, I share everything I've learned and every step I've taken to reach a healthy weight. I also share what I've learned and every step that's been necessary for me to maintain a 160lb weight loss for over two decades. This speaks to the power of never giving up.

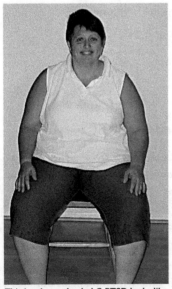

This is what unhealed C-PTSD looks like

This is what healed C-PTSD looks like

## How I've Recovered From My Struggle with Food & Weight

My struggle with food and weight has been part of my story for over fifty-five years. But it wasn't until I discovered I was suffering from C-PTSD in my mid-fifties that I realized that unhealed childhood trauma was the root cause of why I felt so compelled to soothe myself with food and had such difficulty reining in my cravings to eat when I wasn't hungry.

After being steeped in learning about childhood trauma for several years, I finally came to a deeper understanding of the role that food has played in my life.

I learned to turn to food as a little girl because it was a way to get the soothing I longed for but was unable to get from my anxious, depressed, and frequently intoxicated mother. Learning to use food instead of people to soothe my stress continued into my adulthood. This is why healing the relational aspects of childhood trauma has been so important for me. This includes healing my relationship with myself as well as others.

In an effort to learn how to give and receive healthy nurturing through people instead of food, I've spent many years focused on healing my ability to forge and maintain healthy, nourishing relationships. As a result, I've developed several safe, close friendships and a healthy romantic relationship with my partner, Maria.

Now when I'm fearful, sad, angry, or triggered, I intentionally turn to Maria or my friends for support and soothing instead of my old friend, food. This isn't to say that I never turn to food when I'm in emotional pain because I do. What's different is that I turn to food 90% less often than I used to.

## Healing Relational Trauma Is Key For Reaching & Maintaining A Healthy Weight

For a more in-depth look at my journey through healing the relational aspects of C-PTSD, which has been instrumental in my learning to turn to people instead of food for soothing, please review the following chapters:

Chapter 13, "Codependency: An Attempt to Stay Safe in a Crazy Family"

Chapter 14, "Childhood Trauma Is Relational Trauma"

Chapter 15, "The Original Wound: Early Attachment Trauma"

Chapter 19, "How Food Saved My Sanity in an Insane Environment"

Chapter 27, "Redefining Relationships to Meet Your Needs"

Chapter 28, "Shrinking the Critic"

Chapter 29, "Letting Go of Guilt and Shame"

Chapter 31, "Grieving the Losses of C-PTSD"

## How Relationships Impact Your Recovery With Food & Weight

If there's anything that will send me to the kitchen for a binge, it's toxic stress in my personal and professional relationships. This is why a big part of my recovery with food and weight has been about setting healthy standards and boundaries in my relationships.

If you're experiencing emotional or physical abuse, it's vital to get the support you need to stop the abuse before you handle your struggle with food or weight. Please see the appendix for resources for help if you're dealing with emotional or physical domestic violence.

Another critical aspect of reaching and maintaining a healthy weight is who you spend your time with. Whether we want to admit it or not, who we spend our time with influences our lifestyle decisions. My experience has taught me that the quality of my life rises or falls based on the lifestyles of the people I spend the most time with.

If you spend time with people who aren't committed to their health and wellness, it's likely you won't be either. This is why it's critical that you seek out and spend time with people who are just as committed to a health and wellness lifestyle as you are. It also makes it much easier and more fun to stick to your healthy food and exercise plan when you have friends on a similar journey.

A big part of my early recovery with food and weight was finding like-minded women in Overeaters Anonymous who were also committed to recovering from their food and weight issues. We would get together once or twice a week for meetings and fun bike rides and walks. Afterward, we'd enjoy a healthy meal together. Spending time with my recovery friends became the highlight of my week.

## The Connection Between Obesity and Sexual & Physical Abuse

In the mid-nineties, Kaiser Permanente doctor Vincent Felitti was perplexed why so many of his severely overweight patients had lost hundreds of pounds and were close to reaching their goal weight when they would suddenly drop out of his weight-loss program and then quickly gain their weight back. Upon investigation, he discovered that 55% of these patients had been molested as children.

By interviewing these patients, Dr. Felitti discovered that being severely overweight was not so much the problem for them as it was an attempt at a solution. Using excess food helped them numb the emotional pain caused by their trauma, and having a larger body made them feel safe from attracting further sexual or physical abuse. Felitti's discovery became the catalyst that sparked the landmark ACE Study in 1998.

If sexual or physical abuse has been part of your story and/or the idea of letting go of your excess weight feels too uncomfortable to consider, please see the appendix for a trauma-informed practitioner directory to get the support you deserve.

## Why I Had Weight-Loss Surgery

In Part One, I share in detail why I decided to have gastric bypass weight loss surgery. The short version of the story is that I struggled with food and weight for thirty-five years. I'd lost and gained hundreds of pounds several times yet had never been able to maintain a healthy weight for more than a few months. After extensive research on different weight-loss surgeries and traditional weight-loss programs, I chose to have gastric bypass surgery because it was statistically proven to give me the best chance to reach and maintain a healthy weight for the long term.

Even though my surgery was designed to stop me from binge eating and eating high-sugar foods, I knew there were ways to eat around my smaller stomach and gain my weight back because I'd seen many people do so. Since I wanted to give myself the best chance to reach and maintain a healthy weight for life, I decided to put a food, exercise, and self-care plan in place before my surgery so I would be ready to hit the ground running as soon as I got home from the hospital.

In many ways, I saw weight-loss surgery as a last-ditch effort to save my life from an eating disorder I knew was killing me. My goal was to combine the benefits of the surgery with a sustainable food, exercise, and self-care plan to enable me to reach and maintain a healthy weight for life.

Although I'd worked an Overeaters Anonymous (OA) program in the 90s and lost 140 pounds, once I became overwhelmed with grief due to the end of a long-term relationship, I couldn't rein in the overwhelming cravings to eat compulsively. Sadly, over time, I gained back all the weight I'd lost in OA. This wasn't the first time I'd regained a massive amount of weight after an initial weight loss. It ultimately became my reason for finding a more permanent solution through having weight-loss surgery.

I do want to mention that just because I chose surgery doesn't mean I recommend that everyone suffering from childhood trauma and obesity should also have weight-loss surgery. I'm sharing about my surgery because it's part of my story of how I have dealt with my struggle with food and weight. I highly recommend that you discuss any approach to weight loss with your doctor and mental health practitioner before deciding which path to choose.

## Weight-Loss Surgery Isn't a Quick Fix

If you're considering weight-loss surgery, it's important to know that it's not going to be a quick fix or a magic bullet. I've been guilty of latching onto quick fixes and magic bullets, so I don't want to portray weight-loss surgery this way.

I did extensive research before the surgery, so I knew going in that I would need to be committed to healing my emotional eating issues and develop a healthy food, exercise, and self-care plan I could stick to. I also knew if I didn't stay on track, I could easily gain back all the weight and be right back where I started.

Since I looked at having weight-loss surgery as my last chance to reach and maintain a healthy weight for life, the thought of gaining my weight back after surgery and being stuck in the hell of morbid obesity for the rest of my life was unthinkable.

Knowing having weight loss surgery was likely my last chance to handle my weight issue is why I was so motivated to do whatever it took to figure out how to maintain a healthy weight after surgery.

## Long-Term Outcomes for Gastric Bypass Surgery Patients

Although the initial weight loss after gastric bypass surgery often appears to be a quick fix, the bottom line is if you're not in recovery with C-PTSD and lack a structured food, exercise, and self-care plan, you're unlikely to maintain your initial weight loss. In fact, according to the following study*, the odds are you'll gain back 50% of the initial weight you lost within ten years after your surgery.

Whether you use weight-loss surgery or a traditional weight-loss program to reach a healthy weight, once you reach your goal weight, to be able to maintain it for the long term; you must be committed to healing your trauma and learning how to develop healthier ways to regulate your emotions other than using food. Otherwise, when you're upset or triggered, you won't have the capacity to rein in your impulse to overeat and will eventually gain your weight back.

*According to the 2017 study "Weight Regain 10 Years After Roux-en-Y Gastric Bypass" by Daniela Vicinansa Monaco-Ferreira from the University of Campinas and Aparecida Leandro-Merhi from the Pontifícia Universidade Católica de Campinas, ten years after gastric bypass surgery, on average patients were able to keep 50% of their excess weight off.

## Why I'd Be 80lbs Heavier If I Opted Out of A Food & Exercise Plan & Healing C-PTSD

According to the above 2017 study on the average outcomes for gastric bypass surgery, patients were only able to keep 50% of their excess weight off at the ten-year mark. If I had kept only 50% of my excess weight off after my surgery, I would weigh 80 pounds more than I do today and have a BMI of 38.3. According to the World Health Organization, this BMI is only 10 pounds away from the threshold for class III or severe obesity, formally known as morbid obesity.

Although gaining 80 lbs. out of the 160lbs I initially lost is better than gaining all of my weight back, this level of obesity is still correlated with a much higher risk for diabetes, heart disease, stroke, cancer, and chronic pain.

This study reflects how devastating untreated C-PTSD is for those of us who use food to regulate our emotions and nervous systems and become obese as a result. It also illustrates that even after gastric bypass surgery, if the root cause of your food and weight struggles (childhood trauma) isn't resolved, you'll most likely gain a significant amount of your weight back and suffer from the many comorbidities of severe obesity.

These statistics demonstrate why survivors who struggle with food and weight must include trauma-healing practices and therapies and a sustainable food, exercise, and self-care plan to maintain a significant amount of their initial weight loss.

In the following two paragraphs, I discuss which parts of my trauma healing journey and which parts of my weight loss surgery contributed to my reaching and maintaining a healthy weight for the long term.

### How Trauma & Recovery Practices Helped Me Reach and Maintain a Healthy Weight

- Attending Overeaters Anonymous meetings helped me become more aware of what I was hungry for, make new friends who were also committed to their recovery, and learn how to create a healthy food and exercise plan.
- Attending Codependents Anonymous meetings helped me learn how to make healthier relationship choices, reducing my stress and the need to use food to cope.
- Implementing various trauma-healing practices and therapies has helped regulate my nervous system, which has reduced my overall stress and the need to medicate with food.
- Due to healing the relational trauma aspects of C-PTSD, I feel much safer engaging in close relationships. Turning to close relationships for soothing has reduced my need to self-soothe with food.
- I have created a sustainable food, exercise, and self-care plan and have put structures in place to keep my plans on track

### How Gastric Bypass Surgery Helped Me Reach and Maintain a Healthy Weight

- My surgery helped me lose my excess weight with relative ease within two years.
- Since my stomach is smaller, I get full much quicker, which makes my caloric intake lower.
- There's a significant limit to how much sugar I can eat. If I eat more than an average size cookie, I become nauseated and feel extremely ill for thirty minutes or more. I love this feature of the surgery because sugar used to be a major problem for me.
- My surgery reduced my baseline level of hunger. This reduces my caloric intake, making it easier to maintain my weight or lose a few pounds I've gained.

### The Three Main Reasons I've Been Able To Keep My Weight Off For Two Decades

1. I've been committed to my recovery with alcohol, drugs, food, and trauma-healing work.
2. I have created a sustainable food, exercise, and self-care plan and have put structures in place to keep my plans on track.
3. I had gastric bypass weight loss surgery.

### Why Tracking Is Key to Maintaining a Healthy Weight For Survivors

While reading through this chapter section, you may question how it's any different from a typical diet and exercise weight loss plan and wonder when I will discuss the trauma-healing aspects of weight loss and how to maintain a healthy weight.

Since healing relational trauma has significantly reduced my need to self-medicate with food, I highly recommend (if you haven't already) that you read the chapters I've listed on healing relational trauma at the beginning of this chapter.

I've found that combining several trauma-based healing practices and therapies (listed in Chapter 35, "Trauma Healing Practices & Recovery Menu") with the practical weight-management strategies described in this chapter have been the most effective for me in maintaining a healthy weight.

Although using various trauma healing practices and therapies have been enormously helpful, they haven't completely eliminated my impulse to eat when I'm stressed, sad, or triggered. This is why a sustainable food, exercise, and self-care plan that includes tracking and course-correcting has been necessary for me to maintain a healthy weight over the long term.

This doesn't mean my attempts to heal my trauma have failed. As a result of my trauma healing, my compulsion to eat when I'm not hungry has decreased significantly, and for that, I'm grateful. After working on healing my C-PTSD for many years, I've come to accept that I can't completely rely on my willpower to maintain my weight. I still struggle with impulse control when faced with an emotional trigger, so I still need the structure of a food, exercise, and self-care plan to help me stay mindful and on track.

This isn't bad news. This is actually great news because it's helped me develop a proven formula that has worked to help me maintain my 160-pound weight loss for twenty years! It works because I've fine-tuned my food plan to where I've found foods I really love. In fact, I love the foods on my food plan more than most of the treat foods at restaurants and parties. As a result, I don't feel deprived. Another reason it works is that I have boundaries over what I eat, what I keep in the house, and how often I go off my plan. In addition, I have a backup plan for when I gain a few pounds (which is bound to happen), so I can lose it quickly and get back on track.

If you'd asked me twenty years ago if I thought I would ever be at peace with food, weight, and my body, I would have said no because I had never been. But now that I have a proven formula that has worked for twenty years, I can say: *YES, I have found peace with food, weight, and my body.* And after struggling with my weight for over thirty years, for me to be able to say this is a freakin miracle!

Another gift I've received from learning C-PTSD had driven my food, and weight struggles is I have much more compassion for myself around my relationship with food and my body. Just having compassion for the little girl in me who had nothing but food to soothe herself in a chaotic, alcoholic home makes me step back when I'm struggling and just love on her.

This isn't to say that I give myself permission to binge on a regular basis. It's really more about being compassionate with myself when I fall off my food or exercise plan (because I do) and being gentle with myself while I get back on track.

Although OA wasn't a permanent solution for me in maintaining a healthy weight, it helped me get in the habit of putting a healthy, sustainable food and exercise plan in place. My plan includes a couple of treat meals per week. Additionally, I give myself a break from my plan while on vacation. This keeps me from feeling deprived. I know from experience that feeling deprived is a major trigger for me and puts me a risk for food cravings that can lead to binge eating.

OA also taught me the value of tracking my food and exercise. Tracking keeps me honest about my eating and how much I move my body. Now that I understand how trauma has caused impulse control deficits for me, I see why tracking has been such a great tool.

Tracking is not necessary if you don't use food for self-soothing and only eat when you're physically hungry. But for those who do, I've found that tracking my food and exercise has been vital in staying mindful and on track with maintaining a healthy weight.

While writing this chapter, I realized that I've been using digital apps and devices to track my food, exercise, and weight for the past twenty years. In fact, I was tracking my food even before smartphones became the norm with an app on my PalmPilot PDA!

## When We Don't Track, We Get Lost in Terminal Ambiguity

Before I used tracking apps for my food, exercise, and weight, I'd get lost in what I call *terminal ambiguity.* Terminal ambiguity is when you simply don't know why you're gaining weight or why you can't lose weight because you have no idea what's going in (the calories you eat) and what's going out (the calories your body naturally burns).

Since a lot of my eating was trance-like and automatic, I wouldn't always remember every little thing I ate throughout the day. I'd often end up underestimating what I ate and feel like a victim because I couldn't understand why I kept gaining weight when it seemed like I didn't eat that much. Also, I'd sometimes even overestimate what I ate and get anxious about gaining weight when I wasn't even overeating!

I discovered this mystery gets cleared up pretty quickly when you get honest through regular tracking. When you track your food and exercise, you simply can't stay stuck believing that your weight problem is due to a sluggish metabolism or a mysterious thyroid issue that doesn't appear in lab work.

Today I use the free Lose It! app to track my food and weight. This app makes it super easy to log my meals and snacks. Another great thing about this app is that it sends you a weekly update of the foods you've eaten and whether you're meeting the nutritional goals you've set for protein, carbs, sugar, fiber, calcium, sodium, and saturated fat. This gives you an opportunity to get and stay on track with food choices that keep your heart, brain, and gut healthy.

To track my weight, I use a Nokia Withings smart scale. My scale automatically tracks my daily weight and BMI and syncs it to my Fitbit and Lose It! apps. That way, I can see my weight loss and weight gain history. I've tracked my weight through Fitbit and a smart scale for the past ten years.

This enables me to see my weight fluctuations over an entire decade at the touch of a button. I can then tie in what was stressing me out and causing me to medicate with food during periods when my weight was trending up. The beauty of this is that I can learn from what was stressing me out, then do what I can to avoid it to prevent future weight gain.

I use a Fitbit Versa II smartwatch to track my steps, exercise, and sleep. My watch also syncs with my Fitbit and LoseIt weight management app. If I hadn't purchased a smart scale and a Fitbit watch, I would have had to manually enter my daily weight and exercise into my Lose It! app. I know myself well enough to know that I would have eventually stopped doing so and missed out on all this valuable data. This is why I highly recommend investing in your health by purchasing a Fitbit or another smartwatch and smart scale capable of syncing to your smartwatch and Lose It! apps.

## How Gamifying Your Journey Makes Reaching Your Goals Easier and More Fun!

A pleasant surprise I discovered about using a smartwatch, smart scale, and my apps to keep me on track with my food and weight is how it gamifies my weight loss journey. Gamifying means using gaming technology to keep you motivated and on track, while making it more fun and easier to reach a goal.

When Maria and I first got our Fitbit Watches, I immediately noticed how much we loved sharing the latest step count or badges we'd accomplished with each other. Another thing I love about my Fitbit is it keeps me mindful of my activity level throughout the day. When I notice my step count is low, it motivates me to get out for a walk. Once I complete my walk and see my new step count, it feels great to know I'm back on track. The same goes for my sleep and weight.

It's funny how something that can seem so inconsequential can feel so good. Yet, it does, and that's why using these apps with these devices works! They help me celebrate and feel great about reaching my goals. They also help me stay mindful of my goals' progress. And, when I'm off track, they help me to course-correct.

## If You Are Not Willing To Track Your Food or Weight

If you are not willing to track your food and weight and have found a way to reach your health and weight goals without tracking, then, by all means, go for it. I'm a fan of whatever works.

As a survivor with impulse control deficits, after many years of trial and error, I have come to the conclusion that tracking is necessary for me until I reach my goal weight. Once I do reach my goal weight and my weight remains stable, I no longer track my food. However, I still track my weight daily to keep my finger on the pulse of how I'm doing. If I see my weight trend up more than three pounds for over a week, I start tracking my food again until I'm back down to my goal weight. This has been a key strategy in helping me catch a weight gain trend early so I can course-correct and get back down to my goal weight in a relatively short period of time. It's much easier to face losing five pounds vs. 10, 20, or 50lbs.

Although it may be uncomfortable at first to track your weight and food, I have found it makes it much easier when you redefine your relationship with tracking. When you look at tracking and using your scale and apps as allies that are part of a fun game you keep getting better at, you'll be more open to using them.

Today, I actually enjoy and have fun with my scale and apps. Like any new game, it takes time to build your skill level at first, but once you do so, you'll find it much easier to reach your goals. And when you achieve some early wins, your confidence increases, and the game becomes more fun.

One thing that is important to remember is that this approach to weight loss is all about self-compassion, kindness, and being gentle with ourselves. The scale and the tracking apps are just tools to see what's working and what's not so we can get on track and stay on track.

## Creating Your Personalized Weight Loss Formula

Your weight-loss formula should consist of a food plan that's doable, healthy, satisfying, and sustainable for a long-term lifestyle. This is your personal formula, so you get to choose what and how often you eat.

It should include a couple of weekly treat meals and healthy portable snacks for when you're out and about. It should also fall within the calorie range you need to stick to (based on what your LoseIt app calculates) to facilitate the amount of weight you would like to lose each week.

## What Needs To Be Included In Your Personalized Weight-Loss Formula

1. Knowing your goal weight and the approximate date you intend to reach it by
2. A daily calorie budget that will work for you to lose the amount of weight you would like to lose per week while maintaining your health. The LoseIt! app will automatically calculate this.
3. A healthy, satisfying, sustainable food plan
4. An enjoyable, sustainable exercise plan
5. An enjoyable, sustainable self-care plan – see chapter 26, *Building Resilience Is Key In Healing Trauma*. See item 2, Practice Extreme Self-Care
6. Tracking apps and devices to track your weight, steps, exercise, and sleep
7. Protocols on what to do to get back on track when you gain a few pounds

Just knowing you have a weight-loss formula in place that works is extremely calming. Now, when I go through a stressful period and gain some weight, I no longer freak out and think, *OMG, I'm going to gain all my weight back!* (like I always did before). Instead, I say to myself, *Mary, you've got this. You know exactly what to do. You have your weight-loss formula. So now, let's get back on track by using it.*

## How Do You Know If You Have A Viable Weight Loss Formula?

A viable weight loss formula is predictable and reliable in its ability to help you lose weight at the rate you intend to or maintain your weight if you are at your goal. If you are not losing the amount of weight you intend to each week or are not able to maintain your weight if you are at your goal, you have not arrived at your weight loss formula.

This is where course-correcting comes in. If you continually maintain or gain weight when your goal is weight loss, your calorie budget is too high, the amount of exercise your doing is too low, or both. Therefore, you must lower your calorie budget, increase your exercise or push out the date to reach your goal weight to where you are losing the amount of weight you intend to lose each week. Once you consistently get the weight loss results you intend to get each week, you have arrived at a predictable, reliable weight loss formula.

Developing your weight-loss formula requires frequent food, exercise, and calorie adjustments for fine-tuning based on what does and doesn't work for you. This is why your food, exercise, and self-care plan will always be a work in progress.

## Choosing Your Method & Plan To Reach and Maintain a Healthy Weight

Obviously, everyone is different when it comes to what works for them for weight loss and maintenance. Therefore, choosing a food, exercise, and self-care plan to reach and maintain a healthy weight will need to be personalized based on your unique needs. Many survivors can reach their health and weight goals by developing a healthy food, exercise, and self-care plan, along with using a scale, Fitbit, and apps to track their progress.

There are also survivors who need additional support to reach and maintain a healthy weight, such as using weight-loss surgery, anti-obesity medication, or traditional weight management or 12-Step programs. There are many options to choose from to add to what I've offered here in designing your weight loss formula. Below are a few to consider.

## A Trauma Informed Weight Management Program

Relish.life is the only trauma-informed weight loss and maintenance program I'm aware of. It combines a trauma-informed approach to weight loss with medically supervised anti-obesity medication, individual Zoom health coaching, therapist-led group support, and loads of live and recorded online classes, including topics on nutrition, exercise, mindfulness, breathwork, and adverse childhood experiences, to name a few.

Between Dr. Vincent Felitti, co-founder of the ACE Study being on the advisory board of Relish.life and being curious to see how they combined anti-obesity medication with a trauma-informed approach to weight loss, I decided to give Relish.life a try.

I loved the compassionate, trauma-informed approach Relish.life takes with clients and their focus on healing the root cause of obesity: C-PTSD. I also loved the abundance of individual and group support and the live a nd recorded classes included in the program. Contrave, the included non-stimulant anti-obesity medication, significantly reduced my late-night cravings to eat, which was very impressive. The great news is I only had ten pounds to lose and was able to reach my goal with relative ease through the support of Relish.life's program.

## Traditional Weight Loss Programs, 12-Step Groups & Weight Loss Surgery For Weight Management

There are also traditional weight loss and management programs such as WW-Weight Watchers and 12-Step programs such as Overeaters Anonymous and other free weight loss support groups. There are also various weight loss surgeries you can check out to assist you with reaching and maintaining a healthy weight.

These are just a few of the many methods available to support your journey in reaching and maintaining a healthy weight. Be sure to do your due diligence and continue researching your options until you find a method or program that resonates and works for you. Also, be sure to consult your physician and mental healthcare provider to make sure that any approach you choose is also good for your physical and mental health.

Additionally, if you are not getting the results you want from the program you are using, be sure to course correct by trying something else.

## No Matter What Method You Use, Have Compassion For Yourself

No matter what you choose, it's important to have compassion for yourself. Let's face it, it wasn't our fault that we were traumatized as children, and our brains and nervous systems were changed to prime us to have difficulty with food and weight. However, it's our responsibility to manage our health, including food and weight issues.

The most important choice to make is to just begin. Just beginning is an act of self-care. So, do your research, put a plan together, and just start. I've found that just starting shifts my energy to feeling hopeful and proud of myself because I'm moving toward improving my emotional and physical health. If your plan does or doesn't work, you'll know by the results. Then you get to celebrate if it does work or try something different if it doesn't and see how that works.

## Creating A Food Plan & Setting a Daily Calorie Budget

Designing and sticking to (to the best of my ability) a satisfying, healthy, sustainable food plan has been one of the main reasons I have maintained my weight loss for the past two decades.

Since everyone has different dietary needs, I won't go into detail about what I include in my plan. I will say that eating small meals and snacks every two to three hours works best for me. I also include weekly treat meals so I don't feel deprived.

Making sure I get enough protein, healthy fats, fruits, veggies, fiber, and complex carbohydrates is also important. If my plan leans heavily on carbohydrates vs. protein and healthy fats, it sets me up for carb cravings, and I get hungry sooner. In the long run, this means I will gain weight

When you initially use the Lose It! app or other food tracking apps, you'll need to set up your profile. This is where you include your goal weight and the date you want to reach it by. Once you do this, the app will automatically give you a daily calorie budget based on your sex, age, weight, level of physical activity, and the date you intend to reach your goal weight. If this calorie budget feels too restrictive, you can increase it by resetting the date to reach your goal weight further out in time. The further out in time you set the date, the higher number of calories you can eat per day.

The trick with setting your calorie budget is to keep it low enough to see results each week in weight loss but not so low that you feel deprived and get triggered to binge. Also, you can manually set your calorie budget within the Lose It! app.

Part of healing trauma during your weight-loss journey is learning new, healthier ways to calm yourself down and get your needs met so you won't need to medicate with food.

If you're just getting started on your trauma and weight-loss healing journey, it's important to go slow and be gentle with yourself. Not being able to rely on food for comfort and soothing can be extremely hard at first, especially if you haven't learned new ways to calm and soothe yourself. If this is the case, you may want to set your calorie budget higher until you find healthier substitutes for self-soothing.

The goal with your recovery is to get so good at soothing yourself through new, healthy behaviors and relationships that sticking to your food and exercise plan gets easier and easier and becomes an automatic way of life. You may be skeptical that this will even work, especially if sticking to a food plan hasn't worked for you before. Believe me, I get it! But if you trust the process and discover what works and what doesn't, course correct when necessary, and don't give up, you'll eventually find your way.

## Creating An Exercise Plan You Enjoy

Walking outdoors or in nature is my favorite way to exercise. I've been able to maintain my regular walking routine for decades because I enjoy it, it's convenient, and I can do it practically anywhere.

I track my steps with a Fitbit Versa II watch, which syncs to an app on my phone. I set my step goal for a minimum of 4,500 steps per day. This is a very doable goal. I've found that I can meet and frequently exceed this goal by just walking for twenty to thirty minutes per day in my neighborhood. If Maria isn't available to join me, I just plug my earbuds into my phone and listen to an inspiring or healing audiobook or podcast, making my walk fly by.

Plus, I'm killing two birds with one stone. I'm taking care of my body and mind by exercising while simultaneously getting inspired to reach life-enhancing goals by listening to an uplifting audio program.

Also, once I became a regular walker, I noticed that when I didn't walk, I craved it. Walking not only helps me maintain a healthy weight but also keeps my brain's feel-good neurotransmitters firing to give me a natural sense of energy and well-being. And gaining a natural sense of well-being prevents me from needing to medicate a low mood with food.

## Making Friends with Your Scale & How to Handle Weight Fluctuations

To keep a finger on the pulse of my weight, I weigh myself every day first thing in the morning, without shoes or clothes, and before eating or drinking anything. Although this method has been a vital part of why I've been successful at reaching and maintaining a healthy weight for the past two decades, there is also scientific data proving the efficacy of daily weigh-ins.

After comparing weight loss results from millions of users, the LoseIt! weight management app data showed that those who logged their weight daily lost, on average, twice as much weight as those who didn't. Also, according to a study from UNC-Chapel Hill that followed individuals for a six-month period, those who weighed daily seemed to naturally adjust their eating and exercise habits to promote an average weight loss of thirteen pounds compared to those who weighed intermittently and lost less than one pound.

If daily weighing is out of the question for you, I recommend weighing yourself a minimum of three times per week. This recommendation is based on a study from the Journal of Medical Internet Research that showed those who weighed themselves and logged their food at least three times per week achieved clinically significant weight loss compared to those that didn't.

Without weighing yourself at least three times per week, you won't be able to develop your weight loss formula since you won't have the data to do so. And without a weight loss formula to guide you, you won't be able to reach or maintain your goal weight since you won't know what your weight was when you started or what is and isn't working to help you lose weight.

If you're not willing to keep track of your food and weight, you'll end up in what I call *the land of terminal ambiguity.* You know you've landed here when you're frustrated that you're not where you want to be with your size or weight while at the same time feeling confounded about why you struggle since you don't think you eat that much. As I said earlier in this chapter, this mystery gets cleared up pretty quickly once you start weighing yourself and tracking your food.

It's normal to see fluctuations in your weight from day to day. If the scale says you're 2 pounds heavier than yesterday, and you know you've been impeccable with your food and exercise plan over the last few days, don't worry about it. Remember that it takes 3,500 calories above the baseline your body naturally burns to gain a pound of fat throughout the day. If you completely binged and took in an extra 7,000 calories, the 2-pound weight gain would make sense. But if you didn't, it's likely water, constipation, or increased muscle mass from your exercise routine.

What's important is to track the general trend of your weight. If your intention is weight loss and your weight is mostly decreasing, you're on track. If it is mostly staying the same or increasing, it's time to regroup. When my weight trends up two or more pounds for a week or more, I know it's real weight and need to investigate what's causing it. I first take a look at what's going on in my life that may be causing me to use excess food to cope. The most common areas that cause me to medicate with food are late-night eating while watching TV, stress at work, or stress in my relationships. If I identify one or more of these as the reason I'm falling off my food plan; I take a look at what I can change with this habit or relationship, what I can let go of, or what I can choose to accept

I also look at my food and exercise plan to see if they may be the culprit in my weight gain. I know that certain foods or drinks are, or can become, binge foods that I can't control once I start. This is when I look at my food plan to identify problem foods or beverages and decide if I need to remove them from my house and replace them with something healthier. I typically still allow these foods as a single-serving item from time to time on a treat day, but I know I can no longer keep a quantity of them in the house.

Another area to look at is my exercise plan. Have I fallen off my regular exercise routine? Is work getting in the way of moving my body? If so, I need to make scheduling time to move just as important as scheduling time to work. If the weather is the culprit, I can walk in indoor malls or use indoor exercise equipment.

The beauty of investigating why you have gained weight early and adjusting your weight-loss formula is you can catch it before you gain 5, 10, 20, or 50 pounds. It's much easier to face losing 3, 5, or 10 pounds instead of 50. This is why keeping track of your weight is so critical.

Prior to using my weight loss formula, I often wouldn't weigh myself for a year or more and be horrified once I got on the scale and had to face a 50 or 75-lb weight gain. Having to face gaining such a devastating amount of weight (one more time) would often bring on so much shame and feel so daunting and depressing that I would simply give up and stop weighing myself. The only thing putting my head in the sand accomplished was gaining even more weight to where at 42, I reached my top weight of 310lbs.

This is why I look at my scale as my friend today. Instead of viewing it as something that will bring bad news or shame, I look at it as a tool to help me identify when I'm on track with my weight and also to catch when I get off track as early as possible, so I can course-correct and quickly get back on track. Knowing I'm on track gives me peace of mind since it's helped me to let go of worrying about gaining my weight back.

I don't beat myself up when I gain a few pounds today. Instead, I get curious about what caused it, then I course correct and get back on track. It feels so good to be able to look at my scale as my ally instead of my enemy. After all, it has helped me get and stay on track for the past twenty years.

## How to Avoid the Dreaded Late-Night Eating

If there's one habit that can make my weight trend upward, it's late-night eating. I've found that my food cravings increase when I'm tired. Also, my willpower is practically nonexistent by the end of the day. This is a volatile mix for someone with C-PTSD, food, and weight issues.

The best way I've found to avert this pitfall is to go to bed once I've used up my calorie budget for the day. Even when I'm not ready to go to sleep, I've found that lying down in bed relaxes and calms me, reducing my cravings to eat. Also, reading or listening to a good book or chatting with my partner in bed are also good ways to avoid late-night eating.

## What If You Can't Control Your Food or Weight No Matter What You Do?

If your weight or food issues are out of control, you can't get on track no matter what you do, and you feel your weight is putting your life at risk, it may be time to consider your harm-reduction options. The key is to be as compassionate as possible with yourself. It's important to acknowledge that you truly are doing the best you can, given the circumstances of your childhood trauma and how it has impacted your impulse control, emotional regulation, and other aspects of your life.

It's also important to recognize that although your struggle with food and weight isn't your fault, finding a way to get it under control is your responsibility. Like anyone else with a life-threatening illness, you, too, deserve to get whatever support you need to reduce the harm of your food or weight issues to live the highest-quality life possible.

Reaching out for support and guidance from a trauma-informed coach, therapist, weight loss program, or doctor can be extremely valuable when you're unsure what your next step should be.

## Psychotherapy To Treat Eating Disorders and Weight Issues

Over the past three decades, I have worked with over a dozen psychotherapists and several psychiatrists to overcome my struggle with food, weight, alcohol, and drugs. Now that I am aware that untreated childhood trauma had been the root cause of these struggles, and not one of my therapists or psychiatrists had caught on to this fact, I would be extremely cautious about choosing a psychotherapist for your food, weight, and addiction issues.

Although I have significantly benefited from talk therapy for issues unrelated to addiction and C-PTSD, in my experience, the majority of mental health practitioners are not trained to recognize, diagnose or properly treat childhood trauma and those of us who have struggled with eating disorders, weight, or addiction. This is why choosing a therapist specializing in treating C-PTSD and who also specializes in treating eating disorders, obesity, or other addictions are crucial for your recovery.

## Reaching & Maintaining a Healthy Weight Is a Long-Term Process

It has taken me many decades to fine-tune my food and exercise plan and my tracking to where today, maintaining my weight runs relatively smoothly. Along with tracking, a big part of my success is due to learning how to engage in healthy relationships. This is a major miracle for me, given how I struggled for forty years with the pain and shame of food addiction and obesity.

Setbacks are bound to happen and are a normal part of the journey. So instead of letting the inner critic beat you up for not being perfect, it's important to have compassion for the part of you trying to soothe yourself the best way you know how. The last thing you want to do is abandon yourself when the going gets tough around food and weight.

When I do sit with food cravings (when I'm not physically hungry) and attempt to feel into my body's physical discomfort and sensations, my goal is to become the compassionate, wise parent to soothe my inner child. Sometimes I'm able to surf the wave of my urge to eat and get through to the other side of the craving without giving in to the food. Sometimes I'm able to reach out to my partner or choose a healthier food or solution to soothe myself instead. And sometimes I'm not.

I don't gain weight because I do my best to stick to my daily calorie budget and have found many low-calorie, healthy, satisfying snacks that work to soothe my food urges.

I recognize today that my brain, body, and mind have been changed by childhood trauma. Although I do my best to heal the various aspects of my trauma, I still get triggered from time to time and end up using food to calm or soothe myself. And today, that's totally okay with me. This is part of accepting myself as is.

## Looking at Your Life Like One Big Science Experiment

I discovered in my early recovery that I love how it feels to approach my life like one big science experiment. I'm always tracking my goals, seeing what works and what doesn't, and fine-tuning my plan. This makes life fun and exciting. By setting goals, putting a plan in place, and taking action over time, you'll know firsthand that you have the power to change your life. This is when the game gets really fun!

The trick is to do your best to not personalize it when you have setbacks or failures. Everyone has them. They're just part of the game. Do your best to look at failure as feedback about what doesn't work, then try a new approach to find what does. Just because you have a setback or failure doesn't mean you're a failure. It just means your plan didn't work, so learn from it and try a new one.

This is how I've approached my weight management journey for the past twenty years. You just have to start with a plan, track your results, course correct what doesn't work, keep doing what does, and make adjustments as you keep learning.

This is how I found my weight-loss formula and finally found a way to reach and maintain a healthy weight for life. It's also what's helped me to finally make peace with food, weight, and my body.

## The Main Keys That Have Worked for Me To Reach & Maintain A Healthy Weight

- Commitment to a healthy, sustainable food and exercise plan
- Gastric bypass weight-loss surgery
- Commitment to staying sober with alcohol and drugs
- Maintaining relationships with introspective and health-oriented friends.
- Letting go of personal and professional relationships that were not healthy for me
- Tracking devices: Fitbit watch and app, LoseIt! app, Nokia smart scale
- Commitment to sleeping seven or more hours per night
- OA Twelve-Step meetings in my early recovery
- Stress awareness and reduction
- Antidepressant medication
- Mindfulness practice
- Commitment to maintaining my mental, physical, and emotional health
- Reading books and blogs related to healing trauma and recovering from food addiction

### You Deserve to Have a Healthy Relationship with Food, Weight, and Your Body

Navigating food, body, and weight issues as a survivor can seem like a difficult, if not impossible, journey. My goal with this chapter is to relieve you of at least some of the burden by providing the map that has worked for me to finally reach long-term recovery with food, weight, and my body. Achieving this has been nothing short of a miracle. It's the first time I've been able to maintain a healthy weight for more than a few months in my entire life. For this, I'm eternally grateful.

This is what I want for you. It's not only possible; it's probable if you're willing to take the necessary steps to make it happen, course-correct when you get off track, never give up, and reach out for support when you get stuck.

### Trauma Healing Resources For Support In Weight Loss & Management

Please see Chapter 35, "Trauma-Healing Practices & Recovery Menu." This menu includes 36 specifically designed practices and therapies to help calm down your nervous system and improve your ability to connect in relationships. This, in turn, will help decrease your need to self-medicate with food and learn to find nourishment in healthy, sustainable alternatives. You can also find trauma-informed weight loss programs, support groups, directories, books, and other media in the appendix.

# CHAPTER 34

---

# GETTING & STAYING ON TRACK WITH YOUR TRAUMA HEALING AND RECOVERY

It doesn't matter how slowly you go as long as you do not stop.

—Confucius

One of the surprising yet delightful aspects I noticed as I began my trauma-healing journey is how great it felt just to be on it! By taking my first steps and then taking baby steps after that, I noticed a positive shift in my day-to-day life. I felt much more connected to myself and others and more hopeful about my future. This alone would have made embarking on this journey worth it. Yet, this was just a taste of the transformation my healing journey had in store for me.

Although making sense of my past by learning I had been suffering from childhood trauma was healing in and of itself, it wasn't until I began implementing trauma-healing therapies and resilience-building practices that I saw significant improvements in my life.

One of the best ways to stay motivated on your trauma-healing and recovery journey is to view it as an investment for a better today and a brighter future. The added bonus to healing our trauma is we not only improve our own lives but also make a positive impact on those we love and everyone we touch.

To accomplish meaningful change in our lives, we must commit to taking consistent action to bring what we desire into existence. Initially, taking on new habits and practices can be uncomfortable, inconvenient, and challenging. But over time, as our new habits and practices become routine, they have a way of becoming an automatic way of life. Once you get to the place where you're experiencing more vitality and well-being, you'll wonder how you have ever lived any other way.

I'm a living example that healing trauma, achieving long-term recovery from food and substance addiction, and going on to create a life you love are not only possible but probable if you're willing to stay in action, reach out for support, and never give up.

### Resistance To Setting Goals Is Normal For Trauma Survivors

You're not alone if you feel resistant to setting your trauma healing and recovery goals. Given that most of us never knew how trauma had prevented us from being able to achieve our goals, many of us gave up on goal setting altogether due to the painful feelings of shame and inadequacy it brought up.

What's crucial about setting and pursuing goals to heal trauma and get into recovery from addiction or other self-defeating behavior is to make it a no-shame and a no-failure zone. To feel safe, we need to give ourselves a whole lot of space not to be perfect and to look at setbacks as lessons vs. failures. Judging and having contempt for ourselves have no place on this journey. Self-compassion, self-forgiveness, and self-acceptance are what win the day with healing trauma.

### How To Get & Stay on Track to Reach Your Trauma Healing and Recovery Goals

If you want to heal your trauma, achieve long-term recovery and live a life you love, you have to be willing to do your part. Since you can't hit a target you can't see, setting your trauma healing and recovery goals must be your first step. Once you're clear about your goals, you'll need to choose the action steps to take to achieve them. As long as you're willing to take consistent action, step outside your comfort zone, course correct for what doesn't work, and stay committed to never giving up, I have no doubt you'll get there. It's not a matter of if but when.

# THE 5 STEPS TO KEEPING YOUR TRAUMA HEALING & RECOVERY JOURNEY ON TRACK

1. Set your trauma-healing and recovery goals
2. Choose actions to reach your goals
3. Choose a structure to keep your goals and action plan alive
4. Use a weekly accountability coach or partner
5. Make a commitment to take action, celebrate wins, and course-correct when necessary

# SET YOUR TRAUMA HEALING & RECOVERY GOALS

The most effective way to achieve your goals is to set SMART goals. The acronym SMART is designed to help you remember to choose goals that are:

**S**pecific

**M**easurable

**A**chievable

**R**ealistic

**T**ime Specific

Be sure to keep **SMART** goals in mind while completing this exercise.

# TRAUMA HEALING & RECOVERY
# GOALS WORKSHEET

**Directions:** List the trauma healing and/or recovery goals you would like to achieve in the following areas of your life. You don't have to pursue all of these goals at once. Getting clear about your goals and writing them down supports you in deciding which one or ones you would like to pursue first.

Mindfulness & Self-Compassion Goals

_____

Physical & Mental Health Goals

_____

Relationship Goals: Spouse, Family, Friends, Bosses, Co-Workers

_____

Nervous System & Self-Regulation Goals

_____

Food, Weight, Substances, Addiction Recovery or Other Behavioral Goals

_____

Money, Work, Career or Vocation Goals

_____

Healing Shame & Guilt Goals

_____

Nutrition, Hydration, Sleep & Exercise Goals

_____

Self Confidence, Building Agency, Empowerment Goals

# CHOOSE ACTION STEPS WITH DUE DATES FOR EACH GOAL

- Go to the next chapter, 35. "Trauma Healing Practices & Recovery Menu." You can complete this exercise with the menu in this book, or you can go to MaryGiuliani.net/TraumaRecoveryMenu, and download and use a printed-out version of the menu.

- With a pencil, place an "X" next to the practice, therapy, group, or other action items you include from this menu to help you reach the trauma healing and recovery goals you stated you wanted to achieve from step 1. For the action steps you need to take that are not included on this menu, add them in the space provided at the end of the menu.

- Be sure to honor your pace regarding how many goals and action steps you take on. You must take some action to achieve results but taking on too many goals at once is counterproductive since it causes overwhelm and puts you at risk of becoming dysregulated and/or giving up.

# CHOOSE A STRUCTURE TO KEEP YOUR GOALS & ACTION PLAN VISIBLE & ALIVE WORKSHEET

Having a structure where you enter, track, and keep your daily action steps visible is critical for your success. To keep your goals alive, you'll need to enter them in a time or task management system, a spreadsheet, a notepad, or a Post-it note.

- Getting my daily action item to-do list in place is the first thing I do each morning. This simple step helps me stay focused on what I'm committed to achieve throughout the day.

- I number my to-do items in the order that I'll do them, putting my top-priority items first.

- I put the to-do items that require intense focus or ones I have the most resistance with at the top of my list since I'm more likely to do them when I have more energy in the morning.

- I make sure my list is visible on my desk, and I bring it with me when out and about to remind me to stay focused on reaching my goals throughout the day.

- At the end of the day, I review my list, and for any items I haven't completed, I place them on my desk to be carried over to the next day's to-do list.

What structure will you use to keep track of your trauma healing and recovery goals and action steps, and when will you put this structure in place?

_____

_____

# USE A WEEKLY ACCOUNTABILITY PARTNER & GIVE YOURSELF A 95% CHANCE OF SUCCESS

With a twenty-five-year background as a life coach, I've seen firsthand the power that accountability has in helping people achieve their goals. Yet even I was astounded when I found the following study on the power of accountability.

According to the Association for Talent Development, having a specific accountability appointment with someone who knows about your commitment to reaching a goal gives you a 95% chance of achieving it. In contrast, for those who only have an idea for a goal but have no accountability partner, their chances of achieving it drop to just 10%. Below are the details of this study.

**The Association for Talent Development Study on Goal Achievement Revealed That**

- Having an idea or goal: Gives you a **10%** chance of achieving your goal
- Consciously deciding that you'll do it: Gives you a **25%** chance of achieving your goal
- Deciding when you'll do it: Gives you a **40%** chance of achieving your goal
- Planning how to do it: Gives you a **50%** chance of achieving your goal
- Committing to someone that you'll do it: Gives you a **65%** chance of achieving your goal
- Having a regular accountability appointment with someone: Gives you a **95%** chance of achieving your goal

This study drives home how having a specific appointment with someone to whom you've committed your goals is what works best if you're serious about achieving them. If you're committed to healing your trauma and achieving long-term recovery, I highly recommend you work with a trauma-informed coach or find a friend or colleague you can meet with for weekly accountability calls. The key to choosing the right accountability partner is that you feel safe and that they are gentle yet honest with you.

**Find An Accountability Partner**

Would the support of an accountability partner get you to take action to reach your goals?

_____

If yes, who will you ask to be a regular accountability partner?

_____

By what date will you ask them?

_____

What day and time of the week will you meet?

# MAKE A COMMITMENT TO TAKE ACTION, CELEBRATE YOUR WINS, & COURSE CORRECT

Nothing significant has happened in my life without my commitment to getting clear on my goals and taking action to make them happen. **I repeat....**

*Nothing significant has happened in my life without my commitment to getting clear on my goals and taking action to make them happen.*

The only reason I've been able to get and stay sober, reach and maintain a healthy weight, heal my trauma, form, and maintain fulfilling relationships, do the work I love, and write this book is because of the goals I've set and the commitments I've made to taking steps to make them happen. Therefore, if you're serious about your healing and recovery and living a life you love, you'll need to make the necessary commitments to make them happen.

After making a commitment to taking action to achieve your goals, reviewing the progress you're making on a regular basis is the second crucial step to achieving them. Keeping a structure in place to remind you to review the progress of your goals is a key part of this step.

I've found using Google calendar to remind me to review the progress of my goals has worked well. I simply set recurring appointments with myself on a weekly or monthly basis, depending on the goal. You can set alarms with Google calendar so you don't forget to show up for your "goals review" appointment.

By regularly reviewing the progress of your goals, you get to celebrate the wins you've achieved, as well as course-correct for any actions that have not worked in moving your goals forward.

## Staying On Track Worksheet

- Have you completed *The Trauma Healing & Recovery Goals Worksheet* & chosen the action steps with due dates to achieve them?

---

- If not, what's stopping you?

---

- If you aren't able to overcome what's stopping you, who will you reach out to for support, and by when will you do so?

---

- By when will you have your *Trauma Healing & Recovery Goals Worksheet & Action Plan* completed?

---

- How often will you review your progress, celebrate your wins, and course-correct?

---

- What structure will you put in place to remind you to review your goals & celebrate your wins?

# CHAPTER 35

# TRAUMA HEALING PRACTICES & RECOVERY MENU

Do not wait; the time will never be 'just right.' Start where you stand, and work with whatever tools you may have at your command, and better tools will be found as you go along.

—George Herbert

This chapter includes a menu of trauma-based therapies, resilience-building practices, and recovery solutions that have been the most effective in helping me heal my trauma and achieve long-term recovery from my struggle with alcohol, drugs, food, and weight.

Although there are thirty-six items to choose from on this menu, it in no way implies you'll need to complete all or most of them to heal your trauma or recover from self-destructive or self- defeating behaviors.

Since everyone's healing and recovery journey is unique, my intention in providing this menu is to offer an abundance of choices, so everyone can find what works best for them.

A philosophy I learned early on in my AA recovery that applies here is to take what you like and leave the rest. As long as you stay on your healing path, you'll figure out what items to choose and which steps you need to take to achieve your desired results.

### How Often & How Many Practices and Therapies Should You Include?

There's no absolute right or wrong way to approach healing trauma or recovering from addiction other than what works for you. The steps and frequency I suggest for each item on the menu below are suggestions based on what has worked for me. You can change them to what works best for you. The number of practices or therapies you choose to work on at any given time is also up to you.

Obviously, to make progress with your healing and recovery, you must include at least one item from this menu. Also, to stay focused and on track, I strongly recommend including the last two items on the menu, #35. *Declare and track your trauma-healing and recovery goals,* and # 36. *Review your trauma-healing and recovery goals regularly, celebrate your wins, and course-correct when necessary.*

## What Results Can You Expect by Healing Your Trauma or Recovering From Addiction?

Like any program designed to change your life in a significant way, you'll get as much out of it as you put into it. If you're highly motivated to heal your trauma and recover from self-defeating behaviors or addiction, by all means, choose practices or therapies from several different categories that are a stretch for you but not so much of a stretch that you become overwhelmed.

Although this menu contains several items and resources for those who need support recovering from addiction, it is also designed for those who don't struggle with addiction and only need to focus on healing C-PTSD. Also, since many of the practices in this menu are focused on self-care and building healthy relationships, they can help anyone improve the quality of their life, regardless of whether they struggle with addiction or C-PTSD.

It's important to be as patient, gentle, compassionate, and kind to yourself as possible during your healing journey. If you aren't ready to take certain steps or need to do them with the support of a qualified trauma coach or therapist, please honor yourself and your process.

That being said, being kind to yourself doesn't mean you shouldn't step outside your comfort zone or take consistent action. In order to heal, you'll need to do so. The goal is to stretch far enough out of your comfort zone to make consistent progress but not so far that you get overwhelmed. Over time, you'll find the sweet spot for which level of stretching is doable for you.

## For Those Struggling with a Serious Substance or Behavioral Addiction

When you're in the grip of a serious addiction, the addiction takes over and will make it impossible to stay focused to implement the items on this menu. This is why getting the support you need to address serious alcohol, drug, or other behavioral addictions must be addressed first.

Once you find the support you need and are stable in your recovery from a serious addiction, you can return to this menu to work on both your addiction recovery and your trauma healing at the same time.

For support to get into recovery with food, alcohol, drug addiction, or other self-destructive behaviors, see Chapter 32, "Alcohol and Drug Addiction Recovery Options for Survivors," or Chapter 33, "Food Addiction & Weight Loss Recovery Options For Survivors." Also, see the appendix for resources for addiction recovery.

## The Goal of The Trauma Healing Practices & Recovery Menu

This menu is designed for you to select practices or therapies aligned with the goals you set in the Trauma Healing & Recovery Goals Worksheet in previous Chapter 34, "Getting and Staying on Track with Your Recovery."

If you haven't completed the Trauma Healing and Recovery Goals Worksheet in Chapter 34, I strongly recommend you do yourself a favor and take a few minutes to do so now.

Since it's well documented that setting and writing down goals increases your chances of achieving them exponentially, taking a few minutes to do so is a minuscule price to pay when you consider what can open up for you by successfully healing your trauma and/or recovering from addiction.

For a survivor, setting and achieving goals can mean the difference between going on to thrive in a life you love vs. staying stuck in chronic survival. Therefore, if you want to give yourself the best chance at significantly improving your life and haven't set your trauma healing and recovery goals, go to chapter 34, set your goals, and then return to this menu.

# THE TRAUMA HEALING PRACTICES & RECOVERY MENU

- This menu is designed to make choosing therapies and practices easy and convenient by providing the entire list in an organized, central location.
- It's intended to be a handy checklist to help you keep track of what you're working on at any given time during your trauma-healing and recovery journey
- You can either work with the menu directly in this book or print out a pdf version of it by visiting: MaryGiuliani.net/TraumaRecoveryMenu.
- To get started, use a pencil to enter a an "X" next to the To-do items on the menu you'll include to help you reach the goals you set on the Trauma Healing & Recovery Goals Worksheet in previous Chapter 34, "Getting and Staying on Track with Your Recovery." Then start with one baby step.
- When you complete an item on the menu, erase the "X" and replace it with the date you completed it. This will help you quickly identify what items you've completed and which items you're currently working on at any given time during your healing and recovery journey.
- If an item on this menu doesn't work for you, that's okay! Erase the checkmark, make a note, and move on to another item from the menu. When a practice or therapy works well for you, keep doing it. You'll have an intuitive sense when you're complete with specific types of therapies or practices.
- Since trauma impacts your body, brain, mind, worldview, and relationships, it's essential to include a combination of healing modalities and practices that address each of these areas. You can do so by choosing therapies and practices from the different categories listed below.

## Categories For the Trauma Healing Practices & Recovery Menu

To make it easier to choose from therapies or practices targeted toward healing specific aspects of childhood trauma or finding support to get into recovery from addiction or self-defeating behaviors, I've grouped the below menu of 36 items into eleven categories.

1. Cognitive-Based Trauma-Healing
2. Self-Care and Resilience Building
3. Building Competency, Agency, and Sharing Your Gifts
4. Relational Trauma Healing
5. Trauma Recovery and Resilience Coaching
6. Trauma Psychotherapy-Body, Brain, and Mind Based Psychotherapy
7. Healing Shame and Guilt
8. Grieving the Losses from Childhood Trauma
9. Addiction – Alcohol, Drug, Food, and Self-Defeating Behavior Recovery Options
10. Body-Based and Expressive Arts Trauma-Healing
11. How To Stay on Track with Your Trauma-Healing and Recovery Goals

# TRAUMA HEALING PRACTICES & RECOVERY MENU ITEMS

## COGNITIVE-BASED TRAUMA HEALING

**1. Get educated about C-PTSD and how to heal:** Consistently learning how C-PTSD had impacted me helped calm my nervous system since it helped me make sense of and have compassion about what happened to me. It also helped me clarify what types of healing practices or therapies were available so I could decide which ones I wanted to try.

\_\_\_\_**To-do:** If you haven't read this book in its entirety, I strongly recommend doing so. It will save you loads of time and speed up your healing since you'll gain access to the most valuable information I've curated from my five-year journey healing C-PTSD. You'll also access the many tools, tips, and techniques I've used for the past three decades to get and stay sober and reach and maintain a healthy weight. Once you've decided what content you will review to educate yourself about C-PTSD, addiction, or other self-defeating behaviors, list two weekly actions you'll take and commit to taking them.

**2. Practice mindfulness:** In my experience, recovery from childhood trauma is not possible without cultivating a mindfulness practice. Taking classes, reading or listening to books, or watching YouTube videos can help you learn how to develop a mindfulness practice.

\_\_\_\_**To-do:** Write down steps you'll take on a regular basis to learn about and implement a mindfulness practice. See the appendix for books on practicing mindfulness.

**3. Practice Self-Compassion:** Learning how to replace a harsh inner critic with the soothing balm of self-compassion was a huge turning point in my healing and recovery and crucial for healing my trauma.

\_\_\_\_**To-do:** Go to Chapter 29. "Letting Go of Guilt and Shame" and review the section on Self-Compassion. Write down steps you'll take on a regular basis to learn about and implement a self-compassion practice. See the appendix for books on practicing self-compassion.

**4. Minimize stress in your life:** Since C-PTSD is about having a highly reactive and sensitive stress-response system, making personal and professional decisions to keep stress to a minimum is vital for trauma healing and recovery.

\_\_\_\_**To-do:** Go to Chapter 26, "Building Resilience Is Critical in Healing Trauma," and review the section titled "Minimize Stress." Assess the level of stress from 1 to 10 (10 being the highest) you currently have in your personal and professional life. Set a goal for what stress levels are acceptable and what actions you'll take to remove excess stress from your life.

**5. Tell your story:** The original 1998 ACE study by Kaiser Permanente and the CDC showed a 35% decrease in outpatient doctor visits and an 11% decrease in emergency room visits for those who discussed how the adversities that made up their ACE score impacted them as adults.

\_\_\_\_**To-do:** Go to Chapter 26, "Building Resilience Is Critical in Healing Trauma," and review the section titled "Telling Your Story." Determine how and when you'll tell your trauma story. Then commit to a day and time to do so.

**6. Write in a journal or diary:** Writing in a journal is helpful in getting in touch with feelings, reduces stress, and is very beneficial in getting clear on the next steps for your healing journey. Journaling has also been found to increase dopamine and improve the immune system and overall health.

\_\_\_\_**To-do:** Go to Chapter 26, "Building Resilience Is Critical in Healing Trauma," and review the section titled "Journaling." Set a regular schedule for when you'll write in your journal and stick to it.

**7. Make a gratitude list:** Writing down or sharing with another person what you're grateful for can shift you into a calmer, more centered state.

\_\_\_\_**To-do:** Write down the steps you'll take on a regular basis to implement a gratitude practice.

**8. Embrace healthy thoughts:** Questioning and reframing your thoughts are essential to healing C-PTSD.  Thought stopping and thought substitution are excellent practices to cultivate to shrink the inner and outer critics.

\_\_\_\_**To-do:** Go to Chapter 26, "Building Resilience Is Critical in Healing Trauma," and review the section titled "Embrace Healthy Thoughts. Also, read chapter 28, "Shrinking the Critic."  Set achievable goals on shrinking your inner and outer critics.

## SELF-CARE & RESILIENCE BUILDING

**9. Create a rhythm and routine by building structure in your day-to-day life:** Going to bed and waking up at the same time every day creates rhythm and routine in your life.  So does making your bed, eating meals, and exercising at the same time each day. Creating a rhythm and routine in your life is very calming and regulating for the nervous system.

\_\_\_\_**To-do:**  Create a schedule for your regular day-to-day, week-to-week, or monthly tasks or self-care items you've committed to doing and enter it into a calendar system and stick to it.

**10. Choose healthy foods and get adequate hydration and sleep:** Being committed to healthy eating, getting ample sleep, and hydration is foundational for building resilience and healing trauma.  When any of these foundational self-care practices are off track, your trauma and recovery journey cannot help but veer off track.

\_\_\_\_**To-do:** Take stock of your current food, hydration, and sleep habits, and decide on what a healthy, sustainable plan could look like in these three areas. Determine what steps you'll take to track, manage, and reach your goals for your plan.

**11. Make fun types of exercise part of your life:**  Making a commitment to move your body fifteen or more minutes a day is vital to maintaining your emotional and physical recovery. If fifteen minutes is too much for your current health, start with how much time you can manage.

\_\_\_\_**To-do:** Choose exercises that are fun, doable, and sustainable as a lifestyle. The more you can exercise in nature, the better it is for your well-being. Finding an exercise or walking partner is an excellent way to stick to your routine. Write down the exercises you'll include in your day or week and how you'll keep yourself accountable.

**12. Replace self-defeating behaviors with self-care practices:** The activities you engage in and the energy you put into your body and mind have an enormous impact on keeping your trauma alive or helping you heal. If you aren't sure how to manage these behaviors, review the below chapters and implement the suggestions.

\_\_\_\_**To-do:** Go to Chapter 26, "Building Resilience Is Critical in Healing Trauma," and review the section titled "Self-Care." Also, if you need help with food, substances, or other self-defeating behaviors, review Chapter 32, "Alcohol and Drug Addiction Recovery Options for Survivors," and Chapter 33, "Food Addiction and Weight-Loss Recovery Options for Survivors." Make a list of two areas of self-care you'll commit to weekly and two actions you'll take to move in a healthier direction.

## BUILDING COMPETENCY, AGENCY & SHARING YOUR GIFTS

**13. Build a sense of agency:** Developing a sense of agency gives you the capacity to take purposeful, effective action. Since feeling helpless is part of what makes trauma traumatic, building a sense of agency naturally builds resilience.

\_\_\_\_**To-do:** Go to Chapter 26, "Building Resilience Is Critical in Healing Trauma," and review the sections titled "Building Agency" and "Focus on Your Strengths" and complete the *Identifying Your Strengths Worksheet*.

**14. Build new competencies:** Building competency is about acquiring the skills necessary to achieve specific goals, which in turn builds resilience.

_____**To-do:** Go to Chapter 26, "Building Resilience Is Critical in Healing Trauma," and review the sections titled "Building Competencies" and "Focus on Your Strengths." Determine what competencies you need to build to achieve your goals and what actions you'll take on a regular basis to build them.

**15. Find meaningful work:** Having a purpose you're passionate about sets a framework and focus for your life. Meaningful work fosters self-worth and provides satisfaction in knowing you're helping others, which builds resilience.

_____**To-do:** Go to Chapter 26, "Building Resilience Is Critical in Healing Trauma," and review the sections "Discover Your Purpose" and "Focus on Your Strengths" and complete the _Identifying Your Strengths Worksheet_. Determine what steps you will take to find meaningful work. Include the actions you'll take on a regular basis.

## TRAUMA RECOVERY AND RESILIENCE COACHING

**16. Work with a trauma-informed recovery and resilience coach:** A trauma recovery and resilience coach specializes in supporting survivors to move consistently forward in healing their trauma, building resilience, and staying on track to reach their trauma recovery and overall life goals.

_____**To do:** Go to chapter 34. "Getting and Staying on Track With Your Recovery" and review section "Find An Accountability Partner." Contact a trauma-informed recovery and resilience coach who has done significant trauma-healing and recovery work. Set up an introductory session to determine if they are the right fit for your needs. See the appendix for trauma recovery coach listings.

## RELATIONAL TRAUMA HEALING

**17. Build a safe, supportive trauma-healing community around you:** Since childhood trauma is relational trauma, building a safe community of people to accompany you on your trauma-healing journey is essential to healing relational trauma.

_____**To-do:** Go to Chapter 26, "Building Resilience Is Critical in Healing Trauma," and review the section titled "Prioritize Building Healthy Relationships." Write down the types of groups and people you enjoy and feel the safest with, then search for these types of in-person or virtual groups in your area.
Commit to visiting one new group weekly until you've found one or more groups you resonate with, then attend them regularly.

**18. Build healthy one-on-one relationships:** Since we were wounded in the context of close relationships, our healing must occur within relationships.

_____**To-do:** Review Chapter 27, "Redefining Relationships to Meet Your Needs." Do both exercises in this chapter on assessing and improving your relationships. List the qualities of the people you'd like to have in your life. Designate what actions you'll commit to taking each week to help you move forward in reaching your relationship goals.

**19. Learn to get okay with disappointing people:** To build resilience, you'll need to learn how to be okay with others being disappointed when you say no to their requests when it's not in your best interest to say yes.

_____**To-do:** Go to Chapter 26, Building Resilience Is Critical in Healing Trauma," and review the section titled "Getting Okay with Disappointing People." To get okay with disappointing people, you must step outside your comfort zone by practicing it. Begin by setting the goal to disappoint at least two people per week. This isn't to be done in a mean-spirited way. It's about saying no when you genuinely don't want to say yes. If guilt or shame prevents you from disappointing people, review chapter 29, "Letting Go of Guilt & Shame," and complete the exercises in it.

**20. Practice corrective experiences in your existing or new relationships:** Since childhood trauma is relational trauma, practicing corrective experiences in your relationships is crucial for facilitating your healing.

____**To-do:** Go to Chapter 26, Building Resilience Is Critical in Healing Trauma," and review the section titled: "Facilitating Corrective Experiences." Write down what types of corrective experiences you'd like to have in your relationships.  Then list one corrective experience you're willing to initiate weekly and schedule a day and time to do so.  Role-playing with a trauma-informed coach, therapist, or a safe friend is a great way to build confidence when practicing corrective experiences.

## TRAUMA PSYCHOTHERAPY-BODY, BRAIN, & MIND BASED PSYCHOTHERAPY

**21. Work with a trauma-based psychotherapist:** The following body-brain-mind-based trauma-oriented psychotherapies are specifically designed to heal childhood trauma: Internal Family Systems Therapy (IFS), Somatic Experiencing (SE), Sensorimotor Therapy, Neurosequencial Model of Therapeutics (NMT), Trauma-Focused Cognitive Behavioral Therapy (TF-CBT), Psychomotor Therapy, Psychodrama, Attachment-Oriented Psychotherapy, Trauma-Informed Stabilization Treatment—For severe addiction, suicidal, self-harm, and self-destructive behavior (TIST).

___**To-do:** Research the types of trauma-oriented or attachment-oriented psychotherapies and psychotherapists you're interested in working with. Schedule an introductory call to determine if the type of therapy and therapist is right for you.  Make sure the therapist you choose is trauma-informed and specializes in working with adult survivors of childhood trauma, C-PTSD, or developmental trauma. Also, if you're struggling with addiction, make sure the therapist you choose specializes in working with clients with your specific type of addiction and incorporates trauma-based along with addiction treatment approaches.

**22. Work with an Eye Movement Desensitization and Reprocessing (EMDR) Therapist:** EMDR therapy incorporates eye movements or other bilateral stimulation designed to process and release information in the mind and body, which can free clients from trauma, disturbing images, body sensations, distressing emotions, and self-defeating beliefs.

____**To-do:** Find a trauma-informed EMDR psychotherapist in your area and schedule a session for an introductory consultation to see if they are the right fit for you.

**23. Train your brain via Neurofeedback:** Neurofeedback, AKA brain training, is designed to help calm down and regulate the nervous system, emotions, and behavior.

____**To-do:** See chapter 30, "Using Neurofeedback To Regulate The Brain, Body, Mind & Behavior."
Either research neurofeedback equipment providers to purchase a system to train your brain at home or find a trauma-informed, certified neurofeedback practitioner in your area. Schedule an introductory consultation to see if you're a fit for each other. See the appendix for directory listings for trauma-informed neurofeedback practitioners.

**24. Review prescription medication efficacy:**
___**To-do:** If you're on medication for C-PTSD, review whether it is helping to manage your symptoms. See your psychiatrist if you aren't getting the results you hoped for or if the side effects are concerning. See your doctor or find a trauma-informed psychiatrist if you're considering starting, changing, or discontinuing an antidepressant or other medication. DO NOT begin, reduce, increase, or stop psychotropic medications without medical supervision.

## HEALING SHAME AND GUILT

**25. Heal shame and guilt:** Shame and guilt are extremely common among trauma survivors and, if left unresolved, can undermine healing C-PTSD.  Since guilt and shame occur in the context of relationships, healing must take place within relationships.

___**To-do:** Review Chapter 8, "Emotional Liberation: Healing Shame and Guilt," chapter 28, "Shrinking The Critic," and chapter 29, "Letting Go of Guilt and Shame," and do the exercises in chapter 29. Since healing shame must happen in the context of relationships, consider finding a safe trauma-informed coach, therapist, spouse, or friend to begin the process of letting go of guilt and shame. Also, see the appendix for various books on healing guilt and shame.

## GRIEVING THE LOSSES FROM CHILDHOOD TRAUMA

**26. Grieve what you've lost to childhood trauma:** According to trauma expert, survivor, and psychotherapist Pete Walker, grieving the losses from childhood trauma is a critical step to resolving C-PTSD symptoms.

___**To-do:** Review Chapter 31, "Grieving the Losses of C-PTSD." Seek support to process your grief from a trauma-informed therapist who offers body, brain, and mind therapies and who specializes in working with C-PTSD.

## ADDICTION – ALCOHOL, DRUG, FOOD, AND SELF-DEFEATING BEHAVIOR RECOVERY OPTIONS

**27. Get into recovery with food addiction and obesity:** You're not alone if you're struggling with food addiction and obesity. It's extremely common for those of us with a history of childhood trauma to use food to cope. Therefore, self-compassion is the first step to embrace when considering handling issues with food and weight.

___**To-do:** Read Chapter 19, "How Food Saved My Sanity In An Insane Environment," and Chapter 33, "Food Addiction and Weight-Loss Recovery Options for Survivors." Follow the guidelines in chapter 33. Be sure to be gentle with yourself and course-correct where necessary. Note: This recovery approach is primarily for people who suffer from compulsive or binge-eating disorders and obesity. It's not designed for people with anorexia, bulimia, or other types of eating disorders. Search online to find support groups in your area for your type of eating disorder.

**28. Get into recovery with alcohol, drugs, behavioral addictions, or other self-defeating behaviors:** If you're struggling with alcohol, drugs, or other self-destructive or self-defeating behaviors, you are not alone. Self-medicating through substances or behaviors is extremely common among survivors.

___**To do:** Review Chapter 18, "Learning Drinking and Smoking Marijuana Were a Normal Response To An Abnormal Environment," and chapter 32, "Alcohol and Drug Addiction Recovery Options for Survivors." To find support groups for various behavioral addictions, see the appendix. Determine which groups and/or programs will best suit your recovery needs by searching online for information about the group or program's focus and where meetings are in your local area.

**29. Find an inpatient or outpatient recovery/rehab program for alcohol, drugs, food, behavioral addictions, or for C-PTSD recovery:** If you have a serious substance or behavioral addiction and/or will suffer from severe withdrawal symptoms when you stop drinking alcohol or using drugs, you'll likely need an inpatient addiction recovery program.

___**To-do:** Review Chapter 32, "Alcohol and Drug Addiction Recovery Options for Survivors," and/or Chapter 33, "Food Addiction and Weight-Loss Recovery Options for Survivors." To find support groups for various behavioral addictions, see the appendix. Make sure you choose trauma-informed care providers who integrate trauma healing modalities with substance or behavioral addiction recovery.

## BODY-BASED & EXPRESSIVE ARTS TRAUMA-HEALING

**30. Implement a breathwork practice:** Since trauma tends to cause breathing to become constricted and shallow, practicing various breathwork techniques is known to regulate the nervous system and emotions and improve mental health.

___**To do:** Research different breathwork techniques designed to regulate your nervous system (box breathing, diaphragmatic breathing, pursed-lip breathing, etc.) and choose one or more to integrate into a regular practice.

**31. Start a movement practice:** Movement therapies listed here are regulating and therapeutic as trauma-healing tools because they incorporate where the trauma lives—in the body, nervous system, and mind. This can include Y12SR-a 12-step trauma-informed yoga, trauma-sensitive yoga, traditional yoga, tai chi, qigong, rhythmic drumming, or martial arts.
___**To-do:** Choose the movement therapy you'd like to practice, schedule a class, and commit to how often you'll participate in your new practice.

**32. Get bodywork or massage therapy:** Since trauma lives in the body, brain, and mind, body-based therapies are known to be very therapeutic for healing C-PTSD.
___**To-do:** Commit to integrating bodywork or massage into your life by deciding what type and how often you will use it.

**33. Practice somatic mindfulness:** Somatic mindfulness is similar to regular mindfulness, except that instead of just noticing your thoughts, you also include noticing the sensations in your body throughout the day.
___**To-do:** Your goal is to become aware of how your body/nervous system reacts to stress or trauma triggers. The better you can tune into your body's subtle sensations and feelings, the more your nervous system calms down, and the better access you'll have to your emotions. When we can access our emotions and process them in a safe environment, they become integrated, which resolves the trauma. Make a commitment to practicing somatic mindfulness throughout your day.

**34. Do art, music, dance, theater, or other expressive arts:** Dr. Van der Kolk highly recommends expressive arts for their ability to heal trauma. In my early AA recovery, singing, writing songs, and playing my guitar were extremely helpful in regulating my nervous system. It also provided a healthy form of authentic self-expression and a sense of agency for me.
___**To-do:** Choose an expressive art you'd like to pursue, then research classes, groups, YouTube videos, or podcasts. Make an appointment to meet with an instructor or group leader to find out how you can participate. Write down which expressive art you will begin with and commit to how often you will practice it.

## STAYING ON TRACK WITH YOUR TRAUMA-HEALING & RECOVERY GOALS

**35. Declaring and tracking your goals:** One of my favorite sayings is "What you can measure, you can manage." Clarifying your trauma healing and recovery goals and the actions you need to take to achieve them is crucial to your success. In chapter 34, "Getting and Staying on Track with Your Trauma Healing and Recovery," I reference a study that shows that those who declare their goals and have an accountability partner have a 95% chance of reaching them.
___**To-do:** Review Chapter 34, "Getting and Staying on Track with Your Trauma Healing and Recovery Goals." If you haven't done so, complete the exercises in this chapter by declaring your trauma healing and recovery goals and what actions you'll take to achieve them on the worksheet.
Setting up a structure and frequency to track your goals is crucial in reaching them. Using apps, an Excel spreadsheet, or simply writing your goals and daily action steps on a post-it note or piece of paper will get them out of your head and into reality. Remember to keep your goals and action steps visible throughout the day to help you stay focused on achieving them.

**36. Review your trauma-healing and recovery goals regularly, celebrate your wins, and course-correct when necessary:** The reason it's essential to track your goals is to help you stay on top of what is and what's not working so you can course-correct to achieve them. Tracking also helps you celebrate the ground you've gained and the victories you've achieved along the way.

____**To-do:**

    a.    Review Chapter 34, "Getting and Staying on Track with Your Recovery." If you haven't done so, complete the exercises in this chapter by writing down your trauma healing and recovery goals and what actions you'll take to achieve them on the worksheet.

    b.    Make a recurring weekly or monthly appointment on your calendar to remind you to review your progress on your trauma healing and recovery goals.

    c.    Determine what's working and what's not working toward reaching your goals. Continue doing what is working and course-correct for what isn't.

    d.    No matter how big or small, celebrate your wins at least once a month by treating yourself to a nice dinner out, an experience, or another way that makes you feel celebrated.

# ADDITIONAL ACTION STEPS I NEED TO TAKE TO REACH MY TRAUMA HEALING AND RECOVERY GOALS

| Action Step | Due Date |
|---|---|
|  |  |
|  |  |
|  |  |
|  |  |
|  |  |
|  |  |
|  |  |
|  |  |
|  |  |
|  |  |
|  |  |
|  |  |
|  |  |

PART IV

———

# THE
# GIFTS OF THE
# TRAUMA HEALING
# & RECOVERY
# JOURNEY

# CHAPTER 36

──────────

# IT'S NOT ABOUT FOOD, DRUGS, OR ALCOHOL IT'S ABOUT HEALING COMPLEX PTSD

"So I'm not crazy?" "No. Your brain is doing exactly what you would expect it to do considering what you lived through."

—Excerpt from survivor story in, *What Happened to You?: Conversations on Trauma, Resilience, & Healing by* Oprah Winfrey & Bruce Perry, MD, PhD

Food, weight, drugs, and alcohol are not the core problem for those suffering from addiction and obesity. They are all attempts at a solution to solving the real problem, the pain of living day in and day out with a brain, body, and mind profoundly dysregulated by complex PTSD. As long as we see addiction, food, and weight as the core problem, we'll miss healing the trauma that drives it.

This is not to say addiction, whether to substances, food, or behaviors, doesn't cause major problems for the addicted, their families, and society as a whole because they do. It's also not to say that stopping self-destructive behavior is unnecessary. If we want to experience a life worth living and save children and spouses from going through the hell of living with a family member in the throes of addiction, we must.

Believing that food, drugs, alcohol, and obesity are the problem and that when a person stops drinking, drugging, compulsively eating, or reaches a healthy weight, their problem is solved is delusional since they've not addressed and healed the trauma driving it. There's a big difference between abstaining from self-destructive behavior and experiencing true healing and recovery. People who quit drinking, using drugs, food, or other compulsive behaviors but don't do their inner or trauma work are often as miserable or even more miserable than they were while practicing their addictions. Many justify that they don't need therapy or recovery support groups since in their mind, alcohol, drugs, food, or their "self-destructive behavior of choice" was the core problem, and they've solved it by moderating or quitting.

Another common issue for those suffering from addiction is that once they become sober or abstinent and fail to heal their trauma, they often switch to other addictions to replace the soothing they no longer have access to. Examples are those who quit smoking and turn to food and gain weight. Some who quit drinking develop a marijuana addiction to replace how alcohol helped quell their anxiety.

Once I got sober, instead of using alcohol and drugs to tap into the excitement and adrenaline partying provided, I got busy building my business and became a workaholic. Many switch from substances to spending, porn, gambling, gaming, or social media. The point is, if we don't get down to healing the trauma driving the addiction, it will pop up in a different form.

## The Price We Pay For Failing To See The Direct Link Between Trauma, Addiction & Obesity

When we fail to understand or accept that addiction and obesity are a symptom of unhealed trauma, we feed the narrative that addiction and obesity are a choice, and those who "make the choice" to drink, use, compulsively eat, or engage in other addictive behaviors are irresponsible, untrustworthy, weak, and therefore unworthy of being included in "normal" people's circles.

Additionally, allowing this shame-based narrative to continue incents the millions of people who've achieved long-term recovery to stay in the closet vs. coming out and sharing their stories of how they've recovered and turned their lives around so they can be an inspiration for others who struggle to also find recovery.

The stigma and shame around addiction in the U.S. is the exact reason it has taken me thirty-five years to share my recovery story on a professional level. Instead of sharing how I'd overcome my struggle with substances and weight to inspire those who still struggled, I set my target market in my life coaching practice to help business owners grow their companies. As long as I didn't disclose my shameful past, I was comfortable. Yet, over time I knew part of me was dying by hiding such an essential part of what I'd overcome and how much I knew I could help others by coming out about it.

I discovered I wasn't the only one afraid to come out about my addiction and obesity history when I saw that the 2013 feature documentary *The Anonymous People* was tackling this very issue. In it, I learned that 23.5 million Americans are living in long-term recovery from alcohol and drug addiction. But due to deeply entrenched social stigma, fear of discrimination, and many of the 12-step members' belief that they have to stay "anonymous" and not share their recovery stories publicly, the vast majority of the millions in recovery have remained silent.

Tragically the vacuum created by this silence has been filled by the media portraying the dysfunctional side of those in the throes of active addiction. What the media doesn't cover is that addiction is a preventable and treatable health condition and that millions have recovered, gotten well, and are living lives they love while being productive members of society.

The film shares that just like celebrities and athletes with HIV/AIDS came out to help save others in the eighties, courageous addiction recovery advocates have launched a movement to inspire recovering people to come out to tell their stories to help others find recovery.

One of the sober celebrities that touched me in the film was actor Kristen Johnson. I loved watching her play Tammy, Bonnie's (Alison Janey's) foster sister, on the sitcom *Mom*. The series was about a mother and daughter in recovery and how they manage to stay sober with the support of their recovery friends and 12-Step groups.

In *The Anonymous People,* Johnson shares an excerpt from her memoir *Guts* about how massive the problem of addiction is in our culture:

> Here's the truth, whether we want to admit it or not. This is our black plague, a terrible scourge that's just as deadly as cancer or AIDS. It's destroying people by the untold millions, and I believe without a doubt that the embarrassment and secrecy that shroud this disease are just as deadly as the disease itself...
>
> In my opinion, the best slogan when it comes to addiction is not found at a meeting in a church basement or in some book. It's a phrase six gay activists from New York City coined in 1987 at the onset of AIDS. *Silence = Death*. I won't stay silent any longer. I hope you won't either.

What struck me about Johnson's plea for those of us in long-term recovery to come out and share our recovery stories is it had been three years since I'd seen this movie, and even though I knew there was a movement that would support me in coming out about my recovery, I still didn't feel safe enough to do so.

As I've shared, up until learning I had trauma, I'd stayed in the closet on a professional level about my addiction and obesity history for decades. It took empirical data about the direct link between childhood trauma and addiction to prove my addictions weren't my fault for me to let go of the shame I had about them. It was only then that I felt safe enough to come out.

Since this is what it took for me to come out, I figured it might also be the key to helping others in recovery feel safe enough to share not only their recovery stories but also how they've healed the trauma that drove their addictions.

## How Changing The Narrative From Addiction & Obesity Being A Choice, or Solely A Disease To It Being A Symptom of Trauma Can Change The World

Since 90% of people struggling with addiction avoid seeking treatment due to the shame and stigma about it in our culture, when we change the narrative from addiction and obesity being a choice or solely a disease to a symptom of unhealed trauma, we de-shame and destigmatize it. This gives those suffering a much better chance of seeking treatment since they'll see their addiction is not their fault vs. believing they're weak, broken, or a failure.

Changing the narrative from addiction and obesity being a choice to it being a symptom of trauma has the potential to ripple out to every sector of society, helping millions to recover and saving countless lives. It will also save family members from the hell of living with and witnessing a loved one practicing an addiction. And the fewer people who struggle with addiction, the fewer children and families will be traumatized. And just like trauma trickles down the generations, so does healing.

This is the power that those of us in recovery from trauma and addiction have by sharing our stories. In fact, it's the very reason I included the following dedication at the beginning of this book.

*For the survivors.*
*Because sharing our story is the single most powerful thing*
*we can do to heal ourselves and heal the world.*

All of our trauma healing and recovery stories matter. In fact, when enough of us share our stories, we can't help but change the world. I know I wouldn't be sober, maintaining a healthy weight, or have experienced profound recovery from C-PTSD without hearing or reading the hundreds of trauma and recovery stories that gave me hope that I could heal and recover too.

If you have any doubt your story matters or that coming together to share our stories can make a difference, I defer to the wisdom of Margaret Mead.

Never doubt that a small group of thoughtful, committed individuals can change the world. In fact, it's the only thing that ever has.

— Margaret Mead

# CHAPTER 37

---

# HOMECOMING & SHARING MY GIFTS WITH THE WORLD

Ultimately your greatest gift to the world is being who you are, both your gift and your fulfillment.

—A. H. Almas

## Homecoming

As far back as I can remember, all I've ever wanted was a safe, peaceful, loving family. From the time I was eight or nine years old, that was what I remember longing for while lying in bed at night while attempting to cope with the insanity that was my home. When I really got down to it, the food, alcohol, and drugs were simply a way to numb the unbearable pain of this heartbreaking loss.

As an adult, I looked to create the family I longed for through my romantic partners. Yet even after being in several long-term relationships and doing decades of healing work, I still never quite felt like I'd experienced having the peaceful, loving family I'd longed for.

Once I embarked on my trauma healing journey and became aware of how C-PTSD had impacted me not just in childhood but over the entire course of my life, my self-compassion significantly increased. As I continued my healing journey, I noticed a sense of safety and calm emerge in my day-to-day life. As the months rolled by, I began to notice a kind, compassionate, internal voice chime in to soothe me whenever I was upset or struggling. It was the kind of voice you'd expect to hear from a compassionate mother or a kind, understanding sister. Interestingly, I hadn't done any specific work to develop this internal voice. It seemed to be developing naturally from my trauma-healing work.

As I contemplated how this voice came to be and its purpose, I realized it was playing a much bigger role in my healing than I initially thought. It wasn't simply a function of my self-compassion practice. I realized it was the voice I'd been longing to hear and feel from the safe, loving family I'd been searching for. It was as if the trauma therapies and healing practices I'd been engaging with had been coalescing behind the scenes to help me cultivate a felt sense of a loving family from within.

What's so wonderful about my inner family is how safe, seen and loved I feel. I know it will always be there for me and has my back, no matter what.

Now that I have a safe, peaceful, loving inner family, I have a much deeper appreciation for the sense of family Maria and I have created as partners. On top of that, since Maria has a huge extended family, not only did my wish for a loving family come true, but I also feel like I've hit the jackpot with more loving family members than I could have ever dreamed of!

Although I've shared the many gifts I've received from healing my trauma and achieving long-term recovery, I must say that one of the greatest gifts of my trauma healing journey is finally having a family where I feel safe, seen, loved, and know that I matter.

## Sharing My Gifts With The World

I had no idea in 2017 that I would stumble upon a book that would completely change my life. This past five-year journey into understanding and healing C-PTSD has been a spiritual odyssey like no other. Although I knew I'd experienced significant growth and healing since embarking on this journey, it wasn't until I took the time to contemplate how my overall life had changed that I saw something much more profound and transformative taking place.

I realized that healing my trauma had freed up a core part of me I'd been hiding my whole life. Before knowing about my C-PTSD, I'd been in long-term recovery from substances and my weight. I'd spend years working toward creating a successful life as an entrepreneur and life coach. After finally turning my life around to where I felt good about how I looked and what I'd accomplished, the last thing I wanted potential clients to know about me was my history of severe addiction and obesity. I was done feeling bad about myself, so I buried my past and thought I'd moved on from it.

Not only did my trauma healing journey make me realize I hadn't moved on from my past, it brought to light how my past was alive and well and was running my life!

As long as I looked good by projecting I was a together, strong, successful entrepreneur and coach and never disclosed my history, I was comfortable. Although I went on to build a thriving business, it never satisfied the part of me that yearned for a close, authentic connection with my clients.

For years I remember hearing Wayne Dyer say, "Don't die with your music still in you." For decades I worked on trying to figure out what my music was so I could share it with the world. I'd always been called to help my clients learn how to live their purpose and create lives they loved. I'd been trying for decades to figure out how to channel this calling in a way that satisfied my longing to feel an authentic connection with my clients.

In a kind of karmic twist, I found that by hiding my history of addiction and severe obesity (to project a successful image,) I would inevitably attract coaching clients who weren't much interested in life-purpose work. Their interest was solely in my helping them build their businesses. Looking back, I now see that I attracted in clients what I was. A woman who based her value on looking good through external accomplishments.

I remember throughout my fifties, feeling the window of time closing in on me while still not knowing what my "music" was and fearing I might die, having never shared my gift with the world. The idea of being on my deathbed, knowing I would die with my music still in me, not only horrified me, it began to haunt me. Thank God I soldiered on and continued the search because in the fall of 2017, at fifty-seven, I finally hit paydirt when I read *The Body Keeps The Score* and discovered I'd been suffering from C-PTSD, and within a few short months, I knew I'd found my music.

As I began to learn more about C-PTSD and understood that my struggle with addiction and obesity was my best attempt to manage the pain of my trauma symptoms and was never my fault to begin with, I was finally able to lay down the burden of shame I'd been carrying over them.

Once I'd let go of my shame, it was as if the world suddenly opened up for me. My discomfort talking with people about my addiction and obesity history began to evaporate. In a matter of months, it became obvious that my calling was to help fellow survivors who had struggled or were currently struggling with addiction, obesity, or relationships find the freedom I had of understanding their struggles weren't their fault—but were their best attempts at managing the pain of their trauma—and that they could heal.

Little did I know that the very thing I thought was my worst liability was, in fact, my greatest asset. Just being able to walk through life feeling completely comfortable sharing pretty much anything about my journey is a freedom I'd never known until now.  Finally, discovering what my "music" is and being able to share it with the world is one more amazing gift of healing my trauma.  I'm so grateful to Wayne Dyer for his tenacity in continually reminding me not to die with my music still in me because without it, I'm not sure I would have pursued it to the end.

As I near the end of writing this book, I'm feeling a wonderful sense of completion in my life. It's partly due to finally cracking the code of living my purpose, and it's also knowing I get to leave the world a little bit better by sharing what I've learned throughout my healing and recovery journey. And I can't think of a better feeling than knowing I can make the difference I've always wanted to make in the world, even after I'm no longer here.

In October of 2022, I'll be sixty-three years old. This means it's taken over four decades of my adult life to figure out my purpose and share it with the world. This drives home the lesson that it's never too late to give up on yourself or your dreams!

# CHAPTER 38

---

# THE GIFTS OF HEALING TRAUMA & RECOVERY

And the day came when the risk to remain tight in a bud was more painful than the risk it took to blossom.

—Anaïs Nin

If you're on the fence about whether you even have C-PTSD, or if you know you do but question if this or any healing approach will help you since almost everything you've tried hasn't, you're not alone. It's very common for those of us who grew up with a lot of adversity to feel ambivalent about healing the wounds of our past or setting goals for the future.

Since so many of the therapists we saw weren't aware that trauma had driven our most difficult struggles, we never received the correct diagnosis or the trauma-oriented therapies necessary to fully heal. As a result, many of us felt defeated or hopelessly broken when the many things we tried rarely worked to overcome our struggles.

What makes this healing and recovery journey different is we're healing the root cause instead of spinning around in symptom relief. And by doing so, we'll give ourselves the best chance to experience significant, sustainable improvements in many areas of our life.

To give you an idea of what's possible by healing your trauma and getting into recovery from self-destructive or self-defeating behaviors, I've listed the top gifts I've received from my healing and recovery journey below.

## The Top Seven Gifts I've Received from My Trauma Healing & Recovery Journey

**1. A loving, compassionate relationship with myself:** Healing my trauma has enabled me to cultivate a level of self-compassion, self-forgiveness, and self-acceptance I would have never known had I not taken this journey. Today I give myself a whole lot of space to be imperfect. Instead of judging myself for missing the mark in certain areas, I do my best to recognize and have compassion for my limitations due to trauma's impact on my brain, body, and mind. This isn't to say I don't actively work on improving these areas. It just means that I have a much deeper understanding and compassion for why they sometimes can be challenging for me. This awareness alone has transformed how I show up for myself and others.

**2. Being able to forge and maintain close relationships and enjoy socializing:** Once I realized childhood trauma is relational trauma, I dedicated a significant part of my healing toward learning how to feel safe and connected in close relationships. My work in this area has really paid off since I feel a level of safety and connection with my partner that I'd never experienced in a relationship until now. Healing relational trauma has also helped me develop several close friendships with fellow survivors that I truly cherish. I've also experienced a huge shift in feeling safe socializing. Today I even look forward to attending parties and events. Given how lonely and disconnected I felt prior to healing my C-PTSD, I'm deeply grateful for this level of healing.

**3. Resolving shame about my history of addiction and severe obesity:** Once I learned about C-PTSD and discovered that my addictions and my struggle with obesity were never my fault to begin with but were simply the best way I knew how to cope with my trauma, I was able to release the shame I had about them and replace it with self-compassion. Being able to lay down the burden of shame I'd carried for believing these struggles were my own fault has been one of the most life-changing gifts I've received by healing my trauma.

There's such freedom in knowing I no longer need to hide this part of my past, and today I actually enjoy talking about it. I love knowing I'm helping educate the public about the link between trauma, addiction, and obesity since it helps change the cultural narrative from addiction and obesity being a choice or solely a disease to it being an attempt to stop the pain of unhealed trauma.

**4. Deep meaning and purpose in my work:** Since discovering and healing C-PTSD has been such a life-changing experience, I naturally felt called to help fellow survivors heal. This is what inspired me to write this book, speak on the topic, and shift my coaching practice to specializing in offering trauma recovery and resilience coaching. Given how long I'd struggled to find purpose and meaning in my work, this is another gift from healing trauma I am truly grateful for.

**5. Peace of mind and serenity:** Releasing guilt and shame, accepting myself on a very deep level, gaining a new, compassionate narrative about my life, and integrating regulating, trauma-based therapies and practices have dramatically quieted down my inner and outer critics. As a result, a new level of peace, serenity, well-being, and expansiveness has arisen in my day-to-day life. Given how much suffering I used to endure with shame, guilt, and anxiety, this is a foundational level of healing I cherish every single day.

**6. Being unattached to the good opinion of others:** An unexpected yet delightful benefit of my healing journey is once I accepted myself on a deep level, I no longer needed to seek approval from others or from my accomplishments. As a result, I rarely worry about what people think of me anymore, and I'm much less attached to outcomes in my personal and professional life. This is a level of emotional freedom I'd always aspired toward but hadn't completely experienced until I embarked on my trauma healing journey.

**7. Freedom from being a slave to self-destructive addictions:** Finding ways to get my needs met without needing to hurt myself through compulsive eating, severe obesity, smoking, and substance addictions is a gift that I'm grateful for every single day. I know the hell of active addiction and severe obesity, and as I've shared throughout this book, there is a solution. Given how life-threatening my substance, food, and weight issues were, I'll be forever grateful to all who have supported me in achieving long-term recovery.

## What Does It Mean To Experience True Healing?

What I've come to learn throughout my healing journey is that true healing is about finding wholeness. Becoming whole is about facing and accepting ourselves "as is" — the good, bad, and ugly. It's also about honoring our authentic selves. This often involves reclaiming the parts we've denied or abandoned.

While reading Gabor Maté's book *The Myth of Normal,* I was struck by the answer he got from the question *What is healing?* from depth psychologist and wilderness guide Bill Plotkin, Ph.D. According to Plotkin, "It's not so much looking at what's wrong, but where is the person's wholeness not fully realized or lived out."

Plotkin's definition of healing explained the ache I continued to feel due to leaving a part of me behind (my addiction and obesity history) and how it cost me by preventing me from realizing my wholeness. I didn't know until I learned I was suffering from childhood trauma that to live my purpose, I would need to reclaim this essential part of myself.

Once I discovered my struggle with addiction and weight was never my fault to begin with but was a common symptom of untreated C-PTSD, I no longer judged myself over them and felt safe to share all of me. Suddenly I had a compelling desire to share my story of learning that C-PTSD had driven my most difficult struggles and how healing my trauma completely transformed my life.

It's not lost on me that the life purpose work I felt compelled to pursue with my clients was exactly what I struggled to clarify for myself. What unlocked my purpose was letting go of my shame over my addiction and obesity history. By doing so, I reclaimed an essential part of me that has a proven track record of overcoming some pretty daunting challenges around alcohol, drugs, and severe obesity.

The beauty of this is I get to share the gift of how I recovered to help those still struggling. This is the power that de-shaming trauma, addiction, and other stigmatized conditions have to free people up to heal so they can go on to live lives they love and make the contribution they're called to make in the world.

## My Life Today

My life today is literally unrecognizable compared to where I came from before I achieved long-term recovery from my struggle with addiction and obesity and healed my complex PTSD. The common denominator for each gift I've received from my healing and recovery journey is that they're essential ingredients for a meaningful and fulfilling life.

Before healing my trauma and achieving long-term recovery, there was no way I could experience these gifts because of how trauma and my struggle with addiction had disrupted my brain, body, mind, relationships, and work.

This is why I can say without hesitation that doing the work to heal your trauma and embrace recovery is not only worth it. It's essential! If given the opportunity, why not give yourself and your family the gift of a satisfying life filled with meaning and purpose?

## The Easier, Softer Way

Before I got sober and was able to get my weight to a healthy level and maintain it, I hesitated to give up alcohol, drugs, and the freedom to eat whatever I wanted. After all, food, drugs, and alcohol had been my go-to lifesavers for decades.

Just the idea of quitting drinking, getting high, and eating my favorite foods brought up thoughts of how boring, dull and depressing my existence would be without them. Since alcohol, partying, and food were the only ways I'd been able to have fun, relax, or escape life's stressors, I never considered it possible to have "real" fun or be able to relax or escape any other way.

But once I got a taste for what it's like to wake up on a Saturday or Sunday morning hangover free, feel the amazing sense of well-being in a healthier, clear-headed, lighter body, and connect with hysterically funny and super fun recovery friends, I realized I'd been duped.

And when I think of how good I feel about who I've become—and how every area of my life has dramatically improved due to healing my trauma and achieving long-term recovery with substances, food, and my weight—there's no question the healing and recovery path does a much better job of meeting my needs and brings me much more joy and fulfillment than partying and binge eating ever did. Today, I get to look in the mirror and feel proud of who I've become. Before my recovery, let's just say I avoided mirrors.

I'm not saying healing trauma and getting into recovery with substances, food, or other behaviors are a walk in the park. Yes, there will be painful moments to face. But as one of my favorite sayings goes,

*I'd rather feel the momentary sting of pain to give up the never ending river of suffering.*

I've been on this path for thirty years, and every time *I've been willing to feel the pain to give up the suffering,* my life has gotten better. This is what makes getting on the trauma healing and recovery path so worth it. It's a heck of a lot more fun, and believe it or not, it really is the easier, softer way!

## Ready to End the Struggle?

If you're ready to end the struggle, the good news is that in chapter 35, I have compiled a menu of thirty-six therapies, practices, and dozens of resources to choose from that have proven to be effective for me in healing C-PTSD and achieving significant improvements in my relationships, work, moods, and with overcoming my struggle with food, weight, and substances. These resources have not only helped me, they've completely transformed my life!

All I can say is I would have given my left arm for this knowledge and these resources thirty years ago. It would have saved me massive amounts of time, money, grief, and suffering.

Therefore, if you're struggling with any of the common symptoms of complex PTSD—or even if you don't suffer from trauma but just want to improve your health or relationships— if I were you, I would look at this book as a gentle nudge from the universe, offering you a map and a step-by-step guidebook to get on the path toward living a life you love. When you think about it, what do you have to lose? The worst-case scenario is you can always go back to your old life. Yet the upside is limitless.

## Picture What Your Life Could Look Like Without the Struggles Unhealed Trauma Has Put In Your Way

Take a moment to picture what your life would look and feel like if you no longer struggled with close relationships, loneliness, food, weight, alcohol, drugs, shame, guilt, anxiety, depression, unfulfilling work, or financial difficulties.

You're not alone if you picked one or even all of these issues. I've struggled with every single one of them throughout my journey. The good news is I rarely struggle with any of them today. This is what's possible by healing complex PTSD and achieving long-term recovery.

I'm living proof that you really can create a life you love when you get freed up from the shackles of trauma and addiction. I've given you the map I've followed and have outlined every step I've taken to accomplish this throughout this book. Now it's up to you.

If you're willing to take consistent action toward your healing and recovery goals, course correct when necessary, and never give up, you'll get there. It's not a matter of if but when. The only thing left is for you to say yes to the journey and start by taking one baby step.

## Just Take One Baby Step

Starting is simple. Just take one baby step today, and you'll be on your way. To stay out of overwhelm, keep the focus on taking one step and one day at a time. When we get too far ahead of ourselves or feel we have to figure it out all at once, we'll get overwhelmed and quit.

Another principle to embrace is to trust the process and know that more will be revealed when you're ready. Remember that true healing is about what you learn and how you transform while on your journey, not the destination.

You can start your journey by simply picking one easy item from the "Trauma-Healing Practices & Recovery Menu" in chapter 35. One of the easiest steps you can take is to continue learning about C-PTSD. If you haven't read this book in its entirety, and completed all of the exercises in it, you can start by making that your first baby step. If you have, you can choose another baby step by perusing the "Trauma-Healing Practices & Recovery Menu" in chapter 35. Or you can visit the appendix, where you'll find hundreds of trauma healing and recovery resources, including recommended books, media, websites, directories, and groups.

Now it's your turn.

Are you willing to say YES to a better today and a brighter future for you and your family by getting on a healing and recovery path? If so, what baby step will you take today?

## The Power of Saying YES To A Better Today & A Brighter Future

If you've said yes to embarking on this journey and have committed to taking your first baby step, I want to be the first to congratulate you for giving yourself and those you love the gift of healing and recovery.

Welcome to the life where you get to feel safe, seen, heard, and know that you matter. This is the life where you get to reconnect to yourself and others and know that you're loved. It's the life that's been calling you in whispers for years.

It wants to thank you for listening. But more importantly, it wants to say...

*Welcome home!* ♡

# ACKNOWLEDGMENTS

Going through the process of writing this book has brought home the saying *Nobody makes it alone,* more so than practically any other project or journey I've been on. My first attempt at getting it written stalled out after one year and stayed stalled for an additional five years.

It wasn't until I surrounded myself with a safe, supportive partner, kind and loving friends, several editors, accountability partners, and many trauma-informed colleagues that I was finally able to take it to the finish line.

This book would have never seen the light of day if it weren't for the support, encouragement, guidance, and inspiration I've received from the people listed below. For this reason, I am truly grateful and owe a debt of gratitude to the following people:

My wonderful partner, Maria, for the undying love and support she has given me through the many ups and downs as a first-time author. I also want to thank her for patiently listening to me share more than she ever wanted to learn about childhood trauma!

Vincent Felitti, MD, and Robert Anda, MD, for launching the landmark Adverse Childhood Experiences (ACE) Study and disseminating its findings on the long-term health, social and behavioral outcomes of childhood adversity.

Bessel van der Kolk, MD; Pete Walker; MA; Jonice Webb, Ph.D.; Tian Dayton, Ph.D.; Bruce Perry, Ph.D.; Janina Fisher, Ph.D.; and Peter Levine, Ph.D., for being the most important guides in helping me understand the nature of childhood trauma and what is necessary to heal.

Gabor Maté, MD, and Oliver Morgan for being the most influential authors to help me understand that my addictions were trauma responses and were my best attempt to regulate a nervous system profoundly dysregulated by trauma.

My trauma warrior friends and key accountability partners, Carey Sipp and Teri Wellbrock, for providing the wise, empathic support I needed to help me stay focused and on track and, most importantly, never give up on my maiden journey as an author.

PACEsconnection.com founder Jane Stevens, CEO Ingrid Cockhren, organizational liaison Dana Brown, and the entire staff and community managers for providing an extraordinary trauma-informed community of colleagues to connect with and for the abundance of content that's played a key role in educating me about C-PTSD and how to heal.

Brené Brown, Ph.D., LSCW, for being the most important author and teacher to help me understand and heal shame, providing one of the most liberating experiences of my life.

Judith Grisel, Ph.D., for being the most important teacher to help me understand substance use disorders from a neurobiological, genetic, and environmental standpoint, resulting in a radical shift in my view about all mind-altering chemicals and, most importantly, my view of myself.

Psychotherapists Diane Poole Heller, Ph.D., Stan Tatkin, PsyD, MFT, and Terry Real, for being the most important teachers in helping me understand the nature of attachment trauma and how to heal and go on to forge healthy, securely attached relationships.

Ruth Schwartz, Ph.D., for being the most influential guide and teacher for navigating the unique relational dynamics that women who love women encounter and for helping me develop the skills and insight necessary to forge and maintain a healthy, fulfilling relationship with my partner Maria.

Stephen Porges and Deb Dana for being the most important guides in teaching me about polyvagal theory and how to become an operator of my nervous system, resulting in my feeling safe enough to connect with others.

Jeffrey Rustein, Ph.D., Sounds True Founder, Tami Simon, and all of the trauma experts who contributed to supporting me in healing from C-PTSD through the Sounds True Trauma Healing Program.

Sebern Fisher for being the most influential teacher in helping me understand the power of neurofeedback to calm down and regulate the fear-driven brains of trauma survivors and the profound impact a regulated brain can make in a survivor's life.

The entire team at Brain-Trainer.com for providing the support to choose the right neurofeedback system to train my brain and for providing the mentoring I needed to become proficient in doing so.

Oprah Winfrey, for raising awareness about what childhood trauma is and how to heal by sharing your trauma story in *What Happened To You: Conversations on Trauma Resilience & Healing,* as well as on the Oprah Winfrey Show and sharing the survivors' stories throughout your career.

My former therapist for sharing a story of a client writing a book that inspired me to write this book. And for your wise, compassionate counsel, which helped me carve out a solid sense of self while navigating a very challenging period in my life.

Cheryl Richardson and Reid Tracy for providing the inspiration and understanding of what it takes to become a successful author during their Speak Write Promote seminar on a Hay House Alaska Cruise. My cruise mates and friends Cari Palmer and Jesslynn Stull for their supporting me in becoming an author. My first writing coach, Kerri Richardson, for providing the guidance and support I needed to get started as a writer and for helping me to stay focused and on track to complete my first draft.

My developmental editor, Susan Strecker, for helping me shape, develop, and organize my initial manuscript. My copy editor, Kristy Phillips, for helping me clean up the formatting, grammar, sentence structure, and spelling. My proofreader, Karyn Giss, for your meticulous eye in ensuring my manuscript was error-free.

My book cover and interior book designer Saheran Shoukat for making my book come alive by creating an amazing cover and for the wonderful job he did on the interior pages and worksheets!

All of my friends and former sponsors in AA, NA, MA, OA, CoDA, and Al-Anon for providing the vital support I needed to achieve long-term recovery from substances, food, and codependency, which has gifted me with a life worth living.

To my LGBTQ+ recovery family from ASH, where I originally got sober in the late eighties. Without your undying support in my early recovery, I would have never gotten sober and would likely not even be alive to tell this tale.

To the many teachers, coaches, mentors, and facilitators I've worked with over the past three decades for holding the space and seeing what was possible for me until I could see it for myself.

To every trauma-informed and recovery-oriented organization, podcaster, website, and person who has shared their childhood trauma and recovery stories. As I've shared in the dedication of this book, sharing our stories is the single most powerful thing we can do to heal ourselves and heal the world. The very reason I'm sober and a survivor who is thriving is due to the many brave souls who inspired me to get sober and heal my trauma by sharing their stories.

Finally, I want to acknowledge all of the authors, producers, organizations, groups, and people listed in my appendix of resources for helping me wrap my mind around what childhood trauma is, how it accounted for my struggle with addiction, weight, and relationships, and how learning this changed everything.

# APPENDIX

---

## Telephone Hotlines

- National Suicide & Crisis Lifeline Dial: 988
- For Any Other Emergency Dial: 911
- National Suicide Prevention Lifeline: 1-800-273-8255
- National Domestic Violence Hotline: 1-800-799-7233
- National Child Abuse Hotline 1-800-422-4453
- National Sexual Assault Hotline 1-800-656-4673

## Complex PTSD, Substance & Behavioral Addiction Recovery Resources

Below is a compilation of books, self-help groups, organizations, websites, movies, podcasts, music, and provider directories dedicated to supporting survivors in healing C-PTSD and recovering from various substance and behavioral addictions.

## Book Recommendations

I have organized C-PTSD related book recommendations into the following categories:

### Book Categories

- Childhood Trauma
- Addiction and Trauma
- Trauma-Informed Relational Recovery
- Healing Shame & Guilt, Self-Compassion, Self-Forgiveness & Self-Acceptance
- Codependency Recovery
- Building Resilience
- Childhood Trauma Memoirs

### Childhood Trauma

- The Body Keeps the Score: Brain, Mind, and Body in the Healing of Trauma, Bessel A. van der Kolk, MD
- Complex PTSD: From Surviving to Thriving, Pete Walker, MA
- The Tao of Fully Feeling: Harvesting Forgiveness Out of Blame, Pete Walker, MA
- The Soulful Journey of Recovery: A Guide to Healing from a Traumatic Past for ACAs, Codependents, or Those with Adverse Childhood Experiences, Tian Dayton, Ph.D.
- Emotional Sobriety: From Relational Trauma to Resilience and Balance, Tian Dayton, Ph.D.
- Neuropsychodrama in the Treatment of Relational Trauma, Tian Dayton, Ph.D.
- The ACOA Trauma Syndrome: The Impact of Childhood Pain on Adult Relationships, Tian Dayton, Ph.D.
- Running on Empty: Overcome Your Childhood Emotional Neglect, Jonice Webb, Ph.D., and Christine Musello, PsyD
- Running on Empty No More: Transform Your Relationships With Your Partner, Your Parents, and Your Children, Jonice Webb, PhD
- Healing the Fragmented Selves of Trauma Survivors: Overcoming Internal Self-Alienation, Janina Fisher, PhD

- Transforming The Living Legacy of Trauma: A Workbook for Survivors and Therapists, Janina Fisher, PhD
- The Myth of Normal: Trauma, Illness & Healing In a Toxic Culture, Gabor Maté, M.D.
- Childhood Disrupted: How Your Biography Becomes Your Biology, and How You Can Heal, Donna Jackson Nakazawa
- Healing Your Attachment Wounds: How to Create Deep and Lasting Intimate Relationships, Diane Poole Heller, PhD
- What Happened to You? Conversations on Trauma, Resilience, and Healing, Oprah Winfrey and Bruce D. Perry, MD, Ph.D.
- The Boy Who Was Raised as a Dog: And Other Stories from a Child Psychiatrist's Notebook - What Traumatized Children Can Teach Us About Loss, Love, and Healing, Bruce D. Perry, MD, Ph.D., and Maia Szalavitz
- Born for Love: Why Empathy Is Essential—and Endangered, Bruce D. Perry, MD, Ph.D., and Maia Szalavitz
- The Polyvagal Theory: Neurophysiological Foundations of Emotions, Attachment, Communication, and Self-Regulation, Stephen W. Porges
- Befriending Your Nervous System: Looking Through the Lens of Polyvagal Theory, Deb Dana
- Neurofeedback in the Treatment of Developmental Trauma: Calming the Fear-Driven Brain, Sebern F. Fisher
- The Deepest Well: Healing the Long-Term Effects of Childhood Adversity, Nadine Burke Harris, MD
- No Bad Parts: Healing Trauma and Restoring Wholeness With the Internal Family Systems Model, Richard Schwartz, PhD
- Greater Than the Sum of Our Parts: Discovering Your True Self Through Internal Family Systems Therapy, Richard Schwartz, PhD
- It Didn't Start with You: How Inherited Family Trauma Shapes Who We Are and How to End the Cycle, Mark Wolynn
- The Emotionally Absent Mother: How to Recognize and Heal the Invisible Effects of Childhood Emotional Neglect, Jasmin Lee Cori, MS, LPC
- Healing Trauma: A Pioneering Program for Restoring the Wisdom of Your Body, Peter A. Levine, PhD
- The TurnAround Mom: How an Abuse and Addiction Survivor Stopped the Toxic Cycle for Her Family—and How You Can, Too!, Carey Sipp
- Mother Hunger: How Adult Daughters Can Understand and Heal from Lost Nurturance, Protection, and Guidance, Kelly McDaniel
- Lost Connections: Uncovering the Real Causes of Depression—and the Unexpected Solutions, Johann Hari
- Silently Seduced: When Parents Make Their Children Partners, Kenneth Adams, PhD
- It's Not Always Depression: Working the Change Triangle to Listen to the Body, Discover Core Emotions, and Connect to Your Authentic Self, Hilary Jacobs Hendel, LCSW
- The Adverse Childhood Experiences Recovery Workbook: Heal the Hidden Wounds From Childhood Effecting Your Adult Mental & Physical Health, Glenn R. Schiraldi, Ph.D.
- The Developing Mind: How Relationships & The Brain Interact To Shape Who We Are, Daniel Siegel

## Addiction and Trauma

- Trauma and Addiction: Ending the Cycle of Pain Through Emotional Literacy, Tian Dayton, PhD
- In the Realm of Hungry Ghosts: Close Encounters with Addiction, Gabor Maté, MD
- Addiction as an Attachment Disorder, Philip J. Flores
- Addiction, Attachment, Trauma, and Recovery: The Power of Connection, Oliver J. Morgan
- Unspoken Legacy: Addressing the Impact of Trauma and Addiction within the Family, Claudia Black, PhD

- It Will Never Happen to Me: Growing Up with Addiction as Youngsters, Adolescents, and Adults, Claudia Black, PhD
- Trauma and the 12 Steps: An Inclusive Guide to Enhancing Recovery, Jamie Marich, PsyD
- Quit Like a Woman: The Radical Choice to Not Drink in a Culture Obsessed with Alcohol, Holly Whitaker
- The Easy Way to Control Alcohol, Allen Carr
- Chasing the Scream: The First and Last Days of the War on Drugs, Johann Hari
- Alcoholics Anonymous: The Big Book, Anonymous
- Narcotics Anonymous, Anonymous
- Overeaters Anonymous: Third Edition, Overeaters Anonymous, Inc.

## Trauma-Informed Relational Recovery

- Wired for Love: How Understanding Your Partner's Brain and Attachment Style Can Help You Defuse Conflict and Build a Secure Relationship, Stan Tatkin, PsyD, MFT
- We Do: Saying Yes to a Relationship of Depth, True Connection, and Enduring Love, Stan Tatkin, PsyD, MFT
- The New Rules of Marriage: What You Need to Know to Make Love Work, Terrence Real
- Fierce Intimacy, Terry Real
- Us: Getting Past You and Me to Build a More Loving Relationship, Terrence Real
- Conscious Lesbian Dating & Love: A Roadmap to Finding the Right Partner and Creating the Relationship of your Dreams, Ruth L. Schwartz, Ph.D., and Michelle Murrain, Ph.D.

## Healing Shame & Guilt, Self-Compassion, Self-Forgiveness, Self-Acceptance

- I Thought It Was Just Me (but it isn't): Making the Journey from "What Will People Think?" to "I Am Enough," Brené Brown, Ph.D., LMSW
- Understanding and Treating Chronic Shame: A Relational/Neurobiological Approach, Patricia DeYoung
- Self-Compassion: The Proven Power of Being Kind to Yourself, Kristin Neff, PhD
- Radical Acceptance, Embracing Your Life With The Heart of A Buddha, Tara Brach
- The Honest Truth About Dishonesty: How We Lie to Everyone—Especially Ourselves, Dan Ariely
- Radical Self-Forgiveness: The Direct Path to True Self Acceptance, Colin Tipping
- Forgive for Good: A Proven Prescription for Health and Happiness, Frederic Luskin, PhD
- Discomfortable: What Is Shame and How Can We Break Its Hold?, A.J. Bond
- Coming Out of Shame: Transforming Gay and Lesbian Lives, Gershon Kaufman Ph.D., and Lev Raphael PhD
- The Secret of the Shadow: The Power of Owning Your Story, Debbie Ford
- Why Good People Do Bad Things: How to Stop Being Your Own Worst Enemy, Debbie Ford
- Healing the Shame that Binds You, John Bradshaw

## Codependency Recovery

- Codependent No More: How to Stop Controlling Others and Start Caring for Yourself, Melody Beattie
- Beyond Codependency: And Getting Better All the Time, Melody Beattie
- Facing Codependence: What It Is, Where It Comes from, How It Sabotages Our Lives, Pia Mellody
- Codependency for Dummies, Darlene Lancer
- Conquering Shame and Codependency: 8 Steps to Freeing the True You, Darlene Lancer
- Codependents Anonymous, Anonymous

## Building Resilience

- The Art of Extreme Self-Care: Transform Your Life One Month at a Time, Cheryl Richardson

- Nurturing Resilience: Helping Clients Move Forward from Developmental Trauma—An Integrative Somatic Approach, Kathy L. Kain and Stephen J. Terrell
- Daring Greatly: How the Courage to Be Vulnerable Transforms the Way We Live, Love, Parent, and Lead, Brené Brown, Ph.D., LMSW
- The Gifts of Imperfection: Let Go of Who You Think You're Supposed to Be and Embrace Who You Are, Brené Brown, Ph.D., LMSW
- Rising Strong: How the Ability to Reset Transforms the Way We Live, Love, Parent, and Lead, Brené Brown, Ph.D., LMSW
- Beyond Intellect: Journey Into the Wisdom of Your Intuitive Mind, Susan McNeal Velasquez
- Loving What Is: Four Questions That Can Change Your Life, Byron Katie
- The Great Work of Your Life: A Guide for the Journey to Your True Calling, Stephen Cope
- SuperBetter: A Revolutionary Approach to Getting Stronger, Happier, Braver and More Resilient - Powered by the Science of Games, Jane McGonigal

## Childhood Trauma Memoirs

- HOMESTEADING in the CALM EYE of the STORM: A Therapist Navigates His Complex PTSD, Pete Walker, MA
- What My Bones Know: A Memoir of Healing from Complex Trauma, Stephanie Foo
- Garbage Bag Suitcase: A Memoir, Shenandoah Chefalo
- Shattered by the Darkness: Putting the Pieces Back Together After Child Abuse, Gregory Williams, Ph.D.
- Don't Try This Alone: The Silent Epidemic of Attachment Disorder, Kathy Brous

# C-PTSD Related Directories Websites, Organizations, Podcasts, Movies, Music & Support Groups

### C-PTSD/Trauma-Informed Therapist Directories

- Trauma Research Foundation Directory https://traumaresearchfoundation.org/lp/directory
- Trauma Therapist Network Directory  https://traumatherapistnetwork.com
- Trauma Informed Stabilization Treatment-TIST Directory: https://janinafisher.com/search
- Assoc. For Training on Trauma & Attachment Directory https://attach.org/clinical-referral-list
- Trauma-Informed Neurofeedback Practitioner Directory https://traumaresearchfoundation.org/lp/directory

### Trauma & Resilience Coaching

- Mary Giuliani, Trauma-Recovery and Resilience Coaching, https://marygiuliani.net
- International Association of Trauma Recovery Coaching Provider Directory https://certifiedtraumarecoverycoaching.com/directory-of-coaches

### Trauma-Informed Weight Management Programs

- Relish Life https://relish.life

### Childhood Trauma Practitioner Websites

- Bessel van der Kolk, MD, complex PTSD: https://www.besselvanderkolk.com
- Pete Walker, MA, MFT, complex PTSD: http://pete-walker.com
- Janina Fisher, Ph.D., complex PTSD: https://janinafisher.com

- Bruce Perry, MD, Ph.D. complex PTSD: https://www.bdperry.com/
- Anna Runkle: Crappy Childhood Fairy: complex PTSD: https://crappychildhoodfairy.com
- Mary Giuliani, MCC, addiction and complex PTSD: https://marygiuliani.net
- Tian Dayton, Ph.D., addiction and complex PTSD: https://www.tiandayton.com
- Gabor Maté, MD, addiction and complex PTSD: https://drgabormate.com
- Jonice Webb, Ph.D., childhood emotional neglect: https://drjonicewebb.com
- Diane Poole Heller, Ph.D., attachment trauma: https://dianepooleheller.com

## Childhood Trauma Podcasts

- The Healing Place Podcast with Teri Wellbrock https://teriwellbrock.com/podcasts
- Therapists Uncensored: https://therapistuncensored.com/episodes
- Being Well Podcast-Dr. Rick Hanson https://www.rickhanson.net/category/podcasts/
- Breaking the Silence with Dr. Gregory Williams: https://bbsradio.com/breakingthesilence
- Beyond Trauma https://beyondtraumapodcast.com/

## Childhood Trauma Organizations

- PACEsconnection.com https://www.pacesconnection.com
- The Trauma Research Foundation https://traumaresearchfoundation.org
- C-PTSD Foundation https://cptsdfoundation.org
- The Trauma Foundation https://thetraumafoundation.org

## Childhood Trauma & Recovery Movies/Series/Documentaries

- The Wisdom of Trauma
- Cracked Up: The Darrell Hammond Story
- Paper Tigers: One High School's Unlikely Success Story
- Broken Places
- Out of Darkness, Into Light: Child Sexual Abuse
- Wrestling Ghosts
- Generation Found
- Resilience
- The Anonymous People

## Trauma Healing & Recovery Music

- Mary Giuliani, 1992 album of twelve original songs— I'm Showin Up For My Dream
  https://marygiuliani.net/marys-music-for-healing-growth-and-transformation/
  Stream on: Itunes, Amazon Music, Spotify, Apple Music, Deezer & Tidal

## Alcohol & Drug Addiction Organizations

- SAMHSA-Substance Abuse & Mental Health Services Administration https://www.samhsa.gov
- NIH-National Institute on Alcohol Abuse & Alcoholism https://www.niaaa.nih.gov/
- National Association of Addiction Treatment Providers https://www.naatp.org
- Faces and Voices of Recovery: https://facesandvoicesofrecovery.org/

# Twelve-Step Support Groups For Survivors, Alcohol, Drug, Food & Behavioral Addiction

### Trauma/ACOA-Adult Children of Alcoholic Survivors

- Adult Children of Alcoholics: http://www.adultchildren.org
- Adult Survivors of Child Abuse Anonymous: www.asca12step.org
- Survivors of Incest Anonymous: http://www.siawso.org

## Alcohol and Drug Addictions

- Alcoholics Anonymous: http://www.alcoholics-anonymous.org
- Narcotics Anonymous: http://www.na.org
- Marijuana Anonymous: http://www.marijuana-anonymous.org
- Nicotine Anonymous: http://www.nicotine-anonymous.org
- Celebrate Recovery: Christian 12-step recovery https://www.celebraterecovery.com
- Medication Assisted Recovery Anonymous https://www.mara-international.org

## Food/Eating Disorders

- Overeaters Anonymous: http://www.oa.org
- Compulsive Eaters Anonymous: http://www.ceahow.org
- Eating Disorders Anonymous: http://www.eatingdisordersanonymous.org

## Behavioral Addictions

- Workaholics Anonymous: http://www.workaholics-anonymous.org
- Internet & Technology Addicts Anonymous (Internet, Social Media, Smartphone, Streaming): https://internetaddictsanonymous.org
- Love Addicts Anonymous: http://www.loveaddicts.org
- Sex Addicts Anonymous: http://www.sexaa.org
- Sex and Love Addicts Anonymous: http://www.slaafws.org
- Porn Addicts Anonymous: https://www.pornaddictsanonymous.org
- Spenders Anonymous: http://www.spenders.org
- Debtors Anonymous: http://debtorsanonymous.org
- Gamblers Anonymous: http://www.gamblersanonymous.org
- Clutterers Anonymous: http://www.clutterersanonymous.net

- Shoplifters Anonymous: http://www.shopliftersanonymous.com

- Self-Injury Recovery Anonymous: http://www.thesira.org

## Non–Twelve-Step Groups for Alcohol, Drug, Food, and Behavioral Addictions

- Secular Organizations for Sobriety: https://www.sossobriety.org

- Smart Recovery: https://www.smartrecovery.org

- Refuge Recovery: https://www.refugerecovery.org

- Women For Sobriety: https://womenforsobriety.org

## Harm Reduction Organizations For Substance Use Disorders

- National Harm Reduction Coalition https://harmreduction.org

- The Peoples Harm Reduction Alliance http://phra.org

- Harm Reduction International https://www.hri.global

# Support Groups For Family & Friends of People Who Suffer With Addiction

- Co-Dependents Anonymous: http://www.codependents.org

- Al-Anon/Alateen: http://www.al-anon.alateen.org

- Nar-Anon: http://nar-anon.org

- Work-Anon: http://work-anon.blogspot.com

- IT-Anon (for family and friends of those who suffer from social media, smartphone, Internet, or technology addiction): https://internetaddictsanonymous.org/meetings-for-family-and-friends

# Support Groups For People Who Suffer From Mental Health Disorders

- National Alliance on Mental Health Support Groups:

  https://www.nami.org/Support-Education/Support-Groups/NAMI-Connection

# Groups for Family and Friends of People with Mental Health Conditions

- National Alliance on Mental Health Family/Friends of People With Mental Health Disorders: https://www.nami.org/Support-Education/Support-Groups/NAMI-Family-Support-Group

# Want Free Support To End Your Struggle With Food, Weight, Substances or Relationships?

## Stay Connected By Signing Up For Mary's FREE Newsletter

Since Mary has a passion for staying current on the latest science-based research for healing C-PTSD and recovering from food, substance, behavioral addictions, and relationship difficulties, and loves sharing what she's learned with her newsletter subscribers, be sure to stay in the loop by signing up for her newsletter today!

 https://marygiuliani.net/free-newsletter

# Want To Be Part of the Solution to Help Prevent & Heal Trauma & Addiction?

## Leave A Review on Amazon or Goodreads

If reading this book has provided support or value for you or those you love, please consider leaving a review on Amazon or Goodreads. The more favorable reviews this book receives, the more people will purchase it and learn about C-PTSD's direct link to anxiety, depression, addiction, obesity, and difficulty with close relationships. This, in turn, will help facilitate preventing and healing C-PTSD and break the chain of trauma, addiction, and obesity from being passed down through the generations. To post your review, go to Amazon.com and/or Goodreads.com.

## Get Your ACE Score By Completing the ACE Questionnaire

It takes a village to prevent and heal C-PTSD. To be part of the solution to creating a world where all people are given the respect, dignity, support, and care they deserve to heal, whether they struggle with addiction, obesity, or other common symptoms of C-PTSD, you can start by going to chapter 17 and completing the ACE-Adverse Childhood Experiences Questionnaire, and asking your family and friends to do so as well by sending them to:

https://marygiuliani.net/adverse-childhood-experience-ace-questionnaire

The ACE Questionnaire asks ten yes or no questions that takes less than five minutes to complete. Even if you didn't have a difficult childhood, completing the ACE Questionnaire will still help you to be part of the solution since it will give you a better idea of what types of adversity and/or household dysfunction cause children to develop C-PTSD, which will help you become an advocate for preventing and healing it. I'm committed to being part of the solution, and I hope you will be, too, by completing the ACE Questionnaire and asking your friends and family to do so too.

# Ready To End Your Struggle With Food, Weight, Substances or Relationships?

### Heal The Root Cause By Working Directly With Mary As Your Coach

Mary combines her experience in overcoming her own struggle with trauma, addiction, obesity and relationships with her 25 year background as a Master Certified Coach to support you to overcome your struggle with food, weight, relationships and/or other common symptoms of C-PTSD. To inquire about Mary's current openings for individual or group coaching programs contact Mary at:

 https://marygiuliani.net/contact/

# Need A Trauma-Informed Speaker To Inspire & Uplift Your Audience?

### Hire Mary as Your Keynote Speaker For Your Conference or Event

Mary brings compassion, wit, inspiration, and hard-earned wisdom as a keynote speaker by sharing her story of triumphing over complex trauma, addiction, and severe obesity.  She is a fierce advocate for ending the stigma of obesity, addiction, and mental health disorders by providing science-based evidence of their direct link to ACEs (adverse childhood experiences) that result in survivors developing complex PTSD.

She speaks on various topics related to childhood trauma, addiction, obesity, and relational trauma. She provides audiences with a plethora of evidence-based, trauma-informed treatments and recovery practices that have proven to help survivors heal their trauma and achieve long-term recovery from their struggle with food, weight, substances, and relationships. To book Mary for your upcoming event, visit:

 https://marygiuliani.net/contact/

# Connect With The Author

For media inquiries, interviews, or for information about seminar or consulting services:

 Mary@MaryGiuliani.net

# To Connect on Social Media:

📘 https://www.facebook.com/Marygcoach

▶️ https://www.youtube.com/@MaryGiuliani

📷 https://www.instagram.com/Mary.Giuliani/

💼 https://www.linkedin.com/in/MaryGiuliani

🐦 https://twitter.com/MaryMGiuliani

Printed in the USA
CPSIA information can be obtained
at www.ICGtesting.com
LVHW082343030424
776386LV00010B/402